TOP 1000 REALLY USEFUL WEB SITES

VERSION 2.0

KEVIN O'DRISCOLL

ENTER

foulsham
LONDON • NEW YORK • TORONTO • SYDNEY

foulsham

The Publishing House
Bennetts Close, Cippenham, Berkshire, SL1 5AP, England

ISBN 0-572-02648-X

Copyright © 2001 Strathearn Publishing

*This book is dedicated to two people without whom it would not be
possible to achieve what I have. The first is my loving partner
Tracy Davis. Without her help, patience and understanding this
book would never have been finished. The second is my mother,
Gillian O'Driscoll, without whose love I would not have been able
to achieve what I have to date.*

Printed in Great Britain by The Bath Press, Bath

Contents

Introduction	6
Protecting yourself and your children on the Internet	11
Getting connected	19
Project: Connecting your modem to your PC	25
Project: Connecting your modem to your Mac	33
Internet service providers	39
Project: Dialling your ISP or OSP	48
Web browsers	54
Internet Explorer Versions 4.0 and 5.0	59
Changing Explorer options	69
Project: Using the Explorer Content Advisor	81
Netscape Communicator	85
Changing Netscape Communicator options	90
Project: How to browse	98
E-mail	104
Project: Sending an e-mail	117
Project: Receiving an e-mail	121
Newsgroups	123
1000 Really useful web sites	133

Introduction

We are all aware of the cosmic potential of the web available at our fingertips in our own front rooms. It is the most up-to-date source of information possible; it's direct; it's personal; and it's international. We know that it offers us an infinite store of information which will be immensely useful and stimulating for us in our daily lives – whether that involves research resources for work or school, cheap holidays, high-street shopping opportunities or whatever else – but we also know that in order to find what we want, we'll have to wade through a whole mountain of stuff that is of no interest at all – it might be useful to someone else, or it might be just plain garbage, but it's all getting in our way.

Add to that the fact that anyone who knows a lot about the web usually assumes that we are all equally familiar with the jargon (and don't they love it!) and know how to manoeuvre through those sticky snares without getting hopelessly entangled, and you have a recipe for wasted potential – in a big way!

SO WHERE DOES THAT LEAVE YOU?

You have internet access and want to use it for your personal benefit – in whatever way that may be.

You are interested in making it work for you, not finding out the minutiae of what is actually going on in all those fantastic digital messages which are flashing round the world.

You have no intention of wasting valuable time being diverted from your task – and you certainly don't want to waste money running up unnecessary phone bills while you track down the information you are after.

If you know nothing, you want to get started. If you know a little, you want to know more. And if you have tried and failed once, you want a solution to your problems. You want to be a net 'user' – you don't want the web to use you!

That's what this book will give you.

We assume you are starting from scratch, and we explain exactly what you need to get connected to the internet and start finding your way around. All the explanations are project-based and backed up with screen-dump images (pictures of what you see on the screen), so that you can compare what you see on your screen with what you see in the book, making it much easier to understand what you are doing. Much of the jargon is irrelevant to ordinary needs, but you do need to know the new vocabulary that applies to getting the job done; so we explain exactly what things mean as and when you need to know, and show you how they can benefit you. For simplicity, you'll sometimes see the 'translation' in brackets after a particular term, as in this paragraph. Nothing is included for its own sake – it's all application-based (it gets things done!) or provides education-enhancement (you need to know it to get on) – and that's the only time we'll use jargon in the way that many computer buffs bandy it about.

And once you are up and running, of course, you need to have somewhere to go, so we have made a selection of over 1,000 really useful web sites, so that you can go direct to the best sources of information currently available on the net.

By its very nature, the net is in a constant state of change, so as you find your way round and discover new and fascinating sites you would like to share, do let us know about them by providing the address and a sentence or two about what the site contains. Leave your comments on our web site at:

www.foulsham.com

WHAT IS THE INTERNET?

A pretty basic question! But building from the ground up means that you will really understand what is going on and can build securely on your knowledge. If you are already surfing, you may want to skim this part, although even more experienced surfers may find some useful and enlightening information in these early pages.

The internet is basically an **inter**national **net**work of computers. These computers are switched on 24 hours a day, 365 days a year, so when you are connecting to the internet you are just linking your computer into this worldwide, constant network. You can't plug directly into that network, so you go through what is called an internet service provider. This literally provides the link from your computer to another computer which holds the information you need, whether that be in the next street or on the other side of the world. Distance has no meaning on the internet.

Once that link has been established, what can you do with it? There are four basic areas of the internet which you can access. Using these four avenues means that you can use the internet to communicate worldwide in seconds rather than in days or weeks. This can save you time, effort and money, and it can all be done without having to leave your home or office.

The worldwide web: www

This area is like a constantly changing and expanding digital library full of what are more commonly known as web pages or web sites. All web sites have an address which is prefixed with: http:// although not all now include www.

E-mail

This is your electronic postal system through which you can send a letter, memo, picture or whatever you want anywhere in the world. It is cheap, effective and quick. If you are sending or receiving e-mail, you need an e-mail address.

Newsgroups

Newsgroups are where the internet really started and they are like club bulletin boards. They contain e-mail messages which people have sent to a particular discussion group and which are then available to everyone. Those messages can be text, pictures, video clips or anything you can put into an e-mail.

Internet chat

Like digital meetings rooms, here you can hold conversations – sometimes even with a video picture – or just type messages on the screen for other people to read.

WHAT CAN YOU DO ON THE INTERNET?

Anything that can be done in real life! Say you want to book a holiday, read today's newspaper, contact a local maintenance company, check your bank balance or the latest sports results, make a bet on tomorrow's race, purchase software, contact friends and family worldwide, research your school or college homework, buy your weekly groceries – all this and a lot more can now be done electronically on the internet. The only limit is your own imagination. All these tasks can be done through the www or e-mail, both of which are very easy to use. It has even been found that buying goods or paying for services on the net is just as safe as making a purchase in a store with a credit card. The added advantage with the net is that the shops or services are available 24 hours a day, 365 days a week.

Using the internet is simple, straightforward and fun. It is all done by pointing and clicking your mouse with the occasional bit of typing thrown in. It will open up a world of information resources that you never knew existed and which is growing all the time. After a few hours you'll feel as though you have been using the net for years.

THE INTERNET AND THE LAW

As a final point, remember that the laws of the land apply to the internet as to everything else. If you break the law, you are liable for prosecution. If you are viewing information that is legal in the country that is hosting the documents but not in your own country, you cannot download that information on to your hard drive. That is illegal. Ignorance is no defence.

Protecting yourself and your children on the internet

Though the vast majority of information on the net is useful and positive, it is true that anyone can set up a web site, so it is up to you to ensure that if children have access to your web entry-point – i.e. your computer – they are protected from information which is inappropriate. Unfortunately, the web has its seedy side just as real life does. Anyone using the net can access pornographic material or information about drugs or other related issues. It is also possible for you to contract viruses which can damage your computer software. Though it can be difficult and time-consuming to find these sites, they are there, and it is possible to stumble across them while looking for something quite different.

There are three main ways to protect yourself and your computer from this seedy side of the internet so that, while you need to remain aware, nothing need spoil your enjoyment of surfing. The first is to use your common sense. Make sure that children are not allowed completely free access to the net but employ an appropriate level of supervision so that they are guided towards the useful and interesting. Investigate the virus-checkers readily available in all computer stores, and also the software that is available to block information of a sensitive nature from children.

PROTECTING YOUR COMPUTER FROM VIRUSES

There is really no reason why a hacker should invade your computer, but you do need to protect it against viruses.

Computer viruses come in many different forms and have many different effects. They can just be annoying – for example displaying a message on the screen every time you press a certain key combination – or they can be downright destructive – deleting all the data on your hard drive. The more you use the internet, the more chance you will have of contracting a virus and the more careful you should be. The first way to protect your computer is to make sure that you download files only from reputable and well-known sources. However, this is not foolproof and you should also install a virus protector. Once loaded, every time you download a file from the internet, the software will check it and repair it if necessary.

Viruses are tiny programs that hide inside other executable (.exe) files and macros. They are not contained within pictures or sound files. The main rule of thumb is that they are only contained within files that need a run command. The way they work varies, but generally they lie dormant on your computer until they are activated by a particular trigger: pressing the enter key a certain number of times, or using the computer at a certain time or on a certain date, for example. Not many viruses will cause major damage as any that do are quite easily detected and will be destroyed quickly before they are passed on. However, some can make your life very difficult – destroying the contents of files, for example – and need to be avoided.

There are many ways to tell if you have a virus on your system. The most common one is that if you begin to notice that programs take longer to start up or in some cases do not start at all. If this happens, then you should check that you have the latest version of your anti-virus software and then run a check on all files. The programs that are causing the problem should be removed and re-installed if a virus is found.

If you start up your computer and the screen displays nothing but a message saying 'Missing Operating System', it could mean that a virus has attacked your startup files. With most anti-virus software you should be able to create a disk called a repair disk. You boot up your computer using the repair disk, then run your virus checker.

Finally, if you see the message 'Invalid Drive Specification' when you start your computer, then I am afraid that unless you have a relatively new and clean backup you have lost everything on your computer. This message means that your computer's hard drive has been cleaned of all data and become corrupt. The only way to rectify this is to reinstall all your programs and files.

ANTI-VIRUS SOFTWARE

There are two different types of anti-virus programs available, and two reputable and easy-to-use programs which are readily available.

Sentry-like programs

This type of program will stand guard all the time on your computer, operating in the background as you work. Every time you open a file, it will automatically scan that file for viruses. Every time you to start up or shut down your computer, the software automatically scans your memory and system files for viruses. The only drawback that when you want to install new software on your computer, the sentry anti-virus software may not allow it to run or install properly as it will recognise unknown executable files to the system.

Search and kill programs

This type is popular and quite adequate for many home users. It scans the complete hard drive at regular intervals and deletes or repairs any infected files. You can set how often you want to run the scan and nothing is run in the background which could conflict with other programs running in the background.

ViruSafe

This is a simple program to use that will automatically protect your computer and software from virus attacks as soon as you log on to the internet. Once installed, the ViruSafe software automatically detects any installed web browsers and offers to become active to protect them. When you download a file, you will see that your anti-virus software is working as it will be designated as the file's viewer. Once the file has been downloaded on to your computer's hard drive, it will automatically be scanned by ViruSafe and, if clean, you will be asked where you wish to save the file. If a file is infected, you have the choice to:

- **Clean the File** to remove the virus;
- **Kill the Virus** by deleting the virus from the file;
- **Abort the Download.**

You can also use ViruSafe to scan files manually. You will need to use this facility on files that have been copied from the web or files that you select to save from the web, as ViruSafe only works automatically on downloaded files.

ViruSafe is available on the internet from:
**http://www. softseek.com/utilities/VirusProtection/
Review 10237.index.html**

McAfee VirusScan

Another easy-to-use and popular program, McAfee VirusScan is available to you free of charge for 30 days, after which time you will need to purchase the software or delete it from your system. Another good thing about this software is that the anti-virus list is frequently updated and is available to download from the web. All you need to do is to install the new list into your program for it to become active.

Once the VirusScan software has been installed, you will notice a shield in the lower right-hand side of the task bar. This means that the VirusScan software is running in the background and protecting your system. It can be disabled manually – to install new software, for example – in which case the shield will appear in a red circle with a line through it.

To configure the software, click the shield on your toolbar and select **Properties** from the list given to you. VirusScan can be configured to scan every single file on your computer every time you start or shut down the computer, scan only program files (.com and .exe files) when you access them, or anything in between.

You can tell VirusScan automatically to clean an infected file, delete it, move it somewhere safe, or prompt you for an action to be taken. You can also configure it so that your computer is stopped from accessing any infected files. It also allows you to use right-click scanning, which means that to scan a file or folder, you simply right-click it with your mouse and select

Scan for viruses.

VirusScan is available from many web different sources, although the best one is to download from McAfee's own home page: **http://www.mcafee.com/main/asp**

PROTECTING YOUR CHILDREN

There are very different ways of protecting your children from dubious material on the internet.

Explain to children that they should never to talk to strangers online or give out personal details such as their full name, age, address, telephone number, or, of course, the user name and password of their account.

Become familiar with rating systems. Browsers 'rate' particular sites so that you can stop children from accessing specific site ratings. Thousands of different web sites have joined up with the rating system which you can investigate on the browser help pages or visit **http://www.rsac.com**

Learn about the various organisations that offer parents help to enable their children to surf the internet safely. You could investigate
Netparents at: **http://www.netparents.org/**
Safesurf at **http://www.safesurf.com**
or CyberAngels at **http://www.Cyberangels.org/**

Buy software that will allow you to block access to unsuitable sites, or check whether your internet service provider (see page 40) will offer the facilities to block unwanted sites.

BLOCKING SOFTWARE

Blocking software or internet filters are available to prevent children gaining access to adult material. Here is some information on two of the most popular options so that you can decide whether either of them is appropriate for you.

SafeSearch

One of the newer internet filters available on the internet, if you search the web using SafeSearch, it will block out sites that contain offensive material and prevent you from giving out private information in chat rooms. Like many other internet filters, it allows you to create different profiles for different members of your family, so that they can each gain appropriate access. What is unique about this software is that it will also block out responses to searches. The software works well with any internet browser. The software and further information regarding it can be found at **http://www.safesearch.com/**

SurfWatch

This popular and widely available filtering software blocks well over 110,000 web sites and allows you to block sites under different categories, such as sexually explicit, violent, hate speech, gambling, drugs and alcohol. You can also block all Internet Relay Chat (IRC). The software is easy to use and configure by adding specific web addresses or URLs (Universal Resource Locators) and it is easy to unblock sites if you do want to view them. It is also easy to block everything on the internet apart from the sites covered in the Yahoo search engine for children, Yahooligans (see page 175). The downside of this software is that you cannot set up multiple profiles – different user interfaces for different members of the family – or limit vocabulary used when your child is online – such as by blocking specific words in addresses and telephone numbers.

What you need to ask

These are the sort of questions you should ask before you select your blocking software.

- Do you want software that blocks out entire web sites or only pages that are of dubious content?

- Is it possible to fine-tune the software in different profiles for different members of the family, to screen vocabulary, for instance?

- Is it possible to configure the software to different members of your family so that the older members can view a broader range of sites?

- Is it possible to prevent your children from giving out personal and private information to strangers?

- Is it possible to block e-mail from certain sources on the internet?

Getting connected

Connecting to the internet is easy. All you need is the right hardware (the basic equipment or computer) and some free software (the programs which run on the computer). If you have purchased a complete package from a computer retailer, the software will be pre-installed, so if that applies to you, you can skip this section. If you are starting from scratch, read on.

COMPUTERS

If you are buying a new computer to access the internet, then these are the things you need to consider.

First you must decide whether to go for a PC or an AppleMac. Mac computers are supposed to be more user-friendly then PCs, so if you are a complete novice and seriously hate finding your way round computers, then a Mac could be the best choice for you. The other main reason for choosing a Mac is that they excel at image handling, so if you work in graphic art, publishing or the media, then a Mac is definitely for you. There are some drawbacks to choosing the Mac route, however. Mac hardware (computers, printers, scanners and so on) tend to be more expensive than equivalent PC equipment and are certainly less readily available in the major stores. You will also need dedicated software (programs specifically designed for the Mac) and there's a lot less available for Macs than for PCs.

If you choose a PC rather than a Mac, there's more choice of hardware when you start, and more choice when you want to upgrade your computer. Prices are therefore more competitive and you should be able to find a good package which contains everything you need. You'll also find it easier to purchase new software. Most businesses outside publishing, communication and the media tend to use PCs.

The process of connecting your modem to a PC is slightly different from that needed for a Mac, so we have given you full instructions for both. After that, all the instructions apply equally to either PC or Mac although as most people use PC, including me, I tend to refer to a PC when I mean computer!

Whatever you buy, it is best to choose a computer with the most powerful processor you can afford (that's the bit that does the work, the calculator, if you like). The immediate advantage is that the more powerful the processor, the faster your computer will be able to process the data it receives, so you will be able to access information more quickly, and will therefore save time and money. The added advantage is that systems continue to improve at a terrifying rate, so if you have more power, you are more likely to be able to use whatever brand-new systems they introduce next week. As a minimum, you should look for a computer with at least a Pentium processor. If you already have a computer, an older 486x computer will work perfectly well, although it will be slower.

You also need as large a hard drive as possible (the part of the computer that stores all the programs it uses) and as big a memory as possible (memory stores information temporarily while the computer is switched on). It's just the same principle as when you buy a freezer: you think you'll never fill all the space but you have it crammed to overflowing within a month.

After-sales service is also an important consideration and you should make sure that this is provided with whatever computer you buy. Most well-known manufacturers offer many different after-sales agreements, as do the retail outlets – some offer same-day replacement for your PC or faulty parts – so the name of the PC manufacturer is not the most important thing to go for. Check what is being offered as after-sales support. For example, they might provide extended warranties, software help and support or hardware support. If something does go wrong, do they come to you or do you have to take the computer to them? How quick is their response time?

INTERNET SERVICE PROVIDERS

Your service provider (ISP) is your doorway to the internet, the company that provides you – whether you are an individual or a company – with internet access. Different providers have different pricing structures and offer different services, so it is important to choose your provider carefully, depending on your individual needs. We'll talk about how to do this later on (see page 40).

MODEMS

Computers use data stored in a digital format but telephone lines use an analogue representation of sound. Computers 'talk' to each other down the phone lines, so they need a device to convert the digital computer data to analogue – so that it can be transmitted down the phone line – and back to digital – so that it can be read by the receiving computer. This is what the modem does (and it does so very quickly); the word 'modem' describes the conversion process: **mo**dulate and **dem**odulate.

Modems come in different forms, which are more or less

appropriate to different users. In all cases, however, you should buy the fastest modem you can afford (for the same reasons as buying the computer with the fastest processor).

External Modem   Internal Modem   PCMIAI Modem

Three main types of home user modems

Modems are rated by their data transfer speed, which is expressed in bits per second, or bps. Currently, the most common modems you can buy are able to receive data (download) at the speed of 56,000bps (or 56Kbps – K just means a thousand), although they are only capable of sending data (uploading) at a speed of 33,000bps (33Kbps). If you already have a modem, you may find that it will only connect at 33,000bps (33Kbps). This is fine, although you will find that web sites which are graphically intensive (have lots of pictures), will take longer to load. If you are using any form of modem that is slower than 33Kbps, then I would suggest that you upgrade your modem to a more powerful one as soon as you can. You will then be able to access information much more quickly, which will save you waiting time and online costs (which really means telephone bills).

Here is a brief example to show you that upgrades can be worth the money. It can take up to 10 bits to transfer one character (a letter or number), so a modem rated at 2.4Kbps will be able to transfer about 240 characters per second. This works out at about one page of text every eight seconds. With a modem of 28.8Kbps, it would take about *two-thirds of a second* to download the same page.

If you have just bought or are buying a PC, it will already have a modem connected and, depending on the type of computer, will be external, internal or PCMIA, as illustrated on page 22. If you have a desktop or tower computer, it will either be an internal or an external modem. There is no major advantage of one over the other but an internal modem tends to be slightly cheaper, saves desk space and reduces the number of cables cluttering up the back of your computer. It is perfectly possible to install an internal modem on an existing computer, although if you are connecting up your existing PC, you may prefer to buy an external modem to removing the case and working on the insides of your computer. With an external modem, you simply plug it straight into the back of your computer with a cable. Also with an external modem, you can see the lights flashing when you transmit or receive data from the internet, thus showing you the progress of the call you are making, though for this privilege you will also need an extra power supply.

If your computer is a laptop, then you are most likely to need a PCMIA card; these come in various types and work at various speeds. Some manufacturers are now fitting internal modems into laptops, and you can connect a laptop to the internet with an external modem, although since portability is the primary advantage of a laptop, this is not really a great idea. A PCMIA modem is a mixture of both an internal and external modem. It looks like a credit card and it simply fits into a PCMIA slot on the laptop so that it can easily be taken out if the slot is needed for another kind of card.

ISDN LINES

ISDN stands for Integrated Services Digital Network and is an alternative way of connecting to the internet instead of using a modem. Connection is almost instantaneous and handling is far superior, so if you are online for long periods, this is a great idea. However, an ISDN line has to be specially installed as a separate line from your telecommunications supplier and the costs of installation of the line and the connection box for your computer are still fairly expensive. You can choose a single-channel connection, in which case you can expect speeds of up to 64K, or a dual-channel connection, which will give you connections of up to 128K. (64K means 64Kbps or kilo bits per second, which is the speed at which the data can travel from your computer to the one to which you are connected.)

Project: Connecting your modem to your PC

This project will take you step by step through the stages you will need to connect your modem to your computer.

First, switch off all power to your computer.

If you have installed an internal modem, make sure the cover of your PC is back in place.

If you have a PCMIA card, make sure the modem is securely connected into the slot.

If you have an external modem, connect your modem to your computer, then connect your modem to your phone line using the cables supplied. Plug any phones into your modem if necessary. Plug in the power lead.

Switch on the power and check that the lights in an external modem display are on.

Once the modem has been connected, switch your computer back on and as it starts it will auto-detect the modem. It will then ask you what you want to do with it and how to install the drivers for the modem.

You have two options:

Option 1: If a driver disk or CD-ROM was supplied with your modem, place this into the computer and select this option.

Option 2: If you do not have a driver disk or CD-ROM, use the driver that is already supplied with your operating system (the system that runs the computer). If your modem is fairly new, it is unlikely to be on the list in an existing computer. In that case, you must install a common modem driver. This will not use the modem to its full potential but it will allow you to connect to the internet and to download an up-to-date driver from your modem manufacturer or contact them via e-mail.

Once you have chosen the option that installs your modem, the computer will automatically install the modem for you.

It is possible, however, that your operating system will not auto-detect your new modem. This is quite a common problem and easily overcome.

First, check the drivers, make, model and speed of your modem, which will all be listed in the accompanying literature. You will need to tell your operating system the type of modem that you're going to be using, so start by opening up your **Control Panel** option. To do this, click on **Start**, then click on **Settings**, then click on **Control Panel**. (Another route to open the control panel is to click on **My Computer**, then click on **Control Panel**.)

Once you have opened up the control panel, look for the modem icon, then double-click on it to select it. Once it is selected, you will be greeted with the following **Modems Properties** option screen.

To add your modem to your operating system, click **Add**. This will open up the **Install New Modem** dialogue box. This box is the first step of an install 'wizard' (a ready-made, quick way of doing things) especially for modems. This wizard makes setting up new hardware very simple.

You have two options to choose from here. One is to let your system detect that the modem is present. Make sure the modem is switched on and quit any programs which are using the modem, then click on **Next**. It may take a few minutes for

the system to search and select the modem you are using. Once
it has detected your modem, the **Verify Modem** screen will
come up, displaying the name of your modem.

Make sure the correct modem is listed, then click **Next**.

If the modem that is displayed is not the correct one, select
your modem from a list by clicking on the **Change** button until
the correct modem information is displayed. The next step is
for you to click on the **Next** button to end the modem wizard.
You will then be returned to the **Modems Properties** box. It
will be the same as before but you will see that your modem is
now listed and is ready to be used by your operating system.

If your modem was not the one that was listed, then you can use the modem wizard to install it manually rather than by the operating system. Once you have clicked on the **Change** button, you will be presented with the **Install New Modem** dialogue box from the wizard.

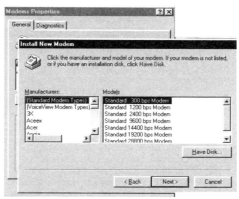

Insert the disk or CD-ROM which contains your modem drivers into your floppy disk drive or CD drive, then click on the **Have Disk** button. This will bring up an **Install From Disk** dialogue box asking you where your drivers are located.

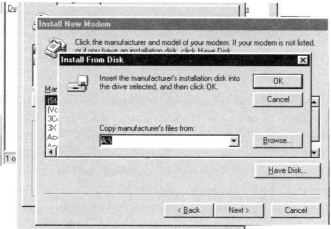

Change the displayed option to either **D:** for your CD-ROM, or **A:** for your floppy disk, then click **OK**. Your system will read the file you have selected and tell your operating system which modem you will be installing. The drivers on the disk may apply to a group of modems, not just yours.

If so, highlight your modem in the new list provided and click on the **Next** button and you will be shown the next dialogue box. You now have to tell your operating system where to find the modem.

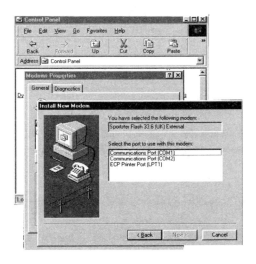

When you connected your modem to your computer, you used what is called a com port. This is just a serial port on the back of your computer designed for communications. Most computers will have up to four com ports; com1 and com2 are external and com3 and com4 are internal. If you only had one com port externally available then this would be com1. If you have two, then they should be numbered com1 and com2. Highlight **COM1**. If your modem is detected, the **Next** button becomes active. If it is not detected, select **COM2** to activate the next button. Click on **Next**.

You will then be presented with the final dialogue box in the installation wizard, which will confirm successful installation. Click the **Finish** button and you will be taken back to the **Modem Properties** box with your newly added modem available for you to use.

ALTERING THE PROPERTIES OF YOUR MODEM

The next step is to connect your modem to your internet service provider, which is the next project we will undertake (see page 40). However, before you do that, you can alter the properties of your modem. You can change the speed at which the modem transmits and receives data, and you can reduce the modem volume so you don't hear all the squealing and squelching it makes when it connects.

Open up the **Control Panel** window again, locate the **Modem** icon and double-click it. This will display the **Modems Properties** dialogue box (see page 27).

From the list of modems installed, click on the modem you want to modify to highlight it, then click on the **Properties** button. This will open up the **Properties** dialogue box and you will be able to alter the appropriate information.

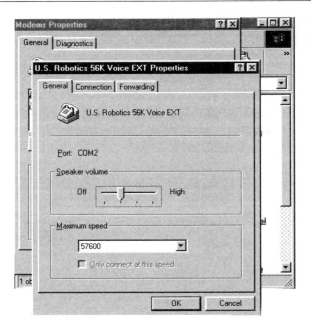

Project: Connecting your modem to your Mac

This project will take you step by step through the stages you will need to connect your modem to your Mac.

First, switch off all power to your computer.

If you have installed an internal modem, make sure the cover of your Mac is back in place.

If you have a PCMIA card, make sure the modem is securely connected into the slot.

If you have an external modem, connect your modem to your computer, then connect your modem to your phone line using the cables supplied. Plug any phones into your modem if necessary. Plug in the power lead.

Switch on the power and check that the lights in an external modem display are on.

Once you have done this, switch the Mac back on, wait for the system to load up and then install the modem software as follows:

Firstly, from the Apple icon in the top left-hand corner of your screen highlight **Control Panels**. Click on the mouse and a sub-menu will open up.

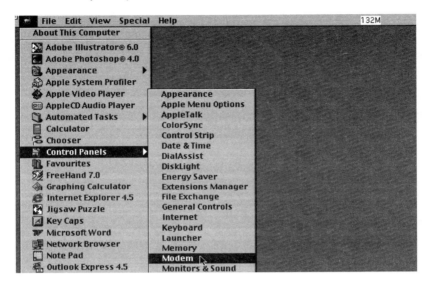

Move the cursor down to the control panel called **Modem** and double-click the mouse.

This will then open up the modem control panel on to the screen.

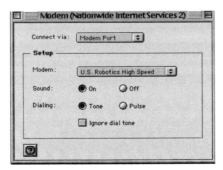

Open up the **Connect Via** pop-up menu and choose the port your modem is connected to, either the **Modem Port** or the **Printer Port**.

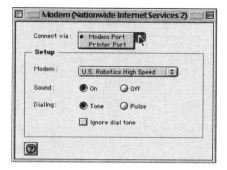

Some Macs have only one connection option; in this case, no pop-up menu will be available.

When you have selected the port you are using, move to the **Modem** pop-up menu and choose the modem you are using from the list displayed. If the name of your modem is already displayed on the screen you can skip this step.

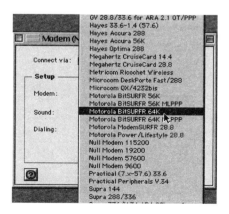

You now need to set up the **Sound** option. The default for these is **Sound On**. This means that when you dial up via the modem, you hear the dialling tones.

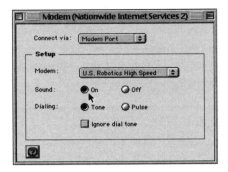

The next option to select is **Dialing**. This asks you whether your telephone uses **Tone** or **Pulse** dialling. In the UK this should be set to **Tone**.

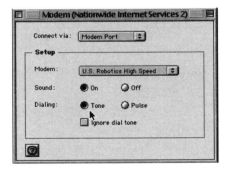

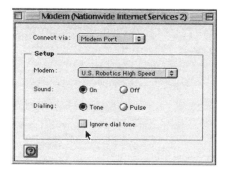

Finally, you have the option to let the modem **Ignore dial tone**. This means that it will attempt to dial up, regardless of whether it can detect a dial tone or not. The default setting for this is to leave it switched off, unless you have an unusual telephone system.

You have now finished setting up the modem. Click on the close box in the top left-hand corner of dialogue box to exit and store the values.

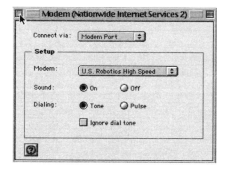

Your modem is now ready for use with your Mac and you are ready for the next project, which is to connect your computer to an Internet Service Provider.

Internet service providers

Now that your modem is connected, you need to connect to the internet; to do this, you have to connect to an internet service provider (ISP).

There are many ISPs available to you and it is worth spending a little time making the choice that is best for you, as services and costs vary. Preferably, you should choose one that has been in business for a long time and so is well established, offers good back-up support, easy access at local rates, a reasonable monthly charge, and free and useful software. There are bad support packages on the market, with poor and slow access once you are online – needless to say, these are the ones to avoid so you do need to shop around before you choose. Ask friends who already have an ISP account, consult your computer stores, and check out internet magazines. Not only do these give you information on ISPs, but they also sometimes carry disks on the cover offering free trial accounts with many reputable ISPs.

To many people, a major concern is the monthly charge, which varies between suppliers. There are some free ISPs, and if you are going to use your access a lot, this can be a good idea. The downside is that because of their popularity, the connection can be slow, or even impossible to achieve in some cases.

You are likely to find that both local and national ISPs serve your area. One way of finding out what is available is to use your browser (see page 54). If you start up Internet Explorer without an ISP account, then it will open up the Internet Connection Wizard. Click the option of **Choosing an ISP**, then fill in the details about your area code and telephone number. The wizard will then locate an appropriate ISP for your location, language and computer operating system.

Netscape Communicator helps you find an ISP in a slightly different way, through a service called ISP Select. Go to the Netscape Home Page (see page 92) and click the **ISP Select** link, which will open up another page for you to read. Click **Start ISP Selection**, enter your telephone details and click **Next**. Your screen will display the ISPs that serve your area. Click the icon of an ISP to see details of their costs and services. When you find one that is right for you, choose **Sign on** and fill in all the appropriate details.

CHOOSING A GOOD ISP

These are the things you need to consider when selecting your ISP.

Reliability
You should expect the same sort of reliability with an internet connection as you do with an ordinary phone line. If you are paying a company a monthly amount for unlimited connection time, then you should be able to connect whenever you want and not expect to experience a lot of busy signals or disconnects. Most of the bigger ISPs have realised that this is a primary function of their service so you shouldn't have to wait for a connection.

Connection type and speed

You want to be able to use the fastest possible connection so that you spend your time doing what you want on the internet and not simply waiting. Check that the ISP you are considering offers a standard service that will support your modem and the connection service you are using.

If you are using a normal phone line connection, all ISPs provide dial-up numbers for connections with 33.6K modems – that is 36 kilo bits per second, or the speed at which your computer can receive and transmit data. Some also provide a standard for the new 56K modems. If you are using an older modem with one of the previous two standards – X2 or K56flex – you will need to make sure that your ISP will support your modem.

Most ISPs will support a connection via an ISDN line. If you have a single-channel connection you can expect speeds of up to 64K, while a dual-channel connection will give you connections of up to 128K. ISDN is expected to be the way to connect in the future as technology advances and the cost decreases.

Local Access

If you are paying per month for access to your ISP and the internet, you do not want to pay for a national or long-distance call to reach your ISP, so one of the first things to look for in your choice of ISP is the cost of the initial call that connects you. Most national ISPs have local dial-up points of presence (POPs) for many cities and towns across the country. Some international ISPs may even offer you local POPs no matter what country you are in.

Support

Good technical support is essential for many people who use the internet at home. Many ISPs offer a choice of support options, with talking to a person on the phone as a last resort. An ISP with a good support structure will offer you some or all the following support options.

Newsgroup: Some ISPs have special newsgroups set aside for people to ask support questions and obtain advice, although this can prove a slow approach to fixing your problems.

Chat support: Some ISPs will provide a chat room which produces the opportunity to discuss problems either with people from the ISP or just willing volunteers.

FAQ: A **Frequently Asked Question** document may be provided by the ISP, answering the most common questions from subscribers.

E-mail: Most, if not all, ISPs will have an e-mail address to which you can send any questions and from which you can expect an answer quickly, although not immediately.

Phone support: This will be a telephone number that you can dial and get help straight away to fix your problem, although ISPs will offer this as a premium rate number (so you pay through the nose for the phone call) to make up for a low-cost connection charge.

Cost

You can connect to the internet free; it can cost you under £10/$10 a month; or it can cost £100/$100 a month for an ISDN connection. Many ISPs will offer you different ways to pay – by direct debit, in advance, by credit card, and so on – and there should be discounts available for some payment options.

Internet services

Many ISPs offer a range of internet services. Although using the world wide web is the main reason people use the internet, with e-mail running a close second, there are more services available to you and a good ISP will give you access to all or at least most of them. Check what is on offer, as different services may be available from one ISP but not another.

Services include the thousands of different newsgroups (although not usually those in foreign languages or on controversial topics), online gaming (online game servers which host online versions of the most popular multi-player games available) and web hosting (if you want to design and create your own website). ISPs offer differing amounts of webspace, but you can usually add the cost of additional space to your monthly payment fee.

Free stuff

One way that ISPs try to persuade you to sign up with them is to offer you free software, discounts on goods and services, and other gifts once you have subscribed to them. Many will offer you free connections for a specified period, often for one month, or even three months' cheaper connection charges. Another popular inducement is to include is free software on their installation disk and this will always include at least one browser (see page 54).

ONLINE SERVICE PROVIDERS

As an alternative to ISPs, you can choose to connect to an online service provider (OSP). The difference is that instead of just giving you an entry point into the internet – where information is stored on a fairly random basis – an OSP takes in the internet information and organises it for you into logical sections. You simply choose your subject, make one click and you will see a listing of all the information on your selected subject in front of you. As an OSP subscriber, you will therefore have access to an exclusive network separate from the internet and a range of additional services. OSPs are more expensive than ISPs but they can be worth it as they are very well organised, easy to use, secure, and regulated for use with children. Also these accounts will give you worldwide access, which is useful if you travel around. The only downside is that they are more expensive, so make sure you need the services they offer before you decide to sign up.

CompuServe
CompuServe has more than five million members and POPs throughout the world. It is one of the more popular OSPs with a comprehensive range of services, although it is set up more for the serious business user than the home user. It has company searches, news, magazines, chat, support forums on anything and everything, program archives, software registrations, flight reservations, professional forums, online shopping and e-mail. Once installed (see page 48), the service is simple to use: just click the CompuServe Icon and it will do everything else for you. Once you open the software, you will see a display page which is the front page of their online content. To access the internet, simply click on the **Internet** button.

AOL (America on Line)

AOL is the world's most popular online service provider with well over 13 million user accounts worldwide. Each main user account comes with five screen names, so you can have one name for yourself and one for each of the family. The main screen name can set up and restrict user access by the other users to various unwanted sites and information, so it is ideal for controlled children's access.

AOL offers a similar range of services to CompuServe, but it is one of the more friendly online services available as it is aimed primarily at home users. Despite its name, AOL is not specifically American. When you log on, you are greeted by Joanna Lumley's voice, and all the news, travel and entertainment guides are UK-based.

One disadvantage with AOL is that it does not have a web/POP3 e-mail system, which means that although you can send and receive worldwide e-mail, you will still need the active AOL program to access it.

MSN (Microsoft Network)

MSN started as an online provider similar to AOL and CompuServe but it quickly changed to being solely web-based. It does not have as broad a content as most online providers and isn't as well organised, although it still has paying subscribers who are given passwords for the web content which is exclusive to them. Of all the OSPs, MSN fits most easily into the internet from its own private network, although as the material from this provider is on web-based you will find that there is no standard look as there is with many of the other OSPs. The big advantage of MSN is that it is included with every copy of Windows 95 or 98.

WHAT YOU NEED TO KNOW ABOUT YOUR ISP OR OSP

Here is a list of questions you should ask your ISP or OSP before you sign up.

Do you have local call access?

The time you are connected to your ISP is charged on your telephone bill, so you want to be paying local call rates for your connection.

What is your user to modem ratio?

You should look for an ISP that will allow as many users as possible to connect to the internet at the same time so that you do not experience delays. Avoid any that have a ratio higher than 10:1.

Do you use POP3 e-mail?

POP3 really is a must as it will allow you to download your e-mail no matter where you are as long as you know the server connections and can alter the e-mail program being used. Unfortunately AOL does not support this but they do have access numbers for you to use worldwide.

Do you have startup costs?

Most service providers have no startup costs, and that is what you should look for when choosing.

How much are your monthly fees?

Most service providers have various price plans based on how you want to use your internet connection. You can pay a monthly fee for a set number of hours, or a higher fee for unlimited hours.

What modem speed do you support?

Modems vary in speed and you need to make sure that your service provider will support your modem, especially if you have an older modem. Older modems are known as **X2** or **V90** and are **56K** modems.

What are your support hours?

Some providers offer support only at certain times of day from Monday to Friday. Make sure your provider will be able to offer support when *you* need it.

Project: Dialling your ISP or OSP

No matter what operating system you have, you need to use the agreed way of talking to the other computer. This is known as protocol. The protocol needed for connection to the internet is TCP/IP. If the operating system you are using is either Windows 95/98/NT or an AppleMac system 7.5 or later, then you will already have all the TCP/IP software you need. If you are using another operating system, you need to install the TCP/IP software first before carrying on.

With Windows 95/98/NT operating software, you also get the dialler needed to dial the modem installed with the operating system. For the Mac operating system, you will need to install a separate program to enable dialling. The two most popular ones that are available from FreePPP at **http://www.rockstar.com** and ConfigPPP/MacPPP which is part of Apple Internet Connection Kit. The following project will show you how to configure the Dial-up Networking software that comes with Windows.

First, double-click the **My Computer** icon to open up the Dial-up networking folder. Double-click the new connection icon and this will open the **New Connection** wizard with the first page of information needed to set up your dialling.

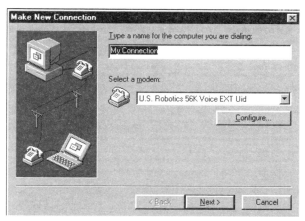

Once the dialogue box is open, you need to input a name for the connection you are about to make. It would be a good idea to name it after the provider you are using to connect to the internet, especially if you will be using more than one.

In the **Select a modem** field, you should see the name of the modem that you have installed on your system. If you do not click the drop-down arrow on the right of the dialogue box and select your modem from the list that is shown.

Click the **Next** button to display the next page of the new connection wizard.

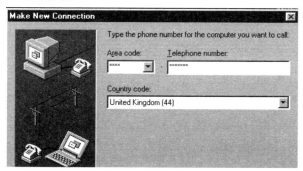

Enter the details of your dial-up connection numbers from your ISP in the **Area code** and **Telephone number** boxes. Enter the country you will be dialling in the **Country code** field.

Click **Next** for the final page of the wizard. This will inform you that you have set up the dial-up connection and that it will be saved in the **Dial–up Networking** folder. To open it, double-click the icon in the folder. If you prefer, you can create a shortcut by copying it on to your desktop.

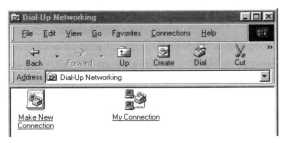

Once the dial-up connection has been created, you will need to configure the connection to suit your ISP. First, right-click the connection you just created **(My Connection)** and select the properties option to open the **Properties** dialogue box.

The dialogue box may look slightly different if you are operating a different version of Windows. If so, you may have the choice of two buttons underneath your **Modem selection** field instead of having different tabs. Use these buttons to configure the selected modem and to configure your connection to your ISP's internet server.

You need to input the TCP/IP address of your computer and the address of the name server. This information will have been provided by your ISP. If you do not have it for any reason, you will need to ring them to obtain it.

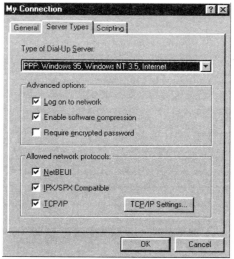

If your provider tells you to let their server handle your TCP/IP addressing, make sure that the Server assigned options are selected in the dialogue box. To access the server TCP/IP settings, click the **TCP/IP** button settings. If you need to input your own addresses, select **Specify an IP address** and enter your computer address in any of the list of numbers, then press the space bar to move on to the next number. Repeat the same process for the name server address. Once you have done this, click the **OK** button.

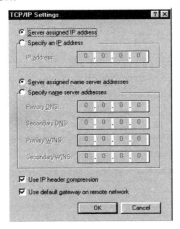

Once you have clicked **OK** and returned to the **Dial-up Network** folder, you are ready to connect to your ISP. Double-click the icon for your connection to open up the **Connect** dialogue box. Here you will have to enter your user name and password for your ISP. When you first enter your password, you have the option to **Save password**. If you are the only user of this connection and computer this is fine, although you may not want to do this if different people use your computer.

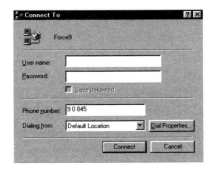

While your connection is being made, you will see the dialogue box change and it will tell you what the modem is currently doing. Once you have connected to your ISP, the dialogue box will tell you what speed you are connected to your ISP and for how long you have been connected. When you see this you can then open your mail software or your internet browser to begin surfing the net. When you are ready to disconnect, open up the connect box and click the **Disconnect** button.

Web browsers

Internet browsers are the software you need to be able to view the information on the worldwide web. Once you are connected to an ISP or an OSP, you can connect to a web browser. Several browsers are available but we will concentrate on the two most popular – Internet Explorer and Netscape Navigator – and also mention an up-and-coming browser called Opera, which is steadily increasing in popularity.

Internet Explorer and Netscape Navigator are both easily available and free to use. Many ISPs give a version of one of them with their set-up disks and many computer magazines contain free CDs that contain either or both of these browsers. For average users, the latest versions of Internet Explorer and Netscape Navigator are both excellent pieces of software which will fulfil all your surfing requirements. The latest versions of the browsers, Netscape 4.X and Internet Explorer 4.0 and 5.0 are far better than the previous versions. Internet Explorer 4.0 is, in fact, part of the operating system of Windows 98.

Although there are some differences between the two browsers, there are many common features.

Both browsers automatically try to match the web address you are typing in the address bar. To do this, the browser uses your history, which keeps a record of all the addresses you have typed in. If the address the browser attempts to insert is not the one you want, all you have to do is carry on typing and it will type over the automatic address.

Both browsers automatically fill in the address prefixes and suffixes when you enter a web address, otherwise known as a URL (Universal Resource Locator). So if you were to type in the address **www.microsoft.com** the browser would automatically place the **http://** in front of it, which is essential to make it a valid web address.

NETSCAPE NAVIGATOR

When you click the **Search** button, it takes you to the Netscape search page, from which you choose a topic. Listed below are the main features which make Netscape Communicator 4.0 different from Internet Explorer.

Powerful history tools

When you visit a web site, the address and contents of that page will be kept in what is known as a history directory on your computer's hard drive. The size and location of this file is entirely up to you and is something you can set in the browser options. When you want to search the history files in Netscape, you can search for words in the web address or document titles, as well as recalling the files by time, date, address, or even how many times you have visited the page.

OLE support

Netscape supports Object Linking Embedding (OLE). This means that you can open up any application that supports OLE, such as Excel, as long as you have the application installed on your computer.

Print preview

It is possible to preview the web page before you actually print it. Since many web pages are now very graphic-intensive, this tool is very handy.

FTP transfer

This option allows you to send a file using File Transfer Protocol (FTP) to any server or computer on the internet as long as you have its address. This is very useful when you design your web page as it saves you having to buy separate software to upload (send your files to your ISP) your website files.

INTERNET EXPLORER

These are the major unique features of Internet Explorer 4.0 and 5.0.

Two–window search

Once you click the search button, Explorer splits the current web page into two different pages. This is ideal as you can view the results of your searches in one window while using the other to conduct new searches or refine your current search.

Two–window History list and Favorites folder

Clicking the **History** button or **Favorites** button opens up a new window in your current window, in the same way as the search function. The contents of both your history and favourites folders are displayed in the new window on the left-hand side. The history contents are listed in two ways. First they are sorted by date, with the most recent first, then every page for the site that you have viewed is listed underneath the address of the website.

Active desktop

You can choose this option of Internet Explorer in the set-up window for Windows 95 and it is pre-installed on Windows 98.

It will update your entire Windows desktop, a feature which can be helpful but can cause problems. If you use the option, you will be able to view your desktop as a web page, add a favourites menu to the **Start** option, enhance your settings option with the ability to search on the internet for people and web sites, set up folders so that they display previews of the documents contained in them, and browse your hard drive with Internet Explorer, although the active desktop option is no longer available with Explorer 5.0.

Full screen option

If you click this option, just a small strip of browser tools will remain at the top of your screen. If you use a small desktop monitor or a laptop, this option is particularly useful.

OPERA: THE UP-AND-COMING BROWSER

Among the lesser-known browsers on the market, Opera is the one that is growing fastest in popularity. It is fast and friendly, and unique in a number of ways.

The software is small and quick to download. At around 1MB (or 1 megabyte of file) to download, the task is completed in minutes rather than hours. Also, the Opera software is only about 2MB (or 2 megbytes of installed software) when fully installed, so is an ideal solution for people with a small amount of disk space.

Because it is small, Opera is fast. As it does not need much of your system's memory to run, it leaves more room free for caching (i.e. storing on the hard drive) the web pages you view. Unlike Netscape or Explorer – which load pages into separate RAM-eating windows – Opera displays all the web pages open within one single Opera window. This means that separate pages can be displayed more quickly and are also more stable.

Opera is very easy and flexible to configure. Although it looks completely different, you can configure it to look like Netscape or Explorer if you prefer.

You can download Opera from **www.operasoftware.com**

CHOOSING YOUR BROWSER

Since browsers are free, the best thing to do is to try several and see which you find easiest to use, then delete the ones you do not wish to keep. If you do this, though, remember to export your bookmarks or favourites from one browser to the other so you don't lose any of your favourite places. Bookmarks are the web page addresses of popular places you visit on the web that you store on your browser (see page 89).

Internet Explorer Versions 4.0 and 5.0

Install Internet Explorer following the instructions on the CD. The method of installation is almost the same for Explorer 4.0 and 5.0, but there are a few differences. On Explorer 4.0, you are offered three installation options, **Minimum, Normal** and **Custom,** whereas Explorer 5.0 offers only **Install now** and **Custom.** The **Install now** option will install all the new features of Explorer 5.0. The **Custom** option means that you can choose the features you wish to install, something that will appeal to more experienced internet users. Explorer 5.0 is particularly well suited to customising, making it easy for you to tailor its features to your individual needs. It is more of a browser suite than its predecessor, offering a web browser, e-mail client, Windows media player and HTML editor. It also has the advantage of new built-in features such as **AutoComplete, AutoSearch, AutoInstall** and **AutoConfiguration,** which the browser itself carries out in the background while you are working.

Explorer 5.0 comes with a range of accessories that allow you to customise your browser by adding, for example custom graphics, toolbar buttons and menu items to suit your own requirements.

Once you have installed the program, an icon will appear on the desktop. You can start Internet Explorer in a variety of ways, the easiest being by double-clicking on the desktop icon. Another way is to use the Start menu: click **Start,** then **Programs,** then click **Internet Explorer** and your browser will open up.

If, when you installed the Explorer 4.0 browser, you also chose to install the active desktop option, or if your PC's operating system is Windows 98, then you can also use the following two options for starting your browser. You can simply click the **Quick Launch** button on the toolbar. Alternatively, you can activate the address toolbar; to do this, just right-click on an area of the toolbar that does not have any icons, choose the **Toolbar** option, then the **Address** option. You can then just type a web address in the address toolbar.

Once you have opened your browser, it will automatically try to open the connection to your ISP. You can then use the options setting to configure your browser however you like.

First of all we shall show you what the browser will look like on your screen and explain some of the major points of it to you.

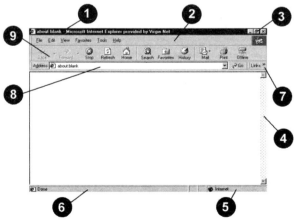

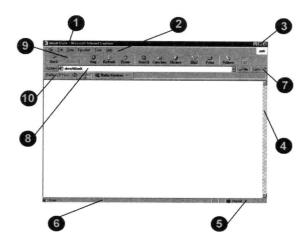

There are buttons, links, address bar, status bar, menus, status lines, and scroll bars. There are also many options open to you to change and configure your browser.

Title bar (1)

Unlike most programs, this displays more than just the name of the program you are currently using. It also displays the web page name of the site that you are currently viewing. This very often differs from the web page address, or may be blank. The bar also contains the **Minimise, Maximise** and **Close** buttons (3) in the right hand-corner.

Menu bar (2)

This displays all the internet drop-down menu options, in a similar way to any other program. Using these options you can change your browser settings, save or print web files, access the **Help** files, and access your **Favorites** folder. These drop-down menus can be accessed either by clicking on the option with your mouse, or by pressing the ALT key and the underlined letter at the same time, so **ALT + a** will open up your **Favorites** file.

Here is a brief run-down of what the menus contain.

File: This opens up another drop-down menu which contains the commands for opening, saving, printing, and sending web pages. With Explorer 4.0, only the HTML files are saved (HTML stands for 'hypertext mark-up language', which is the code used to write web pages), so that when you open them offline, you will see lots of broken image links. With Explorer 5.0, however, there are several options. The default option – **Web page complete** – saves complete web pages from the internet to your computer, including any graphics, sound files etc. to make the page complete. However, you can, if you wish, opt to save HTML files only, or text only, or even web pages to be sent on by e-mail. This improvement also enhances offline browsing using Explorer 5.0.

Edit: This enables you to copy all or part of a web page to your clipboard, edit a local HTML file and also to search for a string on the page currently being viewed.

View: This enables you to change and control the appearance of the Internet Explorer screen, to change the fonts displayed by the web pages viewed, and also to modify how your Internet Explorer program works. Also the Source option will enable you to look at all the HTML programming that went into making the web page you are currently viewing.

Go: This option includes the commands that you will need to move around a web site, to return to pages that you previously viewed, and to launch other functions such as e-mail and your Internet newsreader.

Favorites: This will enables you to view, update or manage your **Favorites** file, and allows you to be able to subscribe to specific information services.

Help: This provides help with Internet Explorer, and allows you to access help resources on the internet.

Title bar buttons (3)

Each one of these small buttons has its own function. The left-hand button is to minimise your browser window. This will place it on the toolbar and therefore open up your desktop so that you can carry out another task without closing down Explorer. The middle button will maximise the window, which makes it take up the complete display. The right-hand button will exit and close down the browser program.

Scroll bars (4)

If the page is larger than the screen, you can use these to move up and down the page. You can use these by clicking on the bar and dragging it up and down or by clicking on the arrows to move the page up and down.

Indicator bar (5)

This is where the browser will display the status of your internet connection – whether you are online or offline.

Status bar (6)

This bar shows the status of the internet activity. When you access a site, it will take some time to download the page to your computer. Once you connect to the site and are downloading, you will see a message saying something along the lines of 'Web site found – waiting for reply'. Once the page has completely finished downloading, then the message will change to 'Done'. The status line also provides information as to the security of the site you are viewing. If you see an open padlock, then the site is not secure for credit card transactions. If the padlock is closed, the site is secure and safe.

Links button (7)

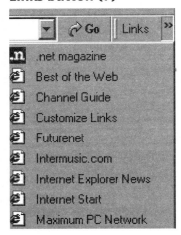

This will enable you to visit web sites with just one mouse click. When you first install the browser it will have several predefined links that will take you to various Microsoft web sites. Clicking the link with the right mouse button will enable you to make changes to the existing links. If you drag the address from the Address toolbar on to the links, that will make a new link for you. On Explorer 5.0, the Links button contains a pop-up menu where you can store up to ten addresses.

Address toolbar (8)

The most important part of the browser, this is where you type in the web site address (or URL) of the site you wish to view, then press Enter to go to that address. To return to an address you have typed in earlier, click on the down-arrow for a list of those previously visited.

Standard button toolbar (9)

This houses the one-click shortcut buttons for all the most commonly used tasks. It is therefore quicker and easier than the menu.

Radio bar (10)

This bar does not exist on Explorer 4.0; it is a new feature specific to Explorer 5.0. It enables you to connect up to radio stations broadcasting live on the internet. In order to use it, you must first install the Windows Media player, which comes with Internet Explorer 5.0.

 Back button

Pressing this button once will take you to the previous page you were viewing. If the page you wish to view is further back, click the small down-arrow for a list of previous pages. You will only be able to return to pages from your current sessions.

 Forward button

Exactly the same operation as the Back button but this time it takes you forward in pages that you have viewed.

 Stop button

This button will stop the current page from loading, which is useful if the page is taking a long time to load and you do not need the rest of the data.

Refresh button

This will re-load the current page you are viewing. This is especially useful if the page you are viewing loads incorrectly.

 Home button

Using this button will take you to what you have assigned as your home page, whether that is a web page or a blank page.

  Search button

This button will split your viewing page into two and open up an internet search engine in the left-hand window, leaving your current page loaded in the right-hand window.

 Favorites button

This will split your viewing window into two and open up your **Favorites** folder in the left-hand pane. From there you will be able to add, organise or visit your favourite web pages.

 History button

This will split your viewing window into two and open up your **History** folder in the left-hand pane so you can return to sites you have already visited. With Explorer 5.0 you can arrange your history list in alphabetical order and search your list for a specific page, rather than just a site.

 Channels button

This will bring up a list of preselected web sites, which you can automatically update. This button is specific to Explorer 4.0 and does not appear on Explorer 5.0.

Full screen button

Clicking on this makes the web page take up the whole screen apart from the button toolbar, which is made smaller but sits on top of the screen. This is a very useful tool if the pages you are looking at are graphic-intensive. This button appears only on Explorer 4.0.

 Folders button

This button is a new feature on Internet Explorer 5.0. It enables you to browse through your own folders on your computer in a left-hand panel of the browser, making navigation and file location easier and quicker.

 Mail button

This will open up your e-mail software program. The default program installed with Internet Explorer is Outlook Express.

 Print button

This will print the currently displayed web pages.

CUSTOMISING THE TOOLBARS

If you are a seasoned internet user, you might wish to customise the toolbars to suit your individual needs. With Internet Explorer 5.0, this is quite simple. First click on **View** on the toolbar, then **Customise**. This will open up a menu containing two panes; the right pane contains buttons already selected and the left pane has buttons available for you to add.

Amongst the new buttons available to you are:

 Size button

This button will invoke a pop-up menu so that you can change the default size of text on the web pages you are viewing.

 Related button

Click this if you wish to find web pages similar to the one you are viewing and it will come up with a list of related pages in your **Search** bar.

WORKING OFFLINE

Working offline means that you download web pages on to your hard disk, to be read at your leisure, thus saving you both time and money on your phone bill. Offline browsing is available on Internet Explorer 4.0 via the **Channels** button. On Internet Explorer 5.0 you click on **Favorites** and then **Add**.

Changing Explorer options

For most people, the basic Explorer set-up is more than adequate, although you can use the Internet Options dialogue box to make even more changes to the way your browser works. It may be necessary to make changes especially if you installed the browser before your ISP software.

To view the Internet Options dialogue box in Explorer 4.0, open your browser, then click on **View** (or **ALT + v**), then click **Internet Options**. With Explorer 5.0, you can open your browser, then click on **Tools**, followed by **Internet Options**. Each of the tabs on this dialogue box has many options, which are detailed below. Most are common to both Explorer 4.0 and 5.0, with one or two exceptions.

THE GENERAL TAB

Home page option

This page is displayed as soon as you open up your browser. If you are connected to the web and the page you are viewing is the one you always want to see, open up the Internet Options dialogue box and click the **Use Current** button. The address space will be filled with the current page's URL. If you want to return to the original setting for a home page that came with the browser when it was installed, click the **Use Default** button. If you do not want to display any pages when you open your browser, click on the **Use Blank** option.

Temporary Internet files

This section controls how the web pages are stored ('page cached') on your computer's hard drive, so that by storing the web pages and their components – such as sounds, graphics, etc. – on your hard drive, the browser can open up those pages more quickly the next time you visit the pages. This is because any items that remain unchanged on the web page you are viewing don't need to be downloaded each time. Although this is a good idea as it will improve performance, it does mean that part of your hard drive space has to be given up to this. If you do find yourself running out of hard disk space, delete the contents stored in the temporary area but remember that as soon as you re-use your browser, the new files will begin to fill the cache again.

The amount of space that is given to these temporary files can be altered to suit your individual needs by using the **Settings** button. Once you click on the **Settings** button, you will be asked to configure how often you want Internet Explorer to check to see if the web pages you have stored in your temporary folder need to be updated. You can choose to have this done in one of three ways.

Every visit to the page: This will get the browser to check for changes to a page every time you visit the page even if you are simply returning to one you have just visited. This will probably slow down your connection as it will force Internet Explorer to check many pages that have not changed in the short amount of time since your last visit.

Every time you start Internet Explorer: This is probably the best of the three choices available. It will force the Internet Explorer to check for changes to the page once per session. This represents a good compromise of speed and making sure that the pages that you are looking at are the current versions.

Never: This option will mean that Explorer will never check for any changes unless you do it manually by pressing the **Refresh** button. This is probably not a good choice because any time you save by always using the changed pages is lost against the time it would take a page to refresh and always having to click the **Refresh** button.

Using the **Amount of disk space to use** slider will help you control how much of your hard disk space is used for your pages to be cached. The minimum size is one per cent. To save any changes that you make, click the ok button which will return you to the general tab of the internet options dialogue box.

History

This section of the general tab will control how long your system keeps the addresses of the web sites that you have visited.

Colors

This can be used to adjust the colours Explorer uses for text, background and links. If you activate the **Use Hover Color**, when your mouse pointer is correctly located over a link, the link will change colour. To save any changes you make, click the **OK** button, which will return you to the **General** tab of the **Internet Options** dialogue box.

Fonts

This button will open up the **Fonts** dialogue box, which will enable you to control the fonts Explorer uses to display web pages. Clicking **OK** will return you to the **General** tab of the dialogue box.

Languages

This button will open up the **Languages** dialogue box, which will enable you to add additional languages so that you can display multi-language web sites. To add another language, click the **Add** button, then select a language from the **Language Preference** box. It will then be displayed in the list under your default language.

When you visit a multi-language site, Explorer will use the language highest in the list to display the site. To change the order of languages, highlight the language you want, then click either the **Move Up** or **Move Down** button. If you no longer require a language to be used, highlight the language you do not need and press the **Remove** button. Clicking the **OK** button will return you to the **General** tab of the **Internet Options** dialogue box.

Accessibility

This button will open up the **Accessibility** dialogue box, which will enable you to tell Explorer to ignore the HTML commands (the hidden codes used in creating the web page) that the web site designers have entered into their web page which may make the text hard to read. Clicking the **OK** button will return you to the **General** tab of the **Internet Options** dialogue box.

THE SECURITY TAB

Internet Explorer has four different security zones for which you can define different security levels.

The level of protection you choose can be from three predefined levels, or from a custom level you define yourself if you understand enough about the objects contained within web pages. Click on the level you want, if you have Explorer 4.0, or use the slider on Explorer 5.0. Note that any changes you make using the Custom facility in Explorer 5.0 can affect the files that you have stored on your computer as well as the pages you are viewing on the internet.

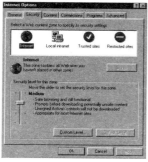

Explorer 4.0   Explorer 5.0

Local intranet zone: This zone comprises your computer, your local network, or web sites that you define as being part of this zone.

Trusted sites zone: This comprises only web sites that you specify as being part of this zone. It should not contain any sites you think might contain damaging or inappropriate material.

Internet zone: This contains all sites on the internet that have not been specifically defined as being part of any other zone.

Restricted sites zone: This contains web sites you have defined as sites that you do not trust.

Click **OK** to return to the **Security** tab of the **Internet Options** dialogue box.

THE CONTENT TAB

Explorer 4.0   Explorer 5.0

The **Content tab** of the **Internet Options** dialogue box enables you to deal with the type of sites you visit and allows you to identify yourself securely to the those sites. This will help you block some, if not all, undesirable sites, although only those sites that have rated themselves in the rating system. As this is voluntary, not many sites participate in the scheme and they may not have honestly rated their content. You do have the option of blocking unrated sites, but by doing so you may block inoffensive sites.

Content advisor

This is where you can set the ratings you want on various materials. This facility has been considerably extended in Explorer 5.0. To set the ratings you want, you press the **Enable** button and then make your choices. As this is important, we will take you through a step-by-step project on page 81.

Certificates

Using **Certificates** enables you to read an electronically encoded document that provides proof that the document is coming from a specific source, either a person or a web page. The **Certificates** section is made up of the following three settings.

Personal: This is for certificates that prove your true identity; many web sites will not need any form of certificate for you to view them but there are some that will require client authentication.

Authorities: This enables you to choose certificates you'll use when you are sending data to secure web sites.

Publishers: This enables you to examine and configure the settings for web sites you have decided you trust. For example, if you need to download a plug-in for a web page (a plug-in is a small program that enables you to view multimedia files over the web, see page 79), you can accept a publisher's certificate so that if you need to download any other software from that publisher you will not have to verify every download.

Personal information

This section of the **Content** tab enables you to store information about yourself in a profile. This is handy to have as it saves you having to type in the same information each time you need it. You can store your address, contact information, and even your credit card information in a password-protected storage, although to store your credit card details securely you will need to have installed Microsoft Wallet, which is an option when you install Internet Explorer 4.0.

There are some changes in Explorer 5.0: the **Payments** button on Explorer 4.0 is replaced with the **Wallet** button, where you can store information about your credit cards for use when shopping on the internet.

The new **My Profile** button replaces the **Edit Profile** and **Address** buttons where you can edit information about yourself and the entries that are contained in your address book.

THE CONNECTION TAB

This tab allows you to control the methods your computer uses to access the internet. With Explorer 5.0, you can also control the connection, and it makes it easier for you to use multiple connections on one computer. To make a new connection using Explorer 4.0, click the **Connect** button and then use the menu to set up its dial-up properties. This is completed by answering some simple questions in a connection wizard. The information you will need will be things like: number to dial, user name, password. On Explorer 5.0, the **Connect** button has been replaced with the **Setup** button.

Explorer 4.0   Explorer 5.0

Connection

If you already have a connection set up to your ISP, you will have to select one of two options. Most home users use **Connect to the Internet using a modem**. If you need to modify your modem settings, this can be done by using the **Settings** button. Most people who use their connection at work or for business will use **Connect to the Internet using a local area network**. On Explorer 5.0 there are three new buttons on the main window of the Connections tab, allowing you to set any of three different dial-up modes.

Proxy server

A proxy server is a security barrier that exists between your local network and the internet. This will mainly be used by people accessing the internet through a network at their business, though you will find that there is no need to go through a proxy server if you are accessing files on your local intranet.

Automatic configuration

Again this will only be needed for people who use this at work. Your company may have established policies to do with internet access. If they have created an automatic configuration, click **Configure** to select this option.

THE PROGRAMS TAB

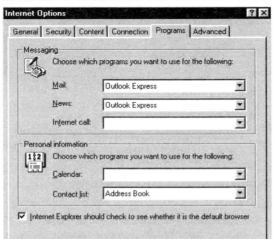

This tab of the **Internet Options** dialogue box allows you to control which programs you would use for newsgroups, e-mail and other programs.

Messaging and personal information

Outlook Express is the default setting for both e-mail and newsgroups. NetMeeting is the default setting for the internet call software. Both are installed with Explorer 4.0 and 5.0, so every time you open Explorer it will check to make sure that this is your selected browser.

If you wish to use another browser to read the HTML files, click the small drop-down arrow next to the software you wish to change. Any other software that you have installed on your computer will then be offered to you as a choice. As soon as you have selected the software you wish to use it will be shown in the box next to the name.

THE ADVANCED TAB

There are many different options to choose on this tab, and Explorer 5.0 has had some extra ones added, for example in the sections on multi-media and searching from the address bar. However, the default options (those that are automatically selected) are usually quite adequate for the general home user; do not change them unless you are quite sure about what you are changing as some of the options can make your browser behave in a strange way.

PLUG-INS

Your web browser is the piece of software that allows you to view web pages but for true interaction with the web you need 'plug-ins'. Available to download from the internet, these are used in both Internet Explorer and Netscape Communicator. A plug-in is a small program that runs in conjunction with your browser, enabling you to view multimedia files – such as animations, sound and movies – over the web. If the relevant software is already incorporated in your browser, you will not even need to know they exist. However, if you access a web page but do not have the relevant plug-ins to view the page properly, you will have a problem.

Before you download any additional plug-ins, check those that come as standard with your browser. If you are using Internet Explorer, type **C:\Windows\downloaded program files** into the address line. If you are using Netscape Navigator, type **about: plug–ins**. This will display the contents of the plug-ins folder in your browser.

These are three of the most popular and widely used plug-ins.

Shockwave www.shockwave.com Many web sites use animated graphics and many of these are produced using a program called Shockwave from Macromedia. You will need to load Shockwave player before you can view these animations.

QuickTime www.quicktime.com Many sites offers videos which you can download and view offline. Many off the videos have '.mov' file extensions, which means they were encoded using QuickTime, so you'll need the plug-in to be able to view them.

Real Player www.real.com Instead of downloading videos to watch offline, you can now use Real Player to watch them as your browser window loads. You can also listen live on the web to many radio stations using the Real Audio plug-in which is part of Real Player.

Project: Using the Explorer Content Advisor

This project will show you exactly how to use the Content Advisor on Explorer.

First, click **Enable** to display the **Create Supervisor Password** dialogue box. If you have set up the **Content Advisor** before, you will see the **Supervisor Password Required** box instead.

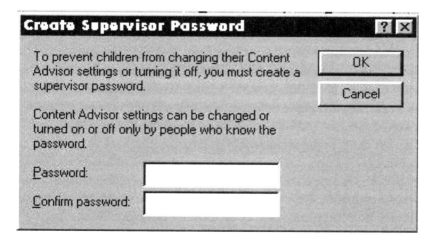

Type the password in the **Password Text** box, then press the **Tab** key to select the next box, then re-type your password in the **Confirm Password** box. You must remember the password you have entered otherwise in the future you will not be able to access this option either to change any setting or to disable the content advisor.

Click **OK** to open the **Content Advisor** dialogue box (see below) under the Ratings tab.

Explorer 4.0	Explorer 5.0

Click one of the categories you wish to block or whose protection you wish to alter. Drag the **Rating** slider to the right if you wish to increase the level of protection or drag it to the left if you wish to decrease the level of protection. Repeat this with all the categories that you need to configure to your preference.

Explorer 5.0 has a new tab in the **Content Advisor** dialogue box, called **Approved Sites**. If you select this tab you can then enter details of sites that you wish either to be made viewable at any time or permanently excluded from view.

Click the **General** tab for complete protection against material you believe may be objectionable. Deselect both the **Users can see sites that have no ratings** and **Supervisors can type a password to allow users to view restricted content**.

Remember, though, that some innocent sites can be blocked by this action. By removing both of these check marks you will not be able to visit any unrated sites. With Explorer 5.0, you can use specified rating listings provided by a third party. Using the **Ratings Systems** button, you can update the rating system that you use and find new systems if you wish.

Explorer 4.0   Explorer 5.0

Click the **Advanced Tab** if you are going to use a third-party rating system and specify the system you wish to use. Some third-party rating systems can be updated from the web so if your third-party software is capable of that, you can enter the rating update page in the **Ratings bureau** text box.

Explorer 4.0

Explorer 5.0

PICS

The people who make the standards for the internet devised the system called PICS which stands for Platform for Internet Content Selection. PICS itself is not a rating system, but it is an internet protocol that allows ratings to be transferred and understood across the internet. Internet Explorer's Content Advisor supports the PICS standard, which gives parents or supervisors control over sites containing certain types of content. Using a password, you can block or allow access to these types of sites. The Content Advisor's built-in rating system is RASCi (The Recreational Software Advisory Council rating service for the Internet), which allows you to choose levels of allowable language, nudity, sex and violence.

The Content Advisor feature allows you to filter out content based on any PICS based rating system. By default, Internet Explorer uses the RASCi rating system.

Netscape Communicator

Netscape Communicator is very similar to Internet Explorer in that it is a suite of internet software in one package. Communicator is primarily used for web browsing, but it also contains applications that enable you to browse newsgroups, use e-mail, online conferencing and web page publishing.

The web browser part of the Communicator suite is called Netscape Navigator. It may look quite different from Explorer but many of the options are the same, even though they may be displayed with different graphics and names, and you use the browser in exactly the same way.

Opening Netscape Communicator is done in the same way as Explorer (see page 59). The easiest way is to click the **Desktop** icon. Alternatively, select the **Start** button, then **Programs**, then **Netscape Communicator**, and you can select the individual parts of the Communicator suite. If you have an active desktop installed on your system, you will find the individual icons for the various components of the Communicator suite there. When you open the software, two windows open: Navigator and the component bar.

FINDING YOUR WAY ROUND NETSCAPE NAVIGATOR

Since so much of this is similar to Explorer, it will be helpful if you read through the information on pages 59–68 before you continue with this section.

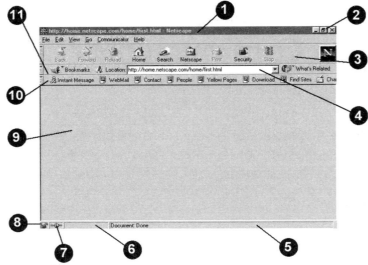

Title bar (1)

This is just like the title bar in Explorer. It also contains the minimise, maximise and close buttons in the right-hand corner.

Title bar buttons (2)

The left-hand button minimises your browser window and gives you more space on your desktop. The middle button will maximise the window, making it take up the complete display. The right-hand button will close down the browser program.

Navigation toolbar (3)

The navigation toolbar is the same as the Explorer standard toolbar and is where you will find all the one-click control buttons for the most commonly used tasks.

Back button: This returns you to a previously viewed page. Unlike Explorer, if you click and hold down your mouse button on the **Back** button it will show you a list of previously visited sites so you move further back than just one page.

Forward button: This moves forward to another web page you have viewed after clicking the **Back** button.

Reload button: This reloads the current page you are looking at in your viewing area. This is handy if the pages you are viewing update regularly in one session. You can also use this as a reset button if the page you want view is taking a long time to load.

 Home button

Pressing this will return you to your home page which by default is the Netscape home page.

 Search button

This will launch a random search engine into your viewing area so you can search the internet.

 Print button

This will print the currently viewed web page. With Netscape, you can see a preview of the page before you print it. If the page is larger than what you see on the screen, Netscape will print out the parts of the web page that you cannot see.

 Security button

This reviews the security settings for the web page you are viewing and for Netscape Navigator.

 Stop button

This will stop the current page from loading.

Menu bar (4)

This is also similar to the one in Internet Explorer, although in Netscape, Netscape Composer – the part of the suite to do with creating your own web page – it is incorporated into the browser and not a separate item.

Status bar (5)

The Netscape status bar from is different from Explorer's. It divides the page being downloaded into all its individual components – image, sound, etc., – and shows you the percentage to completion for that one item.

Connection icon (6)

This icon gives you information about your current connection. If the connection is good you will see two connecting plugs; if the connection is broken, the icon will change to two separate plugs.

Server icon (7)

This shows the status of the connection to the server holding the web page you are viewing. Many sites use secure servers, giving an encrypted connection that makes any data transfer secure. This is vital if you are sending your credit card details, for example. If you are using a secure connection, you will see a closed padlock. If it is not a secure connection, the padlock will be open. Never send sensitive or personal information unless you have a secure connection.

Viewing window (8)

This is where the web pages you are viewing are displayed.

Personal toolbar (9)

You can customise this toolbar to create quick links to your favourite web sites. Click on **Communicator** on the menu bar of the navigator menu, select **Bookmarks**, then **Edit Bookmarks**. Find the bookmark you wish to add to your personal toolbar, then click it and drag it into the personal toolbar folder and it will appear on the toolbar. To remove any unwanted bookmarks on the toolbar, click on the bookmark and press **Delete**.

Location toolbar (10)
This is where you will find the web site address for the current web page and the links to bookmarked web sites.

Closing toolbars (11)
Since there are three toolbars with Navigator, you may wish to close one of them down to make your viewing area larger. To do this, click on the small down-arrow on the left of the toolbar, which will convert it into a small parallelogram under the last toolbar on the screen. To reopen it, click on the parallelogram.

When you start your Netscape suite and browser, the component bar will open, giving you another quick way to access parts of your Netscape suite. With Netscape, the component bar always remains visible at the front of the application you are using. If you want to close it, click on the small down-arrow on the left of the toolbar and it will appear in the right-hand corner of your Navigator window. To reopen it, click on the little bars to the left.

Changing Netscape Communicator options

Within the **Preferences** option you can change the options for all the separate parts of the Communicator suite. For example, if you prefer to read your e-mail or read the newsgroups files first rather than browse, then you can do this with the **Preferences** dialogue box. To access the **Preferences** dialogue box, open the Netscape Navigator window, click on edit, then select **Preferences**.

APPEARANCE OPTION

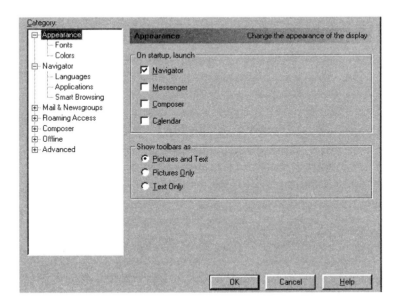

On startup, launch

Use this to specify which parts of the Navigator suite open up when you start Netscape Communicator. You can choose as many or as few as you like, at long as there is at least one.

Show toolbars as

Select whether you display the toolbar buttons as **Pictures Only**, **Text Only**, or **Pictures and Text**. The default selection is for both to be shown, which is the best option for a beginner, although you may find it better to use pictures once you are more familiar with the program.

NAVIGATOR OPTIONS

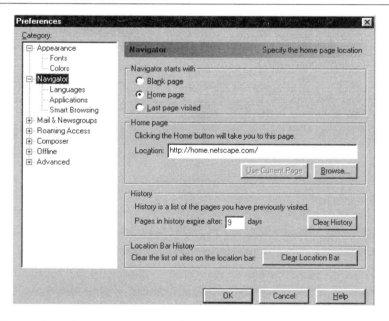

The options here are very much the same as for Internet Explorer (see page 69) although there are these additional options.

Navigator starts with

Here you can select what page is displayed when you first open up the Navigator window, just as you can specify the home page for Explorer. With Navigator, you cannot specify that the current page is your startup page.

Home page

Here, you choose which page is selected as your home page. It can be any page on the web, a page on your hard drive, or the current page.

History

This browser keeps the web pages, images, sounds, etc. from the web sites you visit in a folder on your own hard drive. With Netscape, you can select how many days they should be kept or, if you are even running low on space, you can delete your history files manually.

Location Bar History

Navigator keeps a history record of the URLs you visit but unlike most other browsers – which delete addresses at the same time as the history files – Navigator keeps the two separate.

Other options

As with Explorer (see page 72), you can also edit the languages, but you have two additional options. The **Applications** option enables you to select which of the applications you have installed on your computer will open files of a certain type when you come across them on the web or using your browser. The second extra option is **Smart browsing**. This is a Netscape-specific item that will help you increase your browsing skills when you are looking for information.

MAIL & NEWSGROUP OPTION

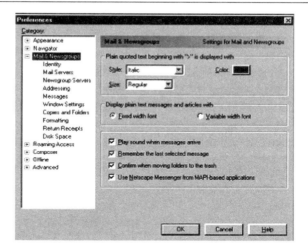

This is where you set up details for sending and receiving e-mail, on Netscape Messenger, or sending and reading newsgroups messages. You can also specify how your computer reacts when there is a new mail message for you. You will need the details provided by your ISP. Because there are so many details, they are covered separately (see pages 117–126).

ROAMING ACCESS

This preference really applies only to people who are using their computer or software on a networked computer, which is mainly in a business context. Roaming access means that when you first open up Communicator you will be asked to create a profile with your name and other details. Your profile will be saved either to your computer's hard drive or to a server to store data on your computer. Each time you use this software, you will need to select a profile so that you only access your own settings and files. Using this option, your profile will be

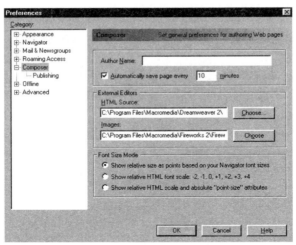

available to you no matter what computer you are using in the network. For some of these settings you may need to contact your computer systems administrator for information.

COMPOSER OPTIONS

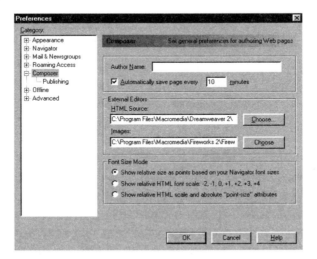

Netscape Composer deals with the creation of web pages. It is a very good HTML editor with some excellent templates and is what is known as a WYSIWYG (what you see is what you get) editor. Explaining how to set up web pages is beyond the scope of this book, however, but you can try it out for yourself and see what happens.

Author Name

What you enter here is stored as person who created the web page.

Automatically save page every

This gives you the option to specify how often your work is automatically saved so that if your computer goes down, you do not lose all your work.

External Editors

This is where you can specify other HTML and graphic editors you have installed on your system. If you wish to edit the source code of your document or edit any of the graphics on your web page, Netscape will start the programs automatically if you have specified them in this section.

Font Size Mode

This selection determines how the font sizes are shown in **Composer** so you can easily alter the font sizes used in your web page.

OFFLINE OPTIONS

This is where you set the way Communicator will start up compared to how it was left from the previous session.

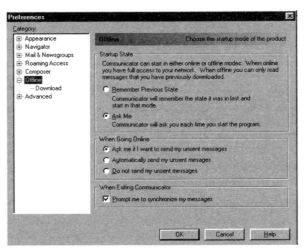

Startup State

The settings here show how Communicator starts and whether or not it automatically makes a connection to your ISP.

Remember Previous State: This starts Communicator in the same way as when it was last used. If you last used it offline, it will not try to make an internet connection straight away. You will remain in offline mode until you decide to go online. If you were online when you last used it, it will automatically try to connect to your ISP.

Ask Me: This will bring up a box of options: **Work Online** to connect you to the internet straight away; **Work Offline** to disable any network communications till you go online; and **Remember Previous State**.

When Going Online

Choose here the Communicator options when you go online. You can send any e-mail messages or newsgroup postings straight away; wait for an instruction to send your messages; or not send any messages.

When Exiting Communicator

If you choose the **Prompt me to synchronise all messages** option, the **Exit Communicator** dialogue box will come up when you exit Netscape Composer. If you decide to synchronise your messages, it will display the **Synchronise Offline Items** dialogue box. Just select what messages you wish either to send or receive before leaving, then click on **Synchronise**.

Download

In this option you will find settings that concern your e-mail and newsgroups messages. It allows you to select by age the messages are that you wish to download and which downloaded items are available to when you work offline.

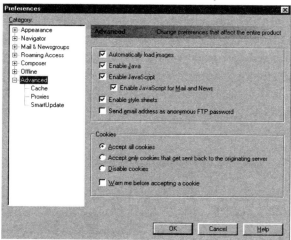

Advanced options

It is best to leave these as the default settings as any changes you make can make your browser very unstable and unpredictable.

Project: How to browse

In this simple project, you will connect to the internet, download a plug-in for your browser and add a bookmark to the site so you can go back to it later. The project is applicable for both Internet Explorer and Netscape Navigator.

First, open your browser window to display your home page. Wait for your connection to be made to your ISP.

Type in the URL for the Shockwave player – **www.macromedia.com/shockwave** – then press **Enter** to try it without the web prefix and see that your browser will begin to find the web page. Although this plug-in comes with a lot of browsers, you may find that it is not the most current version. This is what you should see in your browser window.

This Netscape page gives a list (1) of the many **hyperlinks** that exist on the page. Hyperlinks are the sentences on the web page that you click to move on to another page. The most common form of hyperlink is a word or sentence that is underlined, although they can also be images. If you place your mouse pointer over a word or image and it changes to a small hand, then that is a hyperlink or link.

Click on the link to download the software and your browser will try to connect to that page and you will see one of the pages shown below, depending on your browser. Internet Explorer allows you automatically to install software direct from the web. With Netscape, you will have to download the file, then run it to install the software.

Netscape users: Click the button to indicate from where you wish to download the software: this will be the USA, Europe or Japan. The download is faster if the data is stored on a server close to you. You will then be given a dialogue box asking you where you wish to save the file. You must remember this location as you will need to run this in order to load the software.

Explorer users: Click on the button that will install the software for you and let you choose a country from which to download. The time it will take will depend on your connection and the speed of the modem.

Click the **Next** button.

Now the Shockwave software will begin to download on to your hard drive and the dialogue boxes will change.

Netscape users: The dialogue box will show you the speed at which it is transferring the data to your computer, how much has already been completed and the amount of time remaining for the download to be complete.

Explorer users: The **Security warning** dialogue box will appear because the software has a certificate attached to it which your browser has read. If you click the **Always trust content from Macromedia** box, any other piece of self-installing software from the same source would download without a security warning. Click the **OK** button and the software will start to download.

The box that will now appear is like the one in the Netscape view except that it allows you to fill in the registration details of the software.

Once the software has been successfully downloaded you can move on to a different page if you wish.

Netscape users: Once the software has finished downloading, this will be confirmed in another dialogue box. You can then either shut down your browser and run the downloaded file or continue looking around the internet. We will go back to your home page using the **Back** button rather than the **Home** button, so click on the **Back** button with your mouse and hold the button down. This will show you a drop-down box of the pages you have visited. Select the page you wish to go back to and click on it. Your browser will locate and connect to that page.

Explorer users: Once the software has been downloaded, it is automatically installed for you by your browser. To make sure that the installation has completed correctly, click on the link that will take you to the test page where you will see some Shockwave multimedia playing. If you cannot see the Shockwave animations working properly, click on the link that will take you to the installation support page. If everything is okay, you have the choice of either closing down your browser and connection or continuing to look around the internet.

Now that you have some browsers plug-ins installed, you can try to find some Shockwave sites to view. To go back to the site listings on a previous page, click on the small down-arrow next to the **Back** button and keep the mouse button pressed. This will show a selection of previously viewed pages. Still keeping the mouse button pressed, highlight the page you wish to go

back to, then let go of your mouse button. Your browser will open up the selected page.

Now it is time for you to step out by yourself! Enter the web address (or URL) of a search engine (a site that lists available web sites and will give you lists of what is available on a specific topic) and look for something that takes your interest or visit one of the other sites listed in this book.

One important point to remember is that not all the software you download will be plug-ins; most of it will run outside your browser. These files must to be saved to your hard disk and then run to install the software. While you are downloading the software, you can carrying on viewing different web pages.

E-mail

One of the biggest advantages of the internet is e-mail. No more waiting for days for mail to be delivered, no more postal charges. All it takes to send a letter the other side of the world is a local call to your internet provider and seconds later the recipient has the mail. The other good thing is that you are able to send pictures, sounds, videos and even whole web pages just as easily as text.

There are many different e-mail 'clients' and your choice will depend on whether you want something simple or something with all the bells and whistles. Both major internet browsers come with e-mail software: Internet Explorer 4.0 and 5.0 offer Outlook Express and Netscape Communicator offers Messenger Mail. Both of these are easy to use.

You can also access many free e-mail accounts on the web, such as Hotmail, Yahoo and Rocketmail. You can access these mail accounts from anywhere in the world as long as you have an internet account. One drawback is that they take time to download on your screen as they always contain advertisements.

OUTLOOK EXPRESS

Outlook Express is easy to use, with the traditional Windows menu bar, tool bar and tiled windows. It has a couple of very handy features: it will automatically add every new e-mail address you use to your address book, and also it features an 'inbox assistant' which allows you to customise your e-mail to suit your own personal needs.

There are some differences between Outlook Express 5.0 and its predecessor, Outlook Express 4.0. One new feature that may appeal to a lot of people is that Outlook Express 5.0 offers **Hotmail support**. To set this up, click on **Tools**, then the **New Account** option and a wizard will guide you through the process.

Working offline

With Outlook Express, you have the option of working offline (preparing and reading e-mails, for example) if you have not already made an internet connection. This has the great advantage of saving on your phone bills! If you opt to do this, the articles and folders unavailable to you will be greyed out.

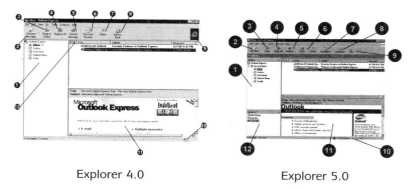

Explorer 4.0   Explorer 5.0

Message folders (1)

Inbox stores files you have received.

Outbox stores outgoing e-mails you have not sent.

Sent Items stores the e-mails you have already sent.

Deleted Items stores erased e-mails.

Drafts stores unfinished e-mails.

Samples stores standard e-mails for general use.

Compose Message/New Mail button (2)

Press this to begin writing a new e-mail. If you click on the down-arrow to the side of the **Compose Message/New Mail** button it will change the background of the e-mail message to a designed piece of paper.

Reply to Author/Reply button (3)

If you highlight an e-mail to read, and then click this button, it will then open a new e-mail box for you to write but will automatically fill in the address and subject box.

Reply to All button (4)

This works in the same way as the **Reply to Author/Reply** button but addresses your e-mail to everyone who received the original e-mail.

Forward Message/Forward button (5)

If you highlight an e-mail message, then click this button and the highlighted message will be forwarded to whoever you decide to mail it to.

Send and Receive/Send/Recv button (6)

Press this if you wish to check for any new mail once you have opened Outlook Express. In Outlook Express 5.0, there is a down-arrow beside it, which you can use to select the e-mail account you want, if you have more than one.

Delete button (7)

If you highlight a message and then press this button, the mail will be deleted from its current folder and sent to the Deleted Items folder. On Outlook Express 5.0, there is a **Print** button to the left of the **Delete** button. (On Outlook Express 4.0, the

Print function is found in the **File** drop-down menu.) You can print or delete a message without opening it, simply by highlighting it in the **Inbox** or the folder you are viewing.

Address Book button (8)

This button will open the address book where you can store or access e-mail addresses of friends and contacts. With Outlook Express 5.0 you have the useful option of using the **Contacts** pane (see below) in the bottom left-hand corner of the screen, which displays the addresses for you to see.

Internet Explorer logo (9)

This button is only found on Internet Explorer 4.0. Double-clicking on it will take you to the web.

Find (9a)

This button is unique to Internet Explorer 5.0. It allows you to search the folder or section you are in for items such as the message-sender, the message subject or even a word or phrase contained within a message.

Indicator (10)

This shows whether you are online or offline. On Outlook Express 5.0, the indicator will also tell you if any errors have occurred when sending or retrieving e-mail.

Message area (11)

This shows you the contents of the highlighted e-mail messages.

Contacts (12)

This button features only on Outlook Express 5.0. It permanently displays the contents of your address book. To send a message to someone listed here, click on their name and this will open a **New Message** window, with their address already in the address field.

CUSTOMISING THE TOOLBARS

As with Internet Explorer 5.0, it is possible to customise the toolbars of Outlook Express 5.0. Remember, however, that you need to be in the correct section of Outlook Express in order to customise the right toolbar – whenever you move to another section, the toolbar will change too.

CONFIGURING OUTLOOK EXPRESS

When you install Outlook Express, some folders are already set up for you, but you may want to create new folders to store your mail in a logical way. Once you have created the folders, you can use the **Inbox Assistant** to configure Outlook Express 4.0 to file downloaded e-mails in the correct folder, forward them or even ignore them. In Outlook Express 5.0, click on **Tools** and then use the **Message Rules** option to define what is to happen to the message.

To create new folders

You could set up a folder for every person who may be sending you e-mail, or for different projects or interests.

Right-click the **Inbox** folder, then click the **New Folder** option in the pop-up menu. The **Create New Folder** dialogue box appears.

In the **Create New Folder** dialogue box, tell Outlook Express where you want to create the folders. If you want to keep your new folders at the same level as your current folders, type in the name and click **OK**. If you wish to make your new folder a sub-folder of a current one, click on the folder in the dialogue box that will hold the sub-folder, type in the name of the new folder, then click **OK**.

To filter e-mail

You don't want to have to drag and drop files into your new folders all the time; you can use **Inbox Assistant** (Outlook Express 4.0) or the **Message Rules** option (Outlook Express 5.0) to filter your e-mail. The most popular form of filtering is to move mail messages to different folders as soon as they are downloaded. You can also use filtering to combat **Spam** – the electronic equivalent of junk mail.

Here's how it's done, using Outlook Express 4.0:

Click on the **Tools** option in the menu bar, then select the **Inbox Assistant**. To add a new rule for e-mail messages, click the **Add** button to open the **Properties** dialogue box.

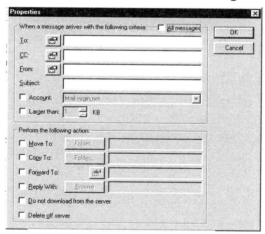

Here is a run-down of the commands that you can choose from with an example of the criteria you need to enter.

To: This will affects messages with the recipient that you choose. Example: **name@isp.com** or Firstname Surname.

CC: This looks for messages copied to the person you specify. For example: **name@isp.com** or Firstname Surname.

From: This will affect the messages from the sender you specify. For example: **name@isp.com** or Firstname Surname.

Subject: This will check for the subject text you enter. For example: Free software.

Account: This will organise messages from the account you specify. For example: **isp.com**

Larger than: This lets you specify the maximum size of messages to be received. For example: 30K.

Move to: This will redirect the message to the folder of your choice. For example: **Inbox**.

Copy to: This leaves the messages in the inbox but copies them to the folder of your choice. For example: **Inbox**.

Forward to: This automatically sends the message on to anybody you choose. For example: **name@isp.com**

Reply with: This enables you to reply and attach a file, for example: any attached file.

Do not download from the server: This leaves all messages on the server and does not download anything to your PC. You may want to use this facility when you are away on holiday.

Delete off server: This will delete selected messages off the server.

To filter using Outlook Express 5.0

Select **New Mail Rule** and the **New Mail Rule** dialogue box will appear on your screen.

At 1, use the checkboxes to define as many conditions as you want for your new rule.

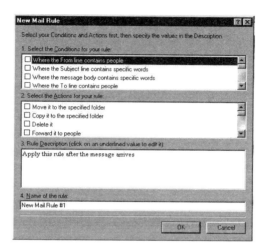

At 2, select what you want to do with any messages that the rules apply to. You can select only one option.

Your instructions will now appear at 3. You can further refine any parts of the rule that are underlined.

At 4, insert the name of your new rule.

When you have completed your new rule, click OK.

To set up a Blocked Senders list

This is another new feature introduced on Outlook Express 5.0.

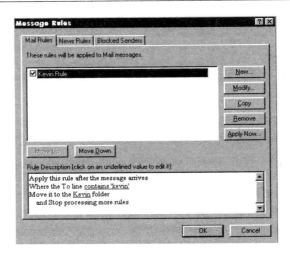

Click on the **Blocked Senders** tab in the **Message Rules** dialogue box. Click on the **Add** button and type in the e-mail address whose messages you wish to block. You can block e-mail or newsgroup postings or both. When Outlook Express 5.0 comes across an e-mail message from a blocked address, it will move it to the **Deleted Items** folder. In the case of newsgroup postings, they will simply not be shown.

NETSCAPE MESSENGER

Netscape Messenger is the e-mail component of the Netscape Communicator suite. It looks different from Outlook Express but shares many of the same features. The main difference is that the small component bar is always available in the lower right-hand corner, as in the browser Netscape Navigator. The features of Netscape Navigator are: **Open** and **Close** tabs so you can display or hide the toolbars; **Search** buttons; **Sort Capability** for mail folders; **Hot Hyperlinks** so you can link straight from your message directly on to the web; and a **Security Advisor** that tells you whether or not a message is secure. When you open Netscape Messenger, you will see this screen.

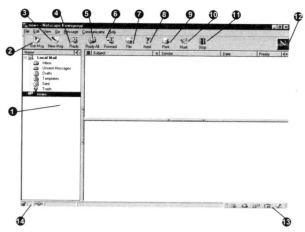

Message Folders (1)

Inbox: This stores all the files you have received.

Unsent Messages: This stores the outgoing e-mails you are waiting to send.

Drafts: This stores e-mails that you haven't finished writing.

Templates: These are standard e-mails for general use.

Sent: This stores e-mails you have already sent.

Trash: This stores erased e-mails.

News: This is how you access the newsgroup available to you on a specific server and turn messenger from an e-mail client into a newsreader.

Get Msg button (2)

Click this button to connect up to your e-mail server and download waiting mail messages.

New Msg button (3)

Click this button to begin writing a new e-mail.

Reply button (4)

If you highlight an e-mail to read and then click this button, it will open a new e-mail box for you to write with the address and subject box already filled in with the address of the incoming e-mail.

Reply All button (5)

In the same way as the Reply to Author button, this will open a new e-mail addressed to everyone who received the original e-mail.

Forward button (6)

If you highlight an e-mail message, then click this button the message will be forwarded to whoever you decide to mail it.

File button (7)

Using this button will enable you to file the current message to your system.

Next button (8)

This will move your currently selected message down to the next message you have to read.

Print button (9)

This will print the currently selected message.

Mark button (10)

This is used when you are viewing newsgroup files. Once you have downloaded the headers, you can mark the files you wish to download so that the next time you log on to your news server they will automatically download to your PC.

Stop button (11)

If a news message is taking too long or creating a problem, use this to stop the data transfer.

Netscape icon (12)

Clicking here will open Netscape Navigator browser and connect to your home page.

Component bar (13)

This bar gives you quick access to the four parts of the basic Netscape Communicator tools which are Navigator (the internet browser), Messenger (this software), Collabra (a piece of discussion group software) and Netscape Composer (the HTML editor).

Online/offline indicator (14)

If you are online, it will show the two sockets joined together; if you are offline it will show the plugs split apart.

CONFIGURING NETSCAPE MESSENGER

Place your ISP details in the Messenger set up and click on the **Get Msg** button to download any mail that is waiting in your mail server. The **Inbox** folder title will appear in bold with a number next to it showing how many new mail messages you have received. The new messages will also be listed in bold in the **Inbox** folder.

To create folders

As with Outlook Express, you can create as many folders or sub-folders as you like and some people find it easier to create folders in Netscape Messenger than in Outlook Express. To create folders, click on **File** in the menu bar, then select **New Folder**. This will then open the **New Folder** dialogue box. Type in the name of the folder you wish to create. If you wish to make this a sub-folder, use the drop arrow to show a list of available folders, click **OK** and your new folder will appear in the **Folders** area.

Project: Sending an e-mail

This project is based on Outlook Express. First, open your e-mail software. Depending on how you have set up your software, it may try to connect to the internet straight away. You need to be online to download messages but not to create an e-mail, so click **Cancel** if it does try to connect.

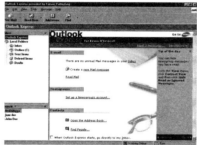

Explorer 4.0   Explorer 5.0

Outlook Express will load its main page, allowing you to select different options. As we want to create a new e-mail, we need to open a new message. To do this, either click on the **Compose Message** (IE 4.0) or **New Mail** (IE 5.0) button in the toolbar, or click on the **Compose Message/New Mail** icon if the front page is shown.

A blank message appears on the screen with its own toolbar, a header section where you fill in details such as the addressee

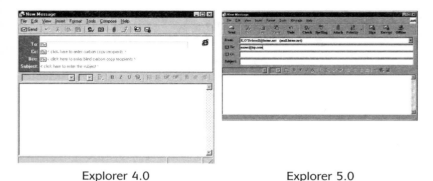

Explorer 4.0   Explorer 5.0

and the title of the message and a blank section at the bottom where you type the message you wish to send. Note that if you are using Outlook Express 5.0, and you have more than one e-mail account, there will be an extra bar, marked From:. Use the drop-down menu to select the account you wish to use.

Place your cursor at the beginning of the line marked To: and type in the address of the person you are writing to. Make sure you type accurately with all the dots and dashes in the right place, otherwise you will not be able to send the mail. Most British addresses will end in **.co.uk** and most American addresses end in **.com**

If the person you wish to send the message to is listed in your address book, you can either click on **Address** and select their name from the list in the address book. If you are using Outlook Express 5.0, you can either click on the book icon to the left of the line marked **To:** and select their name from the address book, or double-click on their name in the **Contacts** pane.

If you want to send the mail to more than one person, repeat the process with the second person's address going into the box marked **CC:**. If you want to send the mail to more than two people, type a semi-colon (;) after the first person's address, then type in details of the other addressees.

Next you need to give the mail message a title, and you write this in the **Subject** box. This is the first thing the person receiving the mail will see, so make it something appropriate to your message.

Now type in the message you want to send. Place your cursor in the large empty box in the bottom half of the screen, click once, then start typing. You can use the **Format** option in the menu bar if you wish to alter the appearance of your text, or click the **View** button so that the **Format** toolbar appears on the screen.

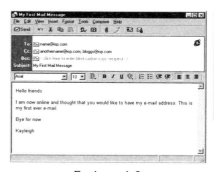 

Explorer 4.0   Explorer 5.0

Once you have finished typing your message, you can spellcheck it by clicking the **Tools** option in the menu bar (OE 4.0) or by pressing the **Spelling** button (OE 5.0).

To send your message, click the **Send** button on the toolbar or click the **File** option on the menu bar. If you do the latter, you have the choice of either sending straight away or sending later.

If you decide to send it later, your message will be placed in the **Outbox** to await your instructions. A number in brackets after the **Outbox** folder will tell you how many messages you have waiting to be sent.

When you want to send your e-mail, click on **Send and Receive (Send/Recv)** and if you are not already connected to the internet, your mail software will start a connection to your ISP and send it for you. The message will still be placed in the **Outbox** but a dialogue box will appear, showing you a progress bar to indicate that the message is being sent.

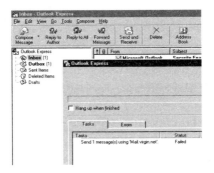

To confirm that your e-mail has been sent, open your **Sent Items** folder and you will see a copy of the mail you sent. Also the number (1) next to the **Outbox** folder will have disappeared.

Project: Receiving an e-mail

When you open Outlook Express and are connected to the internet, all the mail waiting for you will be downloaded from your ISP mail server to your PC. If you have mail waiting to be read, the word **Inbox** on your message folder will be bold and after it you will see a number in brackets representing the number of new mails you have received.

Double-click on your Inbox folder to open it and the right-hand pane splits in two. In the top view is a list of all the e-mails you have received. The new or unread e-mails will be in bold. In the lower half of the screen you will see a preview of the e-mail that is currently selected in the top half of the screen.

Explorer 4.0   Explorer 5.0

To open an e-mail, double-click on it in the top screen. If there is a paper clip next to the message or a picture of one in the right-hand corner of the preview, this means that the e-mail contains an attachment. To open the attachment, double-click on the paper clip on the preview and it will bring up a dialogue box asking what you want to do with it. You can either save it to your computer's hard disk or open it straight away.

If you have been logged on to the internet for a while and you wish to see if you have received any new mail, click on the **Send and Receive** button in the toolbar and any new mail will be delivered to your inbox.

Newsgroups

Newsgroups offer a vast resource for information. You need software called a **News Client** to access the newsgroups. The two main browsers contain the newsgroup readers you need. In Explorer it is part of the Outlook Express package, in the Netscape suite, the newsgroup reader is called Collabra. If you are going to use newsgroups a great deal, you may want a few extra facilities, in which case you could investigate a news client such as Newsmonger or Forte Agent, both of which can be downloaded from the web.

Newsgroups are very much like e-mail. Groups on the server are arranged by topics and anyone can put a message in the group or download a message from the group in the same way as sending or receiving an ordinary e-mail. Just as with e-mail, you can forward messages to someone, reply to the author or reply to the group. You can also add attachments, which can be either pictures, sound, video clips and other files.

One drawback with newsgroups is that because they are public, they open the way to a new problem in the form of unwanted advertisements (Spam), mainly for 'get-rich-quick' schemes or adult sites. They will often have nothing to do with the topic of the site, and may take up to 50 per cent of the newsgroup files. This is because it is impossible to control what gets sent into a newsgroup and because it is easy for someone to hide their true identity when posting.

That said, Newsgroups are a very useful way of communicating on the internet.

To join a newsgroup, you need to connect to a news server. All the major ISPs have a server dedicated to newsgroups. The number of groups carried will depend on the ISP but is likely to be up to 30,000. Access the news server and download the list of newsgroups available, then search for the group you wish to join. Subscribing to the newsgroup does not cost anything. Once you have subscribed and are connected to the newsgroup, headers will download on to your PC. Once this is done, you will be able to view them either offline or online. You can then mark messages for download to your PC and see the complete message. If you mark messages when you are offline, they will download automatically when you go back online. Once downloaded, the messages can be viewed either online or offline.

OUTLOOK EXPRESS

Before you can use Outlook to view news messages you will need to set it up. In order to do this, you will need to place the new server name in your list. Find this out from your ISP and also make a note of your e-mail address.

First, open Outlook Express and connect to the internet if it does not auto-connect.

From the menu bar, click on **Tools** and select **Accounts**.

From the **Internet Accounts** dialogue box, select the **News** tab and click **Add** then **News** as the account you wish to add.

This will open up the **Internet Connection** wizard which will ask you some questions about yourself and your e-mail account.

The wizard will ask you for information concerning the 'domain' name for your news server. This information is available from your ISP, although the format is usually **news.** followed by the ISP name: for example, **news.virgin.net** – you will only need to check the box requiring you to log in if your ISP specifies that.

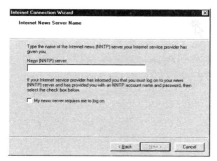

Carry on answering the simple questions, then click **Finish**. A new folder will have opened in the main window, which is your connection to your news server.

Once you connect to the news server, Outlook Express will notice that you are not a subscriber to any newsgroups. It will ask if you wish to download a list of available newsgroups from your server. You have to do this before you can access any of the groups.

Click **Yes** to download your list. Even with a fast connection, it will take a few minutes to download as most ISPs carry over 30,000 groups. The good news is that it will only have to be done once.

To save time searching through the list to select the ones you wish to view, search for a group of sites. Type the first few letters of your hobby or interest in the display newsgroups box and the list will shrink down to the groups that contain the letters or word you specified.

Once you have selected a newsgroup, you have to subscribe to it to read the messages it contains. You can either click the **Subscribe** button or double-click on the group name.

When you click the **Go to** button, the subscription dialogue box will disappear and you will return to Outlook Express and see that message headers are being downloaded. By default, only the first 300 headers are downloaded. If it is a busy newsgroup, there may be more than 300 to view. Click on the **Headers** button in the toolbar menu to download the next 300 headers.

To read the messages, click the **Messages** header and the message will begin to download. Once it has downloaded, you will see a preview of it in the panel below the headers list and the icon to the left of the message will change from a broken to a complete newspaper.

Once you have downloaded the messages, you can view the headers offline and mark the ones you wish to view by right-clicking to mark the headers and then selecting the **Mark Message** option. Alternatively, you can click in the column to the left of the message header.

When you re-connect to the internet and select **Check All Mail**, it will download the messages you have selected from the header list.

NETSCAPE COLLABRA

Collabra needs a basic set-up before you can read any of the newsgroup messages. When you first open up Netscape Communicator, it will run through a series of wizards asking you to set up your e-mail and newsgroups preferences. If you did not set these up, you can do so later by going into the **Preferences** and entering the data required, such as the address of the news server of your internet provider. Once this is done you can then connect up to the news server and download the newsgroup messages.

First, make sure you are connected to the internet, then open Netscape Communicator. Click the **Discussions** button on the component bar to open Collabra in a new window.

Download the list of available newsgroups from your ISP news server by clicking on the name of your news server in the left-hand panel to highlight it. This will activate the buttons in the button bar.

Click on the **Subscribe** button to begin downloading the list. This will take some time, although it will only have to be done once. You will not see much happening on the screen apart from a line moving from side to side in the bottom left-hand corner of the dialogue box with the words **Receiving newsgroups** to the right.

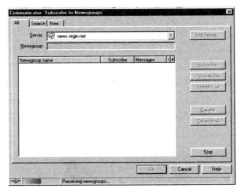

Once your lists have been downloaded, you will have to subscribe to a newsgroup to receive the message from that group. You can find and select groups through the **All** tab or through the **Search** tab.

Using the **All** window it can be difficult to locate the group you want. All the newsgroups are grouped together with submenus instead of in one huge list. You can work your way through this in the same way as if you were using Windows Explorer to browse your computer's hard drive.

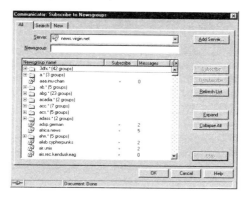

To use the **Search** tab, click on it to bring it to the front. Type in a few letters or a word you wish to search for. The results of your **Search** window will stay blank. To get the results of the search you will need to click the **Search Now** button and a list of the newsgroups themselves will be displayed. The example below shows a result for the search of newsgroups from the word 'computers'.

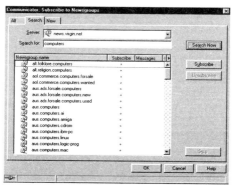

Once you find a newsgroup you wish to subscribe to, click it to highlight it, then either click the **Subscribe** button or double-click the newsgroup. To show that the newsgroup is a subscribed group, you will see a tick by its name. Once you have subscribed to all the newsgroups you wish, click **OK** to exit.

All the newsgroups you have subscribed to are now listed under your news server name in the main Collabra window.

To read messages within the newsgroup, highlight the name of the newsgroup. If there are a lot of messages, you will be asked whether you want to download all the messages or just the first 500. You can also change the number of headers.

Once the headers have been downloaded, you will see them all in the top right-hand pane in the main Collabra window. Highlight a message and it will be downloaded on to your PC. A preview of the message will appear in the bottom right-hand pane. To view messages in their own window, double-click the message.

You can set up messages to be downloaded offline. Download all the messages to your PC and then go offline. Scroll through all the messages and select the ones you wish to view. Highlight the file you wish to view, then click the **Mark** button in the button bar. When you next go online, click the **Get Msg** button and select **Get Marked Messages** to download them on to your PC.

SENDING MESSAGES TO NEWSGROUPS

Adding your own messages to the newsgroup is as easy as sending an e-mail. Highlight the group to which you would like to send a message. Create a new message by clicking the **New Msg** button in Netscape or the **Compose Message** button in Outlook. Fill out your message with title, message, and any other information you want to send, in the same way as creating an e-mail, then simply post the mail to send your message to the news server and then into the newsgroup.

One thing you may notice is that there are some messages which all have the same title. These are called threads, which are replies to an original message.

If you want to respond to a message, there are different sequences for Outlook and Netscape.

Replying to a message in Outlook
In Outlook, you have two options.

Reply to group: If you use this option, the message will be posted to the newsgroup where everyone who has access can read the message.

Reply to author: Using this option, you will reply only to the author of the original message.

Replying to a message in Collabra

In Netscape Collabra, you can reply in the same ways as Outlook, but in two other ways as well.

Reply to sender and all recipients: This will allow you to reply to the sender and also anyone who originally received the message. The message will not be posted to everyone in the group.

Reply to sender and group: This option allows you to reply to the original author of the message and also to post your message to the whole newsgroup.

1000 Really useful web sites

Here is a selection of some really useful web sites so that you can go direct to the source of the information you need without wasting time trying to find that essential gem of knowledge for your household finances, hobby or school project. As the web is growing all the time, we need your input so that we can expand and update the list, so if you have come across other valuable sites in your travels around the net, visit our web site at:
www.foulsham.com
and tell us about your favourites.

ANIMALS

About Gerbils
This site provides a basic guide to looking after gerbils. There are many sections in the web pages that should broaden the foundation of information in this basic guide. Regardless of whether you want information about breeding, general care, naming your gerbils or even funny and serious stories featuring gerbils, you will find it somewhere on this comprehensive web site.

http://www.gerbils.org.uk/index.html

Acme Pet
This site is a huge directory listing of pet sites on the web, as well as having its own newspaper, club, marketplace and multimedia gallery. Also available is the chance to send pet and e-cards and lots more.

http://acmepet.petsmart.com

Allpets.com

This is an online magazine and encyclopedia which provides practical information about caring for all sorts of pet.

http://www.allpets.com

Animal Information Database

SeaWorld, the major theme park in Orlando, switches on its webcams at meal times, but in between the shows it provides games, quizzes and guides on the animals to give you an insight into their behaviour.

http://www.seaworld.org

Animal Omnibus

The Animal Omnibus is a reference list of animal web sources, indexed by the name of the animal, so provides links to information and booklists on any specific animal.

http://www.birminghamzoo.com/ao/

Animals Around the World

A wonderful source of information on animals for all animal-lovers and students.

http://www.chicojr.chico.k12.ca.us/staff/gray/animals.html

Bird Box Company

A unique site selling wildlife boxes into which you can fit a camera to connect to your TV or PC so you can watch and hear the birds or mammals from your armchair without disturbing them. They are in the process of establishing an eco-network so you can also view other people's images.

http://www.thebirdbox.com

British Aquatic Resource Centre

This site aims to provide interesting and informative articles both on a general level and from specialist societies. Information is included about clubs and societies in Britain that you can join, including local clubs and national specialist societies for people with particular interests in this field. There's also information on interesting books and CDs, and shops for you to browse and information on where to buy what you need.

http://www.cfkc.demon.co.uk/

The Dinosauria
What does modern science tell us about the dinosaurs? How did they live? Are they really obsolete, long-extinct relics of a more primitive stage in the history of life, or is there more to them than meets the eye? Find out the facts and theories here. The Dinosauria includes a section on myths and contains links to numerous other dinosaur sites.

http://www.ucmp.berkeley.edu/diapsids/dinosaur.html

Feline Advisory Bureau
This charity is based in Wiltshire, England, and supports research into the health and welfare of cats by making the latest information available to vets, cat breeders and owners. FAB members receive a quarterly colour journal outlining the latest information and treatments in the feline world. Over 50 information sheets are also available on feline diseases, behaviour and breeding for you to download and read on your own computer.

http://web.ukonline.co.uk/fab/

Fish Information Service
Free information service about topics of interest to the aquarium hobbyist. FINS is constantly changing as new information is added and old information is updated. All that you need to know about aquariums is included. There's also a glossary, a catalogue of fish and invertebrates, information on diseases, diagnosis and treatment.

http://www.actwin.com/fish/index.cgi

Hamster Site
This site is packed with information about these popular pets. The site includes an in-depth guide to the various species, health and care advice, plus links to breeders, clubs and shows.

http://www.hamsters.co.uk/

The Horse Interactive

This site is concerned with all aspects of equine health, and it is written for hands-on horse owners, trainers, riders, breeders, and barn managers who want to know more about taking the best care of their horses. There is extensive information on topics of concern, supplemented by timely features on horse health and news from researchers, veterinarians in the field and other equine professionals.

http://www.thehorse.com/

Net Vet

Whatever queries you may have about any animal, you are bound to find the answers here. The site contains an electronic zoo, the Net Vet gopher, many specialist directories and the veterinary medicine page of the web's virtual library.

http://netvet.wustl.edu/vet.htm

Panda Camera

A live panda to watch as it sleeps, plus facts and information.

http://www.sandiegozoo.org/special/pandacam/index.html

Pet of the Day

This is a free site on which one pet is selected to be honoured each day. Dogs are featured on the web site dedicated just to dogs called Dog of the Day. Cats are featured on Cat of the Day. If your pet is selected, they will let you know in advance which day will be your pet's special day.

http://www.petoftheday.com/

Pets Park

Pets Park has been created for anyone who loves pets and animals. There's information and advice provided by their vet Gina and animal behaviourist Laila to help you understand, care for and cherish your pet. You'll also be able to buy all you need for your pet at the Pets Park superstore. It's convenient, fun and safe. It will soon be the largest internet pet shop in Europe. Their goal was clear – to create a place where pet and animal-lovers can meet and share their experiences as well as shop for all their pet-care needs.

http://www.petspark.com/

Pets Pyjamas

Pets Pyjamas is a major European site catering for the needs of pet owners by offering shopping, information, services and entertainment. Pets Pyjamas has sister sites in France, PetsPyjamas.fr, and Germany, PetsPyjamas.de, and further European expansion is planned. In addition to the web site, a Pets Pyjamas catalogue is also available in which you will find the full range of products and services offered on the internet.

http://www.pets-pyjamas.co.uk

Planet Koi

This site is dedicated entirely to Japanese koi carp, or Nishikigoi. Here you can find information about koi varieties, koi health, koi breeding, feeding koi and what to look out for when buying koi. Also available is a great links page and the opportunity to buy koi and accessories online and find out about koi clubs.

http://www.koicarp.demon.co.uk/

Royal Society for the Protection of Birds

For all bird-lovers, you can find out about the society and read interesting articles on nature reserves, conservation issues and generally looking after our feathered friends. Also contains information on membership of the society.

http://www.rspb.com

Royal Society for the Prevention of Cruelty to Animals

This is the official site of the Royal Society for the Prevention of Cruelty to Animals. It is full of information about the work done by the RSPCA and also how the public can help them. You can also download a foxy screensaver, adopt a cyber pet, and receive online advice on how to deal with common pet ailments. Enter into the kids' zone and you can read the zany zodiac and meet the mystic monkey.

http://www.rspca.org.uk

Virtual Memorial Garden
The VMG is not a place of death, but an online free memorial – somewhere people can celebrate their family, friends and pets; to tell the rest of us about them and why they were special. You can also place an ode on the site, and this service is currently free.

http://catless.ncl.ac.uk/vmg/

Virtual Pet Cemetery
At this site for a small fee you can immortalise in cyberspace the pets you have loved and lost, telling the world just how much they mean to you. In this American online memorial garden, it'll cost $15 (about £10) to display your tribute.

http://www.mycemetery.com/my/pet_menu.html

ZooNet
ZooNet has useful information on various zoos and contains all kinds of picture sections. Visit the animal galleries, where the pictures can be viewed in two different sizes: a small 'thumbnail' size and a larger versions to help you get a better look at the contents of this interesting site.

http://www.mindspring.com/~zoonet/gallery.html

ANTIQUES

Chelsea Clocks

Antique clocks and other similar objects with online ordering and e-mail for further information.

http://www.chelseaclocks.co.uk

Cyber Antique Mall

The purpose of this page is to provide a web directory that categorises quality antique dealers and antiques-related sites on the web. Most of these links have been checked out for quality and usefulness. Cyber Antique Mall guarantees that all antiques posted on their site are authentic, although they will not be responsible for authentication of antiques from other web sites.

http://www.cyberantiquemall.com/

The Internet Antiques Shop

This site contains a unique group of antique and collectible cybershops that can't be found anywhere else on the web. Tens of thousands of antiques and collectibles are available online from antique shops around the United States, Europe, Canada and South America. Pictures, text and complete online catalogues. If you like to browse antique shops you will love this. The Tias Bookshop is one of the largest of its kind on the web, with almost 1000 new books about antiques and collectibles.

http://www.tias.com/

Portobello Market

For many years, collectors and the general public have flocked to the Portobello Road in London, England to roam around the stalls and shops, which offer an unending source of reasonably priced antiques. The web site gives you information on which stalls are on the market and the range of goods available. There is also a map of the market area and travel directions, which you can download to print out.

http://www.portobelloroad.co.uk/

ART

see also Books and Culture, Museums and Galleries

About Design
Good for the creative and design world, which seems to be becoming more pervasive. Glossary, chat, links, etc.

http://www.aboutdesign.co.uk

ArtAIDS Link
The AIDS patchwork quilt consists of thousands of personal tributes made by family and friends of those who have died of AIDS. You can now add your own tributes by connecting up to this site. ArtAIDS Link is the internet equivalent of this incredible quilt.

http://www.illumin.co.uk/artaids/

Artchive – Theory and Criticism
This is a museum-style site where they say that 'At the Artchive, the only constant will be change'. Each gallery will include new material so that each visit offers variety, taken from new scans in the Recent Acquisitions gallery, to additional art criticism excerpts and new installations of feature exhibits. The museum is divided into several galleries: The Artchive, Art Reviews, Theory and Criticism, Juxtapositions, CD-ROM reviews and Art links.

http://www.artchive.com/

The Art Connection
If you are interested in seeing what artwork is for sale in some of London's top commercial galleries, then this is the site for you.

http://www.art-connection.com

Art Guide – The Art Lovers' Guide to Britain and Ireland
There are hundreds of magnificent public art collections in Great Britain and Ireland, and each year they are enjoyed by millions of visitors from all over the world. Art Guide is for anyone who has ever

enjoyed a trip to one of these collections, or for people who are planning a visit to one of them. Art Guide is organised by artist, by museum and geographically. The database currently contains more than 1900 named artists, more than 650 museums, over 4500 individual listings and comprehensive exhibitions listings. For each artist there is a list of their works and where they can be found; for each museum a list of outstanding works in the collection, an address, telephone number and links to other museums in the same region.

http://www.artguide.org

ArtLex

ArtLex is a dictionary of definitions of all 'artistic words', containing the explanations of more than 2800 terms along with illustrations, pronunciation notes, quotations and links to other resources.

http://www.artlex.com/

Art for Sale?

This site is the US government-sponsored index to the arts. Its main objective is to help those who are interested in acquiring different works of art.

http://www.artsusa.org/clearinghouse/

Design Council

Find out all about the many people around today who have helped add substance to the arts in the UK, whether or not you agree that they have made such a contribution! Find out about the latest movements and exhibitions here at the Design Council's web site.

http://www.design-council.org.uk/

The Fray

On the site it is stated that 'the Fray is a place for people who believe the web is about personal expression and a new kind of art'. If you choose to visit this site, you will definitely find it is provocative, perhaps disturbing, too. You have been warned!

http://www.fray.com/

Grove Art

The Grove Dictionary of Art is the most comprehensive online reference resource for all aspects of the visual arts from prehistory to the 1990s. You will also find links to further information in museum and other art-related web sites. You will need version 4.0 or above of Internet Explorer or Netscape to view the site and either one can be downloaded free from here. It is a subscription site.

http://www.groveart.com

Spike Magazine

Spike is about people, books and ideas. The site continues to update on a frequent but erratic basis, publishing interviews, features, reviews and new writing both by established and unpublished authors. The site features not only the famous and the up and coming, but also the totally obscure.

http://www.spikemagazine.com/

World Art Resources

This site is an enormous interactive guide to art and culture on the internet. It has information on over 7,800 artists and over 100,000 further arts resources on top of that. The site covers visual and performing arts too, so you can find out about dance, antiques, opera, theatre, architecture, film and literature here as well. Finally, when you have completed your research you can then use the site to send artistic e-postcards to all your friends.

http://www.wwar.com/

ASTROLOGY

see also New Age

Astronet

This astrology magazine consists of a wide selection of regularly updated articles and different types of horoscope. Astronet also includes advice columns and offers interactive features including personalised horoscopes, relationship compatibility and instant readings that can be obtained by various methods using only a birth date. You can also join a workshop and have a basic astrology lesson. There are message boards and a chat room for you to use, together with links to other related sites.

http://www.astronet.com/

Astrology on the Web

This is a huge astrology resource with detailed horoscope information, topical astrology features and horoscope readings. The site can be viewed in English, French, German, Italian, Portuguese and Spanish.

http://www.astrologycom.com/

Internet Horoscopes

At this site you can bookmark the page or fill out the form to have a free horoscope e-mailed to you daily. 'Use your zodiac sign to unlock the astrological outlook on the things that matter most: romance and sex, health and fitness, career and finance – all aspects of your life!' The site also includes a handy link to a translation tool that enables your horoscope to be viewed in any language.

http://www.internethoroscopes.com/

Netstrology

This is analysis of the stockmarkets with a difference! For your investment, technology, career and money astrological profiles, do your 'research' at the Netstrology web site.

http://www.techweb.com/horoscope/

Your Yastrologer – Daily Horoscope

This is truly an unusual horoscope site. Your Yastrologer not only gives you a daily horoscope prediction but also includes a list of links to web sites that match your birth sign. All you have to do is pick your birthday from the list and the site will do the rest.

http://www.zdnet.com/yil/selector/getsign.html

ASTRONOMY

See also Space

Aboriginal Star Knowledge: Native American Astronomy

Stone medicine wheels were in use about 2,200 years ago on the northern plains of Alberta and Saskatchewan and you can discover how they work at this interesting site. Study Native American legends and folklore behind the stars at this site too.

http://indy4.fdl.cc.mn.us/%7Eisk/stars/starmenu.html

Bradford Robotic Telescope Observatory Site

Anyone can access this telescope and ask it to look at anything in the northern night sky. This is a real 'hands-on' site and is a must for all astronomy enthusiasts.

http://www.eia.brad.ac.uk/btl/

Center for Mars Exploration

This site presents historical references to Mars, together with previous Mars mission information and current Mars news. It also gives you the tools to analyse Mars and take your studies further.

http://cmex-www.arc.nasa.gov/

The Constellations

Do you need information on the stars, how they are grouped into constellations, and the Milky Way? The first thing that might surprise you is how far apart the different stars in a constellation actually are! A source of all sorts of fascinating information about the stars is to be found at this site.

http://www.astro.wisc.edu/~dolan/constellations/

Earth and Moon Viewer

This site 'presents an earth map – you can see where it is day, or night, right now'. View either a map of the earth showing the day and night regions at this moment, or view the earth from the sun, the moon, or the night-side of the earth. You can view it above any location on the planet that has been specified by latitude, longitude and altitude, from a satellite in earth orbit, or above various cities around the globe.

http://www.fourmilab.ch/earthview/vplanet.html

History of the Light Microscope

The microscope has become one of the most recognisable symbols of science. This site covers the early history of the microscope, starting with use of a simple lens in ancient times, to the first compound microscope developed in about 1590, up to the microscopes of the nineteenth century.

http://www.utmem.edu/personal/thjones/hist/hist_mic.htm

Hubble Space Telescope's Greatest Hits 1990–95

The Hubble space telescope evokes a new sense of awe and wonder about the infinite richness of our universe in dramatic, unprecedented pictures of celestial objects. This site presents a selection of Hubble's most spectacular images.

http://oposite.stsci.edu/pubinfo/BestOfHST95.html

The Jason Project

After world-famous explorer Dr Robert Ballard discovered the wreck of RMS *Titanic*, he received thousands of letters from students around the world wanting to go with him on his next expedition. As a result of this, Dr Ballard and a team of associates dedicated themselves to developing ways that would enable teachers and students all over the world to take part in global, year-round explorations using advanced interactive telecommunications. Hence the Jason Project was founded and is now a leader in distance-learning programmes. It continues to extend its reach by adding more 'components' regularly and is a site not to be missed.

http://www.jason.org

The Messier Catalogue

Images of the brightest and most beautiful diffuse objects in the sky, including nebulae, galaxies and star clusters, can be found here. A fascinating discovery.

http://www.seds. org/messier/

The Nine Planets

This site is a collection of information about our solar system intended for a general audience with little technical background. No special expertise or knowledge is needed; all technical and astronomical terms and proper names are defined in the glossary. The bulk of this material should be familiar to planetary scientists and astronomers but they may find a few interesting tidbits, too. This document consists of about 90 web pages, one page for each major body in the solar system. Each page has: a large picture of its object and usually several smaller thumbnail images (all linked to their full-size originals); some scientific and historical facts about it; if the object has satellites, then its page has a table of data on them and links to their pages; links to more images and information about the object elsewhere on the web; and a list of open issues for which we as yet have no answers.

http://seds.lpl.arizona.edu/nineplanets/

Northern Lights Planetarium

The Northern Lights, or Aurora Borealis, has been called 'nature's own gigantic light show'. This special light phenomenon can be seen on the northern and southern hemispheres, only when the circumstances are right. Basically, the Northern Lights occurs when particles from the sun are thrown against the earth by the solar wind. When the particles collide with the earth's atmosphere, the energy of the particles is turned into light. Go on a ride in the universe at this Norwegian planetarium and see it all for yourself.

http://www.uit.no/npt/homepage–npt.en.html

Saturn Watch

Cassini Mission to Saturn allows you to follow along with the spacecraft as it makes its 6.7-year journey to the planet. Launched in

October 1997, every step of the project can be found on this site. You can find out about the mission design, watch movies of the launch to navigation, or look at photos taken along the way.

http://www.jpl.nasa.gov/cassini/

Search for Extraterrestrial Intelligence

Are we alone in the universe? That is the question being asked at the SETI Institute. At this site you can see the effort that is currently being made to detect evidence of technological civilisations that may exist elsewhere in the universe, particularly in our galaxy. There are potentially billions of locations outside our solar system that may host life. Find out more about it all here.

http://www.seti-inst.edu/

Skyview

A good site if you need a telescope.

http://www.skyview.gsfc.nasa.gov/skyview.html

Views of the Solar System

Go on a vivid multimedia adventure of the solar system from the comfort of your own home! This site shows the splendour of the sun, planets, moons, comets, asteroids, and more. Discover the latest scientific information, or study the history of space exploration, rocketry, early astronauts, space missions, and spacecraft through a vast archive of photographs, scientific facts, text, graphics and videos. The site is available in English, Spanish, Portuguese and French.

http://www.hawastsoc.org/solar/homepage.htm

Windows to the Universe

Windows to the Universe is a user-friendly site helping people to learn about the earth and space-related sciences. It uses the web to allow easy access to numerous sources of space information. The project is aimed at people using publicly available platforms with high-speed internet connections at libraries, hands-on museums and classrooms.

http://www.windows.umich.edu/

AUCTIONS

The Auction Channel

The Auction Channel is 'the first interactive themed television and internet channel offering live coverage of auctions and related programming, broadcasting via satellite and cable to television and internet users'. However the live auctions are accessed, viewers can take part in the bidding using the unique interactive bidding system. Fine and contemporary art, antiques, memorabilia, classic cars, country estates, jewellery, collectable toys and posters are all on offer.

http://www.theauctionchannel.com/

Because-We-Can

Are you worried about security when joining an online auction? According to this site you should be, because it is apparently very easy for malicious persons to assume control of eBay accounts. Because-We-Can tells you all about this scam and how to protect yourself when using an online auction, which is not easy but is essential.

http://www.because-we-can.com/ebayla/index.htm

Bullnet Auctions

This UK-based site free auction specialises in selling items from the normal to the bizarre! Here you can bid for anything from surveillance equipment to toys and novelties once you have given over your credit card details. This site may be of particular use to subscribers interested in electronics and computers. Existing clients can use their current login and password, although if you are selling goods you can add more information about yourself, if you wish.

http://www.bullnet.co.uk/auctions/

EBay

EBay is 'the world's largest personal online trading community'. It is a British-based auction site, selling everything from pottery to pianos. Browse and shop at EBay by category, location or availability. Enter your own goods for online auction and sell here too. Prices can be viewed in pounds or dollars. Auction times are given in GMT or BST.

http://www.ebay.co.uk

EBid

EBid has been carefully designed and is good to use because it has an extensive and well-organised list of categories. It is a person-to-person auction site that offers items for sale in the UK. Prices are in sterling, and the site requires no credit card registration.

http://www.ebid.co.uk/

Icollector Online Auctions

At Icollector Online Auctions, lots are put up for sale by a wide range of auction houses from around the world. It has a glossary of terminology and the facility to enable bidding directly from the site. It gives details of how to use the site and how to pay for lots, but it does not arrange shipping. You can get advice about this in the Terms and Conditions section or you can ask at the Customer Help desk.

http://www.icollector.com

QXL

QXL is an online auction for Europe only and it lets you buy quality goods at great prices. Auctions are opened and closed each day and they offer a variety of goods in computer, electronic goods, jewellery, gifts, hosehold and travel. The site is also available in German, French and Italian.

http://www.qxl.com

BANKING

See also Finance and Insurance

Barclaycard

Pretty much everything you can do at a bank, you can do from your PC with this site dedicated to Barclaycard customers.

http://www.barclaycard.co.uk

Barclays

Online banking, business park, stock brokers, newsroom and recruiting from one of Britain's biggest banks. You'll also find investor information on this site.

http://www.barclays.com

First-e

Operating offshore, this totally virtual bank has no branches but functions only online. Interest is calculated without paying tax.

http://www.first-e.com

MasterCard International

This site contains everything you could possibly want know about MasterCard. Look into the future of banking, too, with electronic payments, smart cards and online transactions explained.

http://www.mastercard.com

Natwest

Another site offering all their usual banking services online plus useful information on holidays, running a business and other topics relevant to your financial life.

http://www.natwest.com

Online Banking

Do you want to find a bank that is open 24 hours a day so you can sort out your finances at a time that suits you, or do you want to know more about the one you are already with? Use this site to check out the banks. It gives you all the banks' web sites so you can find out more about each one.

http://www.netbanker.com

Visa International
Visit the Visa site to find out all about the services they provide. Visa International has the edge where electronic banking is concerned and does not fail to tell you so on the web!

http://www.visa.com

The World Bank
Find out how the World Bank balances its books. Helping developing countries to reduce poverty and sustain economic growth is the main aim of this organisation.

http://www.worldbank.org

BEAUTY AND HAIR

See also Health, Fashion

AFE Cosmetics and Skin Care
AFE offers lots of information plus a full line of the highest-quality skin-care and cosmetic products which, until recently, were only been available in professional skin-care salons. They are comparable in quality to the expensive European brands, but because they are manufactured in the United States, they are offered at costs that are reasonable for consumers. You can also have an online make-up lesson at the cosmetics counter. As well as defining what the products do, you can also get a very thorough free skin-type test.

http://www.cosmetics.com/

Beauty Link
Here you can consult the style guide on what's in fashion in the world of beauty. You can also find out which hairstyle suits you best, and

even try out a few tried-and-tested beauty secrets. If you're under 21, Cyber Teen offers tips on beauty basics, skin conditioning and even relationship problems. You will need to register first but this is free and quick to do.

http://beautylink.com/

Beauty and Soul

Get all your fashion and beauty tips from international model Wendy Mason, as well as information from several other health and beauty experts. The site focuses on inner beauty and feeling good without giving you a massive list of products that you should use. It states that it is 'a web site devoted to inner and outer beauty'!

http://www.beautysoul.com/

Changes Lives

Divided into four sections – beauty shop, magazine, community information and interactive make-over – this site, primarily for women, gives you a whole range of information on beauty needs and products available.

http://www.changeslives.com/

Clinique

This is the web site of Clinique Laboratories. Clinique was first launched in 1968 with prestige skin-care, make-up and fragrance products. The skin-care and make-up products have been designed to address individual skin types and needs and are all allergy tested and 100 per cent fragrance-free. The site offers information about Clinique, its products and which ones are right for you. Check out the health and beauty tips and even shop online.

http://www.clinique.com

Cosmetic Connection

For cosmetic counselling, including monthly features, weekly product reports and a question-and-answer section, look no further. The highlight of this site is a comprehensive product-review section. Even though the product list has been compiled for American readers, there is plenty that European make-up users will find relevant.

http://www.cosmeticconnection.com

Cosmetic Surgery

Beauty is more than skin deep, so they say. However, if you are considering getting nipped or tucked in order to modify what nature intended, this is the site for you. It is devoted to plastic surgery and is a good place to check out before you go under the knife. Pick the body part you are interested in having altered, then read about the options available. From hair transplantation to breast augmentation, it is all covered in detail.

http://www.surgery.com/

Health 'n' Beauty

If you are looking for health and beauty tips or weight-loss secrets, it is worth paying a visit to this site. It offers advice, reviews and recommendations from a health and beauty expert, and gives details of new products to help you achieve optimum health, beauty and well-being.

http://www.healthnbeauty.com/looks.htm

The Make-up Diva

Although this is not the most extensive of sites, the advice here is realistic and relevant to the average woman. The Make-up Diva does not deal with specialist beauty issues, it simply brings you new answers to your make-up and skin-care questions every week. You can subscribe to a free newsletter sent by e-mail and view past questions. The site is well designed and very easy to navigate.

http://www.makeupdiva.com/index.html

Nailtech

Nailtech is a site for both professional nail technicians and consumers. There is a question-and-answer section for consumers who want to know more about caring for artificial nails, and there are links to other related sites. Look up the articles on nail care, including health and hygiene advice that is well worth reading before you book yourself in for that manicure. You may find the latest pictures from recent nail shows either appealing or appalling – so be warned!

http://www.beautytech.com/nailtech/

Vidal Sassoon

This site will be of interest to both clients and stylists as it offers details of all the Sassoon products currently available to buy, and the nearest salon to you. The site has salon addresses for many major cities in Canada, Germany, UK and the US. For the stylist, there is information on courses, job availability, new product ranges and forthcoming events.

http://www.vidalsassoon.com

Virtual Makeover

Do you fancy a complete change of hairstyle but are not sure what will suit you? Do you wonder what you would look like if your hair were a different colour? Do you wish you could to see what you would look like if you changed any of your features? If so then look up this site, order the demo, scan in your photo and start to change your look.

http://www.virtualmakeover.com

BEER

See also Drink, Wine

Beer Information

Are you a connoisseur of beers? Do you wish to know more about the multitude of different beers available? If so, then this site has all the information you need.

http://www.beerinfo.com

Beerstalker

Concentrating on real British beer, this site offers a complete listing of bottled beers brewed in the UK, along with ciders, wines and spirits,

Beer

with a mail-order service.

http://www.beerstalker.co.uk/

BreWorld

This is Europe's largest web site devoted to the brewing industry, which has all the 'news, information and entertainment regarding the brewing industry'. It also includes a beer database, a list of the top ten beers, articles from *Grist* and *Beerscene*, a bulletin board, information on beer-making and a beer-specific search engine.

http://www.breworld.com/

City 2000 Pub Guide Directory

The pubs in this directory – categorised according to their attributes such as whether or not they have gardens and are child-friendly – have been listed by UK county. When using this site as a guide, it may be worth remembering that it is the pub owners who submit descriptions and pictures to the directory, so they will not be objective.

http://www.city2000.com/entertainer/directory/index.html

The Good Pub Guide

Register here and open up the book to discover thousands of pubs around the UK. You can search the site by region or locality and state preferences according to recommendations in quality of beer, food, value, surroundings, etc. It has been well designed, is quick to use and is an excellent basic interactive pub guide for the UK.

http://www.goodguides.co.uk

London's Real Ale Guide

London's Virtual Real Ale Pub Guide now includes over 250 pub reviews in the London area. Each review gives a brief description of the pub, the atmosphere, the clientele and even the toilets. These pages have been thoroughly researched over several months and are occasionally changed as they find new pubs or revisit pubs that have altered since they first visited.

http://alt.venus.co.uk/vpub/welcome.htm

On the Sauce

A collection of photographs of pubs around Britain, with reviews posted by local drinkers giving a personal view of the pubs.

http://www.on.the.sauce.dial.pipex.com

Real Ale

Another site all about British pubs, you can find reviews, pub locations and all kinds of related information at this useful site.

http://www.grum.clara.net

Real Ale Database

Find out about the quality and diversity of British real ales at this site. It is a database that contains the details of around 2,000 beers from over 400 breweries, as well as having links to other sites. The database is searchable by brewer, name or beer strength and there are contact details available for the breweries as well.

http://www.personal.u-net.com/~thepub/beers.html

Real Ale Guide

This is a comprehensive site that will tell you all you need to know about beer. Find out what is on offer, where to get it and when. Check out their brewery of the month or browse the information on independent breweries. There is a pub directory, a guide to upcoming beer festivals, pub news, a trade directory, a landlords' forum, articles about ale, a section about related societies and associations and lots more.

http://www.real-ale-guide.co.uk/

BOOKS

See also Reference, Shopping and online sales at specialist sites

Achuka

This is an extensive and enthusiastic guide to children's books, which have been broken down by age group and genre. It has a listing of events and a growing online cuttings catalogue that points you to reviews of a long list of authors. This is essential browsing for book-lovers of all ages.

http://www.achuka.co.uk/

Advanced Book Exchange
An excellent source of out-of-print books, although the site is Canadian, access is world-wide.

http://wwwabebooks.com/

Aesop's Fables
This site is an online collection of Aesop's Fables that includes more than 650 fables, indexed in table format, with morals listed. There are images from the Dore illustrations and the beginnings of audio texts.

http://www.pacificnet.net/~johnr/aesop/

Aesop's Fables Read
Students studying Computing in the Fine Arts, were instructed to illustrate each fable in a traditional style and then in a modern style. Some students also wrote modern text to accompany their designs. See the results for yourself at this site.

http://www.umass.edu/aesop/

Amazon.com
Amazon.com is an online retailer of books, music and more. If you do not know anything about a particular title, then look up the various synopses, excerpts and reviews made available by the publishers and labels. The site has easy-to-use search and browse features, customised e-mail notification, personalised shopping services, secure web-based credit or debit card payment and direct delivery. Amazon.co.uk is the British subsidiary with more than 1.5 million locally published titles.

http://www.amazon.com/

http://www.amazon.co.uk/

Arts and Letters Daily

This site is an intellectual guide to literature on the internet. It covers many different topics ranging through literature, philosophy, art, science, history and more. Some people may find the site controversial, but it is well worth a visit and may encourage you to join the discussions yourself.

http://www.cybereditions.com/aldaily/

Authors and Illustrators

This site gives an extensive list of links to author/illustrator information.

http://www.users.interport.net/~fairrosa/cl.authors.html

Authors and Illustrators (Simon & Schuster)

If it's information on an author or illustrator that you require, this site has just what you need.

http://www.simonsays.com/kids/mtb/index.cfm

Barnes and Noble

With worldwide despatch and discounts on all titles for sale online, Barnes and Noble are well worth looking up. If you are considering buying a book but want to know more about it first, you can do so here because this site includes links to press releases and literary excerpts. It is easy to see why they are currently the biggest booksellers in the world.

http://barnesandnoble.com

Bibliofind

An excellent site for finding out-of-print, rare or unusual books.

http://www.bibliofind.com

Bibliomania

At Bibliomania you can read some 60 classic novels as well as reference works. Science, economics, some biographies and ancient texts are all included here. To top it all, you will also find that there is a good selection of poetry at this site.

http://www.bibliomania.com/

Book a Minute

Check out this site for the condensed versions of classic, children's and science-fiction literature. The classics section covers everything from Shakespeare to Steinbeck. The bedtime section enables you to read to your children without plodding through every last word of the 'epics', and covers everything from Dr Seuss to the Hardy Boys. The science fiction section gives you your favourite science fiction and fantasy stories at light speed and covers everything from Tolkien to Dragonlance.

http://www.rinkworks.com/bookaminute/

The Bookplace

Hammicks, the well-known UK high street chain of bookstores, stocks over 1.5 million books. It is worth remembering that its online shop, The Bookplace, has descriptions that are indexed by its search engines. Want to know the best title on a particular topic? Then put this site to the test! When you are ready to order, just do so; they offer worldwide delivery.

http://www.thebookplace.com

Books Unlimited

This site from the *Guardian* newspaper is full of interesting information. It has a range of news stories, literature reviews, and articles from both authors and celebrities. There are many interesting parts to this site, two of which are the author profiles – providing you with background information about your favourite writers – and the mood-matcher, which will pick you a poem in seconds to suit your mood.

http://www.booksunlimited.co.uk

The Bookseller

The weekly magazine of publishing and bookselling available online.

http://www.thebookseller.com

Borders
This company is the main rival to Barnes and Noble in terrestrial bookselling. The online site has been well designed and allows the worldwide ordering of books, CDs and videos.

http:www.borders.com

British Literature
Specifically, this site's goal is to collect, in the most organised manner, a large collection of articles, information and photos covering every aspect of literature in the British Isles. The reasons for creating the site is to create an internet resource useful to the world at large.

http://www.britishliterature.com/

British Magazines
Ideal for ex-pats, this is almost as easy as popping down to the corner shop for your favourite magazine, as they deliver over 3,500 British magazines throughout the world.

http://www.britishmagazines.co.uk

The Brontë Web Site
This site is from Japan (!) and offers excellent photographs and links to all kinds of resources on the famous, literary Brontë family.

http://lang.nagoya-u.ac.jp/~matsuoka/Bronte.html

The Camelot Project
The main menu lists Arthurian characters, symbols and sites. You can move from any highlighted element to a sub-menu of basic information, texts, images and a bibliography.

http://www.ub.rug.nl/camelot/

Children's Bookshop
Based in Hay-on-Wye, Herefordshire, UK, this bookshop sells only children's books and currently has approximately 15,000 titles. It specialises in twentieth-century fiction and has a free book search service for finding books they do not have in stock. You can visit the

web site or visit the actual shop! The site has an online catalogue and ordering system, plus useful information and links on Hay-on-Wye itself. With worldwide delivery, the site also has an online currency converter.

http://www.childrensbookshop.com

Children's Storybook Online

This site is divided into three sections, one containing stories aimed at young children, one containing stories aimed at older children, and the third aimed at young adults. Read lots of exciting things such as: *Alphabet* by Rolando Merino, which is an animated story of the alphabet; *The Littlest Knight* by Carol Moore, an illustrated fairy tale; and *Sliver Pete,* also by Carol Moore, which is an illustrated story.

http://www.magickeys.com/books/

Future Fantasy

The Future Fantasy Bookstore offers worldwide delivery and an order by e-mail service. The categories available include science fiction and fantasy, but they also cater for fans of horror and mystery.

http://futfan.com

The Goosebumps Page

Beware maximum horror ahead – enter if you dare! For those without children, *Goosebumps* is a successful series of story books for youngsters designed to be mildly scary. Meet R. L. Stine and the many tales he has created for youngsters in this scary place.

http://place.scholastic.com/Goosebumps/index.html

Harry Potter

There are many sites devoted to these phenomenally successful books, where you can read about the author, preview the books, and find out other people's opinions.

http://harrypotter.okukbooks.com

http://www.connectingstudents.com/lessonplans/potter/index.html

Hergé and Tin Tin

Hergé (pseudonym of Georges Remi, 1907–83), the Belgian author and illustrator, created Tin Tin in 1929 and produced 23 volumes of the internationally famous *bande dessinée* by the time of his death. A must for intense lovers of Tin Tin and his adventures, this site contains links to a large number of Tin Tin sites around the world.

http://www.regiments.org/bd/tintin.html

Jane Austen Information Page

Find here an electronic text of *Pride and Prejudice*, as well as information and links to other sites with details on Jane Austen.

http://www.pemberley.com/janeinfo.html

Learning About the Author and Illustrator Pages

Many readers are curious about the creators of the books they like. The more than 500 links to author/illustrator sites included here will help to satisfy that curiosity.

http://www.scils.rutgers.edu/special/kay/author.html

Lewis Carroll Collection

For anyone interested in the author of *Alice in Wonderland*, this site must not be missed.

http://www.users.interport.net/~fairrosa/carroll.html

Louisa May Alcott Web

This site is an excellent collection of resources on the author of *Little Women* and many other books. Her books have been on the best-seller list for more than 100 years since her death.

http://www.alcottweb.com

Many Faces of Alice

Fully illustrated by students at the Dalton School in New York, this site gives you a full-text version of Lewis Carroll's *Alice's Adventures in Wonderland* with student essays and a teaching packet.

http://www.dalton.org/ms/alice/

Mark Twain and his Times

This site focuses on how 'Mark Twain' and his works were created and defined, marketed and performed, reviewed and appreciated. The goal is to allow readers, scholars, students and teachers to see what Mark Twain and others from his times said about each other, in ways that can speak to us today.

http://etext.virginia.edu/railton/

Natural History Bookshop

This is the largest environmental mail order bookshop in the world. Search for any title here. It has thousands of titles describing and explaining the amazing diversity of the natural world: field guides, textbooks, monographs, reports, CDs, videos and cassettes on every environmental subject you can think of!

http://www.nhbs.co.uk

The Peter Rabbit Web Site

This is the official and definitive site on the world of Beatrix Potter. Beatrix Potter's favourite characters and other aspects of her work can be viewed at a wide selection of art exhibitions, theatrical performances, displays and local events. Find out everything there is to know at this address.

http://www.peterrabbit.co.uk/

Pick a Book

Author and publishers profiles, news, reviews and offers feature on this site. You can search by author, title, publisher, ISBN or classification to find the information you want on your favourite books, and also buy online.

http://pickabook.co.uk

Robin Hood Project

The Robin Hood Project is designed to make available in e-format a database of texts, images, bibliographies and information about the Robin Hood stories and other outlaw tales.

http://www.ub.rug.nl/camelot/rh/rhhome.htm

Seamonkey Oz Home Page

Here you will find links related to the world of Oz (as in *The Wizard of Oz*!), philosophical musings, creative writing and lots of artwork by the inhabitants of Oz created by Baum. Many of these 'Ozians' are very young, but they have e-mail addresses and would like to hear from you.

http://seamonkey.ed.asu.edu/oz/

Shakespeare

Resources, discussion, quotations, lists and text of plays and a useful glossary with plenty of links is provided by this useful and informative site on everything about the Bard.

http://www-tech.mit.edu/Shakespeare/works.html

Snow White

This site examines the Snow White story in text and images drawn from the last 100 years.

http://www.scils.rutgers.edu/special/kay/snowwhite.html

Treasure Island

An informative site very neatly designed for children by a librarian in Britain. Here you can learn about this novel by Robert Louis Stevenson.

http://www.ukoln.ac.uk/services/treasure/

UK Online Bookshops

Although you will find UK Online similar in most respects to Amazon, it offers a wider range of UK releases. It is also worth remembering that if you are shipping within Europe, postage and packing will be cheaper.

http://www.bookshop.co.uk

http://www.bookpages.com

http://www.alphabetstreet.com

WH Smith

The site for the major high-street chain selling books, stationery, CDs, games, etc.

http://www.whsmith.co.uk

The Wonderful Wizard of Oz Web Site

Oz first started as a book by Frank L. Baum, which then became a series of books. You will find the incredible world of Oz is explored here in detail.

http://www.eskimo.com/~tiktok/index.html

The Yarn

Don't just read it, write it too! Read a chapter of the story and then choose one of two options: go on to the next chapter or write your own. See how the plot thickens then!

http://www.theyarn.com

BUSINESS

See also Employment

Asian Net

This site contains all the information you need to conduct business with Asian companies. It contains a huge search engine of businesses and organisations in Asia, which will display information about the companies' products and services available to you.

http://www.asiannet.com/

Big Yellow

Big Yellow contains the contact details of 11 million US businesses. You can search by category and/or by business name. Click on any address to see detailed maps and driving directions too.

http://www.bigyellow.com/

Biz Pro Web

This web site is to connect you with the resources available on the internet to help you with your business. It is specifically targeted toward the needs of small-business owners, professionals and home-office entrepreneurs so that you don't have to spend time searching for useful links.

http://www.bizproweb.com/index.html

Business Resource Center

A good source of information on getting started in your own business or in self-employment, it is designed for Americans but much of the information is practical and appropriate to other countries as well.

http://www.morebusiness.com

Companies Online

Find out all you need to know about over 100,000 public and private American companies.

http://www.companiesonline.com

Digital Women – Women in Business

This site is for women in business who are looking for a place that contains resources for all their needs. Here you will find free business tips, free sales tips, free marketing tips, home business ideas and a place to communicate and meet business women all over the world.

http://www.digital-women.com/

E-commerce Guidebook

This site is an excellent resource for helping you get your business e-commerce-ready. At the site you will find reviews, a step-by-step tutorial for making a business e-commerce-ready, get a list of companies offering payment gateways, and many links. The tutorial is an excellent place for people to start who are new to this enterprise as it provides the basic understanding necessary to get you started, and allows you to make a better decision about which company to go with.

http://www.online-commerce.com/

Electronic Commerce

This site offers links and information to answer the many questions you may have and can help you understand the confusion and complexity of e-commerce. It also offers help and information on the technology of smart card and processing data.

http://ecommerce.about.com/

Europages

This gives the basic details of 500,000 companies from 30 European countries, which are searchable by name or by product. The site also offers a company search by activity sector, plus links to online *Yellow Pages* from all over Europe.

http://www.europages.com/home-en.htmlges

Home Office Help

These pages are to help people working from home to design the right kind of home-office, read about the keys to running a home-based business and learn how to create and sell information products.

http://www.bizproweb.com/pages/features/home_office.html

IBM Patent Server

The Intellectual Property Network (IPN) lets you search and view patent documents from the US, Europe and Japan that go back to 1971. You can also check out patent applications published by the World Intellectual Property Organisation (WIPO). The site has an entertaining gallery of obscure patents containing all things strange and wonderful.

http://www.patents.ibm.com/

Internet Business Guide

This resource presents ideas, tips and instructions for creating, maintaining and promoting commerce-related web pages. There are news profiles too. At this site you can find the resources necessary to establish home-based internet businesses and to find experienced merchants.

http://www.ibguide.com/ibg.htm

Institute of Logistics and Transport

The Institute of Logistics and Transport site, a good source of information both about the institute itself and any matters related to supply-chain management.

http://www.iolt.org.uk

Mondus

An online market for small and medium-sized businesses who are tired of spending too much time searching for new suppliers and want to expand their business. This site will help buyers purchase more quickly and conveniently while saving money, and help suppliers acquire new customers and increase sales.

http://www.mondus.com/index.htm

Net Source Asia

This site will help business find trade information in Asia and connect to financial resources about trade law, travel, transport, currency and conventions.

http://www.netsource-asia.com/info/resource.htm

Sell it on the Web

Want to start selling on the web? Then sell it! The number one e-commerce resource is here to help! Peruse news, reviews and step-by-step guides about selling goods or services on the web. Also get free books, business ideas and newsletters. The world of e-commerce can be confusing but this site aims to make it easy for you.

http://sellitontheweb.com/

Smarter Work

This site bills itself as 'the global market place for business services'. Clients can post details of projects they need to commission and experts can bid for the work.

http://www.smarterwork.com

Training Zone
A comprehensive site dealing with aspects of human resources, particularly training and learning resources. A very useful site for exchanging ideas with other site users.

http://www.trainingzone.co.uk

UK Patent Office
The United Kingdom Patent Office is the official body for the granting of patents and for the registration of designs and trademarks in the UK (through its Designs Registry and Trade Marks Registry). It is also involved with domestic and international policy on intellectual property, including copyright, design right and other unregistered rights (through its Policy Directorates). This is the official site on which you can make searches but the information is not intended to be comprehensive and readers are advised to seek independent professional advice before acting on anything they find here.

http://www.patent.gov.uk

CARDS

See also Flowers, Gifts

Blue Mountain
Sometimes it can be hard to find the right card for the usual occasions such as birthdays, weddings and births, but have you ever found yourself wondering where on earth you will be able to get a card that says 'Happy Left-handers Day'? Blue Mountain provides relevant animated cards for all current and upcoming events – however obscure – and also includes a selection of international and multi-denominational cards.

http://www.bluemountain.com/

Card Central
Card Central is a one-stop site for virtual postcards and greeting cards on the web. The site is a growing searchable database of many

hundreds of card sites, whatever the occasion.

http://www.cardcentral.net/

Care Mail

Choose from the many cute animated cards, with optional music accompaniment, and with each card sent Care Mail will donate a portion of its advertising revenue to a wildlife charity. Care Mail has dedicated itself to saving wildlife around the world and to helping protect the remaining wild places. Through its network of talented artists, environmentalists and business leaders, and together with your help in making use of this free service, they have found a practical way to do this.

http://www.care2.com/

E-greetings

Yet more cards to send and receive, including animated greetings. Particularly good on hello cards and cheaper than a phone call.

http://www.egreetings.com

Virtual Insults

If you feel that the majority of greetings cards on offer are filled with over-the-top sentiment or are too 'nice', help is at hand. This site provides plenty of choice, and there are insults for all occasions for anyone who has ever wanted a card to say what they really feel!

http://www.virtualinsults.com/home/

CHILDREN AND YOUNGSTERS

See also Books, Education, Fun and specific subjects

Breakup Girl

Are you smarting from a recent breakup? Do you want to wallow in your misery, or wreak shrewd revenge? If so, then this site is for you.

There is an advice column where you can ask Breakup Girl everything you need to know about breakups but were afraid to ask!

http://www.breakupgirl.com/

The Bonus Supersite for Kids
This site is well equipped with a limited browser that only allows the user to access the kid-safe sites. There are various sections: explore, inspect, colour, imagine and play. All contain educational projects and games, making this a great site for fun and learning.

http://www.bonus.com

The Bug Club
Do you have any pet insects? If so, this fan club for owners of creepy crawlies will help you to look after them properly and keep them alive! The Bug Club with its e-pal page, newsletters and pet care sheets has everything you need know.

http://www.ex.ac.uk/bugclub/

Chick Click
This site lists all the most notable independent girl web sites in one place. Full of news, views and gossip, this might be your thing!

http://www.chickclick.com/

Children's Literature Web Guide
Want to find out more about any new children's books that are available? If so, then you will find this site very useful as it gives a critique of all recent publications together with links to texts.

http://www.ucalgary.ca/~dkbrown/

Club Girl Tech
All girls should look at this site at least once. It has been designed to encourage girls to consider studies and careers in technology.

http://www.girltech.com

Cyberteens

This site enables you to submit your artwork, musical compositions or writing to a public gallery. It is well worth considering doing this as you may win a prize!

http://www.cyberteens.com/ctmain.html

Disney

If you want to know more about the Walt Disney Company and all its movies, other products and theme parks, this site catalogues it all. It's the official Disney web site with games, stories, films, musical theatre, videos, competitions and, of course, information on all the Disney theme parks.

http://www.disney.com

Fantastic Fractals

Did you know that a fractal is a complex self-similar and chaotic mathematical object that reveals more detail as you get closer? Well you do now! Learn about fractals with the step-by-step tutorials or use the site to download software that will enable you to generate some amazing graphics. This is great fun for adults too.

http://library.advanced.org/12740/msie/

Funschool

This site is packed full of educational games for the very young.

http://www.funschool.com

Global Gang

This site is aimed at getting children and teenagers interested in the what is happening in the wider world. The site is set up by Christian Aid and through the use of good news and games they aim to raise children's awareness of important global issues. The site also aims to put children in touch with other children in different countries all over the world.

http://www.globalgang.org.uk

Greatest Places

Check out this site for the greatest places in the world. Do you agree with them?

http://www.greatestplaces.org

The History Net

If you want to learn a thing or two about the past, check out this site for the history of the world.

http://www.thehistorynet.com

KidPub

The name stands for 'kids' publishing' so the only thing to be served up here is a good story. KidPub contains thousands of stories that have been submitted by children from around the world.

http://www.kidpub.org/kidpub/

Kids' World

This is full of entertaining and educational activites for kids of all ages. Each section has a suggested age limit so that kids can get the the most out of their visit here.

http://www.kidsworld.com/

Learn2

A general interest site for adults and children. Find out how to do all sorts of things here from throwing a flying disk or boiling an egg, right the way through to repairing a broken window or reading music.

http://learn2.com

Mathematical Magic

Find out how to perform all sorts of tricks without becoming a member of the magic circle. Here practice does not make perfect, a basic understanding of maths does!

http://www.scri.fsu.edu/~dennisl/CMS/activity/math_magic.html

Something Strange to Make and Do?

When you are feeling creative but don't know what to make or do, try out this site for some very strange ideas – especially the kind of science projects you are unlikely to do at school, such as making stink bombs and fake blood!

http://freeweb.pdq.net/headstrong/

A Space for Children to Play

This site is designed to be a sharing space for children on the internet. There are illustrated stories by children from all over the world and pictures for the children to write further stories about. There is even a concert hall where they can put sound files of their own musical performances online. There should be enough on the site to keep them occupied for more than 20 minutes!

http://www.kids-space.org/

Star Child

Attention all budding young astronomers – look up this site before you next look up at the stars. StarChild is a fun-filled site on all aspects of astronomy that is easy to use, entertaining and extremely educational.

http://starchild.gsfc.nasa.gov/docs/StarChild/StarChild.html

Teen Advice Online

Teen Advice Online (TAO) provides support for teenagers. A team of non-professionals, ages 13 and beyond, provide suggestions for your problems so you can get the answers to your questions, and offer the chance to network with other teens around the world.

http://www.teenadvice.org/

Thomas the Tank Engine & Friends

This is the official site of the children's favourite Thomas the Tank Engine. The site is full of fun and games with the children's favourite steam trains. There are puzzles and riddles, a chance to paint and colour pictures – and of course a trip round the depot to meet Thomas and all his friends.

http://www.thomasthetankengine.com/

UK Kids

It's hard to think of much that they have left out of this site. There's games, film reviews and music plus more 'serious' features on careers and school.

http://www.UKkids.co.uk

White House for Kids

Let Socks, the resident cat, take you on a tour of the White House. Socks will show you who all the previous inhabitants were too, including all the boys and girls as well as the pets. You can even write to Socks if you wish.

http://www.whitehouse.gov/WH/kids/html/kidshome.html

Wild World of Wonka

This site is committed to developing the premier web site for kids, making the site an entertaining and educational forum for children to learn. Here you can use the magical colouring-in to explore a vast range of information and music. There's a load of stuff here and most of it can be downloaded to play offline to save your telephone bill.

http://www.wonka.com/

Xplore Kids

A great fun site with lots going on, children can investigate science, sport, an underwater world and everyone's favourite: the world of dinosaurs. They can also contribute their own stories to the site. A good one for keeping them busy on a rainy day.

http://www.xplore.com/xplore500/medium/kids.html

Yahooligans

This is a version of the well-known search engine Yahoo, aimed at the youngsters now using the internet. You use the site exactly as you would the main search engine but the links are more fun and interesting and also educational for kids of any age. This is a search engine that will be enjoyed by adults as well as children.

http://www.yahooligans.com/

You Can Find Out Why

Here you'll find the answer to many everyday questions, such as why feet smell or how a refrigerator makes itself cold. Great for school projects!

http://www.beakman.com

COMPUTERS AND SOFTWARE

See also Internet, Newsgroups, Reference, Search Engines

Adobe

Here is where you can find some of the best and most professional imaging and publishing software on the market. Not only is this the home of the most-used professional software PhotoShop but also one of the internet's most-used plug-in, Adobe Acrobat Reader. You'll find information on the software available and software to download as well as patches, help and tutorials on how to use your software.

http://www.adobe.com

Allexperts

Experts here will answer any questions related to Windows, browsers, word processing and graphics programs. To put it simply, this site is a one-stop shopping source for free questions and answers on virtually any topic!

http://www.allexperts.com/default.asp

Apple Products – QuickTime

QuickTime is the standard for digital video and streaming media. On this site you can see examples of how QuickTime is used in live programming and on-demand programming on the web. The BBC, Bloomberg, and WGBH Boston use QuickTime in their digital media offerings, as do industry giants like Pixar, Lucasfilm, Macromedia, Microsoft, Disney and CNN. This is an essential plug-in for your browser to enhance your multimedia experiences on the web.

http://www.apple.com/quicktime/

Big Rom

Another computer supplies company, but this one promises really low prices combined with quality goods and a reliable service.

`http://www.bigrom.co.uk`

BBC Webguide

A section of the massive web site created by the British Broadcasting Corporation, this section gives you a guide to the information available on the web on the arts and culture, nature, business and finance, children's information, reference, science, sport, travel – and television and radio!

`http://bbc.co.uk/webguide`

Bigfoot

Bigfoot is a really good site which not only offers free e-mail for life but also offers one of the largest search engines. It is also available in five different countries and languages: Arabia, United Kingdom, France, Germany and, of course, America.

`http://www.bigfoot.com/`

`http://www.bigfoot.de/`

`http://www.arabia.bigfoot.com`

`http://www.fr.bigfoot.com`

`http://www.uk.bigfoot.com`

Blacklist of Internet Advertisers

This site is intended to curb inappropriate advertising on usernet newsgroups and via junk e-mail. It works by describing offenders and their offensive behaviour in order to help people avoid their 'services'. The list is posted regularly to several newsgroups, stored on a number of FAQ archives around the world, and the most recent version is always available on the web.

`http://math-www.uni-paderborn.de/~axel/BL/`

Browser Watch

One of the leading sites for information about browsers, plug-ins and ActiveX controls, this site offers up-to-the-minute news in the browser and plug-ins industry, as well as one of the most complete lists on development of different plug-ins and browsers. A quick check of your browser allows you to find the plug-ins or browsers you want quickly and effortlessly.

http://www.browserwatch.com

Buying Guides

This is one of the most comprehensive computer-buying resources ever published, covering computers, hardware (parts) and software. It is the only tool created to guide each customer through the entire buying process, from the realisation of their need for a computer product to intelligent fulfilment of that need in order to make the best buying decision possible.

http://www.buyinguide.com/

Computer Chaos

The Y2K fun page is a collection of humorous explanations of computer problems. In a light-hearted and fun way, find out about the effects of the turn of the millennium on all our computer systems.

http://www.leonardsloan.com/about/y2k/

Computer History and Development

Where would we be now if we did not have computers? For better or worse, computers have infiltrated every aspect of our lives and today they do much more than simply compute. But where did all this technology come from and where is it heading? To understand and appreciate fully the impact computers have and what the future holds, it is important to understand their evolution. This is also a useful site for detailed information on computer background projects.

http://www.digitalcentury.com/encyclo/update/comp_hd.html

Computer and Internet Zone

Having problems with your computer system? If so, then visit the

Computer and Internet Zone with its question-and-answer board. You can also browse the highlights of current news topics, all relating to the computer and internet industries.

http://www.cizone.com/

Computer Manufacturers

All the main computer manufactrers have their own web sites on the internet – in fact, many of them have sites in different countries all over the world. From their sites you can find out a vast amount of information on all the companies' products and it is the best place to get support for your computer. You can also find updated drivers for your hardware. Many of the companies are based in America but from their main site it is possible to connect to a site closer to home for faster downloads. Some of the computer manufacturers' sites even allow you to buy new computer systems, base units, monitors or other hardware online.

Compaq: http://www.compaq.com

Hewlett Packard: http://hp.com

Packard Bell: http://www.packard-bell.com

Dell Computer Systems: http://www.dell.com

Gateway Computers: http://www.gw2k.com

Toshiba: http://www.toshiba.com

Dave Franklin: Hunter Gatherer!

Here is a site that all Windows and Linux users should check out. Dave Franklin collects the addresses of all the latest software for Windows and Linux PCs. Whatever you need he should be able to take you to it. There are a huge number of catergories to choose from on his site. If there is some software you would like to see here, you can either e-mail Dave or use his submit page to inform him of the software, though new listings are added every day.

http://www.davecentral.com

Deja News

Deja News is a great starting point for joining in with a debate and for taking part in a discussion on almost any topic that comes to mind. Discussions take place in newsgroups or usenet groups, which normally require the use of a difficult newsreader programme to be accessed. The Deja News web site allows you to access newsgroups easily and is well worth looking into.

http://www.dejanews.com

Download.Com

Download.com offers people quick and intuitive access to more than 20,000 Windows, Macintosh, DOS, Linux, Palm OS, Windows CE and BeOS software programs that are available for download over the internet. The programs are evaluated and categorised by the people at Download.com – also available here is the information needed about them to help you decide if a program is suitable for your system and needs. Download.com allow users to download the software programs they want from several web and FTP sites around the world, and offer a reliability guide which points users toward the download location most likely to be successful.

http://www.download.com

The Easter Egg Archive

This site contains hundreds of software Easter eggs for all computers, operating systems and applications. What is an Easter egg? In computer terms, it is any amusing tidbit that software creators hide in their creations. They could be in computer software, movies, music, art, books or even your watch. There are thousands of them, and they can be quite entertaining, if you know where to look. This site will help you discover Easter eggs in the things you see and use every day, and let you share Easter eggs you discover with the rest of the world.

http://www.eeggs.com/

FAQs

This archive contains all the newsgroups' Frequently Asked Questions (FAQ) postings in hypertext format and in FTP archive textual format. Each FAQ is converted into a single hypertext document. All FAQs are scanned for various references and have hypertext links automatically inserted when such references are found.

http://www.faqs.org/

Free Web Space

At this site you can use a simple search for free hosts. You can also view the complete list of free personal web space providers available on the internet. There are also special pages if you want free hosting for your business site or a non-profit organisation or your game site. There is also a page for special interest-free hosts.

http://www.freewebspace.net/

Freeserve

If you have not already found this free web browser, take a look. It offers a good level of service.

http://www.freeserve.net

Gooey

Gooey can be downloaded from the web so that you can enjoy real-time communication between people using the web at the same time.

http://www.hypernix.com

Help–site

Help-site contains links to hundreds of computer-related documents and sites. If you are looking for a FAQ list, a tutorial, a manual or an official or unofficial support site, as long as it is for a computer-related subject, you have come to the right place. This is not another free-for-all links site, however. Only the more useful sites and documents will be added, allowing you to find the information you need much more easily.

http://help–site.com/

Mac Connect

The first and largest national Internet Service Provider exclusively for users of the Mac OS in America. Here they are dedicated to providing

Macintosh users with access to a superior data network with excellent Mac support from folks that love the Mac as much as you do! MacConnect provides dial access with over 1,000 access numbers, world-class Mac-centric web hosting, and full-time high-speed connections nationwide.

http://www.macconnect.com/

MacFix-it

MacFix-it is more of a troubleshooting site than a news site. Here's the type of information you will find: troubleshooting tips, hints, work-arounds and solutions of any sort; news about documented bugs, conflicts and problems with existing versions of popular software and hardware; announcements of new and/or updated products. Their Download Library is a collection of troubleshooting-related freeware and shareware utilities and a lot more.

http://www.macfixit.com/

Mac Orchard

This site is a careful list of the most vital internet applications and links for Macintosh internet users, as well as internet software reviews contributed from the Mac Orchard's audience. Also available is a very good FAQ about the site for new users of the site and Macintosh machines.

http://www.macorchard.com

Mac World

This is the online version of the magazine *Mac World*. You can find out all the latest information for the Mac machines and software, and you can even subscribe to the magazine from the site. This site is also available in German, Italian, English, Chinese, Russian, Swedish and Spanish.

http://macworld.zdnet.com/

Mail Start Plus

One of the first and best web-based universal e-mail clients, this site gives you all the features and benefits you have come to expect from a well-made e-mail program, with the added advantage of being accessible any time you find yourself on the internet. The best part is that you get all these advantages and services free of charge.

http://mailstartplus.com/

Microsoft

This is the largest company involved in the computer business and on their site you will find downloadable versions of many of their software products – such as word processors, spreadsheets, games and many more. The site also contains lots of utilities for you to download, as well as all the information you may need to solve any of your problems with their software.

http://www.microsoft.com

Micro-warehouse

Both hardware and software are on sale from this site, with a good range of software products, next-day delivery (free for orders over £30), and a quality service. Not the best place for games, but good for general software.

http://www.microwarehouse.co.uk

Modem Help

Modem Help is a support service for individuals who need assistance using their modem and communications software. The web site is a free service for everyone looking for modem-related support information. There is an exhaustive link library and support forums where people can help each other. Their technicians maintain the support links and participate in the forum discussions.

http://www.modemhelp.com/

Netscape

This is the home of the popular and well-used browser suite of software Netscape Communicator. Here you will find the latest version free to download. You will also find tutorials on using the suite of software to its maximum potential. The site also doubles up as a search engine as well with a full and comprehensive site list.

http://www.netscape.com

Netspeak
A dictionary of jargon for the techno-minded.

http://www.erols.com/amato1/AC/

PC Mechanic
PC Mechanic is one of a minority: a unique site on the internet. There are not many sites like this one that offer such a wide variety of computer hardware information in one place. Not only that, but the information and tutorials are written in plain English for the newcomer to computers. They also offer (for a small fee) a downloadable book which contains all the site's tutorials and information.

http://www.pcmech.com/

PC Show and Tell
Puzzled about how to fulfil a task or action with your software or even on the internet? PC Show and Tell will guide you through the answer, step-by-step, while you actually see and hear how to do it. This site is your best source for understandable and quick computer help – and it's free of charge! They have shows for Word, Excel, PowerPoint, Outlook, Hotmail, ICQ, Internet Explorer, Yahoo and more!

http://www.pcshowandtell.com/

PC Technology Guide
The idea of this guide is to cover the PC's major internal components and peripheral devices and, as its name implies, is more concerned with PC technologies than products – and at present just hardware technology. In general, specific products feature only in the context of major technological innovation. Topics are covered at the overview rather than detailed technical level and the guide is aimed more at the PC hobbyist than the IT professional.

http://www.pctechguide.com/

PC Webopedia

This is an online encyclopedia of computer technology and information together with an extensive links page. The site's online encyclopedia and search engine is dedicated to computer technology and nothing else.

http://www.pcwebopedia.com/

Real Player

RealNetworks is the pioneer and established market leader in streaming media technology on the internet. Their Real Player software allows you to watch video clips and listen to live music or radio while you are on the internet. Once you have downloaded the software, just go to the guide page to see what's on. The Real Player software is available free of charge, though you can upgrade by paying for the latest release.

http://www.real.com

http://www.realaudio.com/

Scambusters

Internet Scambusters is a site created as a result of watching hundreds of companies get blatantly wrong information and baseless hype while trying to learn how to use the internet to promote their businesses successfully. If you want to learn from other people's mistakes, subscribe here to find out what others have done wrong and how to avoid being taken yourself

http://www.scambusters.org/

Shareware.com

Shareware.com is from the same people that bring you Download.com except the site allows users to search a variety of existing internet software archives containing 250,000 freeware and shareware files. These files are organised by archive and are not categorised. File descriptions at Shareware.com are provided by third parties and may not include system requirements or other relevant details.

http://www.shareware.com

Slashdot

Only for the computer enthusiast, this is a magazine-style site full of news and features about what is happening in the techno-world.

http://www.slashdot.org/

Software Paradise

Concentrating on sales of software, this site offers a wide range at good prices with plenty of special offers.

http://www.softwareparadise.co.uk/

Symantec

Symantec offers both the home and business users with the computer software they need to help with their networks and security. Symantec offers award-winning solutions for corporate help desks, mobile and telecommuting professionals, as well as the industry leading anti-virus and protection applications.

http://www.symantec.com/

Technology Dictionary

This is an online encyclopedia that contains everything you need to know about computers. This site is a must for experienced users as well as novices. Search for definitions to more than 7,000 high-tech terms! So, if you are not sure what CCYY is, or what data ageing means, check it out here.

http://www.currents.net/resources/dict/dictionary.html

Timecast

This site is a huge listing of available real-player shows, videos for you to listen to and watch. Just select what category you wish to view from: stations, news, music, showbiz, shopping, sports live, real jukebox. Once you select the item, your real player will start up and you will be able to view or listen to as much or as little as you want.

http://timecast.com

Tracing Software

Have you ever wondered where the signals you are sending are actually going or have you wanted to trace that computer address that is giving you a headache? Neoworx have come up with the answer. Their software, NeoTrace, traces the route your data takes all around the world and displays it to you graphically. You have to purchase the software but you can download a demo version first.

http://www.neoworx.com/

Tucows

Tucows is one of the world's best collections of internet software available for people to download. It offers software for Windows 95/98, Windows NT, Windows 3.1, Macintosh and BeOS internet software. All the software available for you to download is both performance-rated and checked for viruses. You can choose to download from servers in Africa, Asia, the Middle East, Australia, Canada, the Caribbean, Central America and Mexico, Europe, South America and the United States.

http://www.tucows.com

UFO Resources

Despite the confusing name, a huge range of computer-related products is available from this site, all available for you to download free of charge. So if you find yourself missing a file or DLL in your computer set-up then the chances are that you can find it on this site. It also offers loads of free cut-and-paste Java scripts for the web designers out there.

http://www.uforesources.com/

W3C

This is site for the the Worldwide Web Consortium, the people who made the internet what it is. Come to find out about all the latest and up-and-coming standards and tools used on the internet.

http://www.w3.org

Web66

This is one of the internet's oldest and most complete list of school web servers. You will find links to schools in countries all over the world and their web sites. The resource centre also has everything you need to get started setting up a Windows NT server to handle your school network and internet needs, as well as information about the worldwide web, browsers, servers and other useful topics.

http://web66.coled.umn.edu/

Windows 95/98 Annoyances

Windows Annoyances is a web site devoted to not only pointing out the flaws in Microsoft Windows but providing solutions to those flaws. It is just not based on the information in the web site but expanded with much more information and examples, and includes coverage of Windows NT 4.0.

http://www.annoyances.org/

ZD Net

This is one of the best places to start researching anything that is computer-related. ZDNet produces original, compelling content and communities of common interests in technology and is consistently ranked by Media Metrix as the number one web site in the news, information and entertainment category.

http://www.zdnet.com

COOKING

See also Beer, Drink, Food, Wine

Barbecues on the Internet

Everything that you ever wanted to know about outdoor cooking is at this entertaining American site. Find out about marinades, cooking tools and even barbecues in history, together with some tasty American recipes for you to try. There are even some excellent FAQs and monthly wisdom from an expert on the subject. The site is aimed at both beginers and experts on all aspects of barbecues and their success.

`http://www.barbecuen.com/`

Culinary Connection

There are over 73,000 recipes to choose from at the Culinary Connection, so there is something for everyone. The site covers many culinary categories and each section contains recipes listed alphabetically by title. In addition, there are links to other food-related sites, a selection of affiliated online shops and topical food and health news.

`http://www.culinary.com/index.shtml`

Internet Chef

Do you find yourself stuck for culinary ideas or wondering how to create a certain dish? Then take a look at this site and you will never have those problems again. Choose from over 30,000 recipes and read the cooking tips. If you wish, you can get involved in the kitchen talk or look up the many links.

`http://www.ichef.com`

RecipeXchange

There is a glut of cookery web sites on the internet if you want recipes and cooking tips, but this one is definitely worth checking out. RecipeXchange contains thousands of tasty recipes submitted by cooks around the world. Why not submit some recipes yourself? You can join in at the live cookery chat rooms or read the many articles on food.

`http://www.recipexchange.com/`

The Repertoire

You will find that this 'culinary workstation' serves up a feast of food facts and recipes. There are helpful articles, recipes and guides to the most delicious uses of bread, fish, meat, game, cheese, wine, vegetables and preserves. There is also a handy guide that shows what foods are in season and some useful conversion tables to help you navigate the recipes.

http://www.therepertoire.com/

Seasoned Cooking

This is the online version of the *Seasoned Cooking* magazine. The site is mainly about cooking but there are also more general pointers on how to keep a healthy body and mind. In fact, the web site is full of interesting and informative articles on healthy eating, it has a searchable recipe index and a full archive of back issues online.

http://www.seasoned.com/

Spice Guide

Do you want to know more about spices and their uses? This site is an encyclopedia of spices and gives details of their origins and purposes together with recipes and tips on what is best combined with what.

http://www.spiceguide.com

Vegans

If you are vegan and need to know more about how to follow a healthy diet, look up Vegan.com for lots of recipes and tips. The site will show you how to get your recommended daily intake of calcium from vegetables instead of milk, for example. It is well worth looking at: just be prepared for all the accompanying political issues.

http://www.vegan.com/

DANCE

See also Entertainment, Theatre

Ballet Companies

This site is simple in design and contains pages devoted to the biggest national, local and touring UK ballet companies. It also contains useful and interesting performer pages and listings information. It is an indispensable guide to ballet and will appeal to ballet dancers and enthusiasts alike.

http://www.ballet.co.uk/

Ballroom Dancing

Use this ballroom dancing resource to find a list of competitions around the world. It also has a ballroom media gallery and information about dancing organisations and publications worldwide.

http://www.dancescape.com/

Dance Index

Focusing on music and dance, this site has all kinds of information on dance throughout the world, in all styles, including lists of forthcoming events.

http://www.ftech.co.uk/~webfeet/

Dance Service

This site is an impressively large resource, covering contemporary dance in Britain. There is information for dancers as well as dance fans and a useful dance directory. You will also find it contains a comprehensive collection of internet links, articles, reviews, a dance discussion area and much more.

http://www.danceservice.co.uk/

International Folk Dance Resource Guide

Find out about the many different types of folk dancing including Morris dancing, country dancing and various international varieties here at this site.

http://www.io.com/~hbp/folkdance/fd.html

Worldwide Web Virtual Library: Dance

As the title suggests, this is a virtual library of dance web sites. Browse through the library's index to find information on exactly the type of dance in which you are interested.

http://www.artswire.org/Artswire/www/dance/dance.html

DELIVERIES

DHL

DHL Worldwide Express is the world's largest international air express network which serves more than 675,000 destinations around the world. At their site you can track any parcels you have sent with them or even place a new order to be picked up. You can also get online help filling out the forms required for overseas and internal parcels. There is a different page for each country DHL serves, together with service information pages on each country in case of problems with deliveries.

http://www.dhl.com

FedEx

This is the official Federal Express web site where – all online – you can track packages, find the nearest drop box, place orders and get help with your forms, even filling them out, saving time in the office or home. From the main page you can access any country's page that has a Federal Express office. You can even download from this site the FedEx World Tracking Software free of charge.

http://www.fedex.com

UPS

UPS, the world's largest package distribution company, transports more than 3 billion parcels and documents annually. It uses more than 500 aircraft, 157,000 vehicles and 1,700 facilities to provide service in more than 200 countries and territories. This site enables you to ship and track packages quickly and easily from the web.

http://www.ups.com/

DISABILITY

Disabled Data Link Group

This site is an advice and support group open to the disabled around the world, though it does focus more on those people living in the UK. The group provides services including companionship, information on disability aids, motoring help and the rights of the disabled. An excellent site for information.

http://web.ukonline.co.uk/ddlg.uk/

Disabilities

National Information Centre for Children and Youth with Disabilities NICHCY is the 'national information and referral centre that provides information on disabilities and disability-related issues for families, educators and other professionals. A US-based organisation, it specialises in children and teenagers and this site is a useful reference point for anyone to investigate.

http://nichcy.org/

Disability Net

This site is an excellent resource for those with disabilities. The site contains information and news in all areas including job listings and links to local, national and international groups. An interesting part of the site is the penfriends section.

http://www.disabilitynet.co.uk/

DTour

This site is for disabled people who wish to visit the country of Ireland. The site contains a huge directory of property, and guides to transport around the country. In its current form it focuses mostly on the wheelchair-bound, but it has plans to extend in future to those people with hearing and visual impairment.

http://ireland.iol.ie/infograf/dtour/

SpeecHTML

This site advertises software for people with sight problems. The software is a written version of HTML that turns text from web sites into speech so that people can dial up and interact with web sites by phone. There's a free one-month trial of the service designed for visually impaired people and those who don't have access to the net.

http://www.speechtml.com/

DO IT YOURSELF AND HOME

B&Q DIY Guides

B&Q is Britain's largest DIY retailer. If you want to learn how to do it yourself, then check out this B&Q site. You will find detailed guides to help you achieve your aim, whether it is painting and decorating or making your house more secure. Voted the best retail site of the year and recently expanded.

http://www.diy.com

DIY Fixit

With clear, step-by-step instructions, even those who blank at the thought of a flat-pack should find help here.

http://www.diyfixit.co.uk

Do it Yourself

This site contains all the information you need to carry out projects on your own home, ranging from 19 different areas. These include lighting, electricity, flooring, kitchens, plumbing, painting and woodworking. Each area contains user-friendly advice guides, relevant books and links to web sites. Should you need further help, go to the forums where you can post your tricky DIY questions and have them answered.

http://www.doityourself.com/

Do It Yourself, Do It Right

This site will appeal to anyone who enjoys making things with their hands as it provides project plans and patterns for a variety of DIY projects. All project plans for sale in the catalogue/showroom contain professionally drafted drawings, hints and tips on problems, and a list of the tools required for the job. Also contained within the package is a construction sequence with detailed step-by-step instructions, which has been written with the novice in mind. Finally, it is good to know that each project has been carefully designed, constructed and tested before making the plans available for purchase!

http://www.do-it-yourself.com

E-commend

A useful site to help you with your design and decoration, including extensive home improvements and advice on choosing a builder.

http://www.e-commend.co.uk

Handy Home Advisor

Home Advisor gives advice on DIY, home improvement, good housekeeping and interior decoration. A must for all home owners!

http://homearts.com/helpers/homecare/00homcc1.htm

Home Improvement Encyclopedia

Do you watch the DIY programmes in complete confusion as to what is going on? If so, then before you attempt to do any DIY yourself, visit this encyclopedic site. The site is organised by area and gives enough information on most of the jobs that you are likely to tackle. The animated examples are especially helpful.

http://www.bhglive.com/homeimp/

Interior Design and Decoration Village

If you prefer to wander round a virtual showroom to choose your fabrics and soft furnishings, then this is the site to visit and buy online.

http://www.iddv.com/

Interiors and Sources

This online version of *Interiors & Sources* magazine brings to you the best of the commercial and residential design and architecture fields. It gives in-depth trend analyses, opinion pieces, case histories, product specification guidelines and reviews, plus the profiles of some of the designers and architects. Get all the features from the magazine and back issues here but do not expect to see lots of pictures!

http://www.isdesignet.com/

World of Interiors

This is the online version of the magazine *World of Interiors*. The site features all the articles from the publication plus a searchable catalogue of all the top names in British interior design from antique dealers and furniture makers to lighting consultants and fabric designers.

http://www.worldofinteriors.co.uk/

DRINK

See also Beer, Wine

Cocktails at the Mining Company

This site has a 'mine' of information on the subject of drinks: cocktail recipes, ideas for cooking with spirits, guides to consuming spirits, help for would-be bartenders, links to online shops and the chance to e-mail virtual drinks.

http://cocktails.miningco.com/

I-drink

I-drink is a quick and easy reference tool for information on mixing drinks for yourself and your guests. From traditional favourites to the latest trendy concoctions, you can look like an expert in no time. The information on 5865 drinks has been compiled from recipes submitted by professional and amateur bartenders everywhere. The next time you are planning to entertain a few friends or throw a big party, you can enter all your bar ingredients in their quick checklist, then let the program match your ingredients against their database and display all your options. You will be surprised at the number of drinks you can make, even with a limited number of ingredients, and will have more fun and enjoy your new bartending skills.

http://www.idrink.com/home.htm

The Virtual Bar
Search the archive containing over 3,000 cocktails by ingredients, drink type or name. The site is also home to Corky the bartender, who provides a guide about alcohol, a virtual jukebox, a selection of toasts for all occasions and, most importantly, a list of hangover cures.

http://www.thevirtualbar.com/

Web Tender
This is a great site to find out how to mix that elusive drink. Webtender contains over 4,800 different drinks for you to try, including cocktails, alcoholic drinks, soft drinks and many more. If you find that your favourite drink is not listed here, then why not submit your own drink using the form supplied?

http://www.webtender.com/

EDUCATION

See also Children and Youngsters and specific subjects

American Institute for Foreign Study
Here you will find information about cultural exchange programmes, summer jobs in the US and studying abroad for both American and non-American students. The American Institute for Foreign Study® (AIFS, Inc.) and its family of companies organises cultural exchange programmes throughout the world for more than 40,000 students each year.

http://www.aifs.org/

BBC Education

Designed to work in support of the National Curriculum, the BBC offers a high-quality site filled with research and revision information, games and stories. There's also an e-mail service for posing questions to teachers.

http://www.bbc.co.uk/education/schools

Connecting Students

Puzzles and links to all kinds of sites on all kinds of subjects.

http://www.connectingstudents.com

Datalake

This web site allows you to search for universities and colleges worldwide via its learning stream. Increasingly, this is possible by subject, department, faculty and course. Useful to students and widely used by them, Datalake is also a resource for locating wider research expertise for a variety of applications. This operates in parallel with a job locator (Earning) – with links made between learning outcomes and available work at all stages of your search.

http://www.datalake.com/datalake/homepage.htm

Digital Education Network

The Digital Education Network enables students to get information on study programmes around the world. You can also search for a wide range of other educational service providers including student advisors, education agents, accommodation agencies, publishers, examination boards and funding organisations.

http://www.edunet.com/

Hobsons

This is the premier site for details of thousands of career and education opportunities in the UK and around the world. Hobsons is a British and US-based company with over 25 years' experience in publishing educational and recruitment guides for students making career and course decisions. A guide to UK boarding schools is also produced.

http://www.hobsons.co.uk/

http://www.boardingschools@hobsons.com

Homework Elephant

This site is a valuable resource for both children and mature students. It helps you find answers to questions and problems and information you need for homework or research.

http://www.homeworkelephant.free-online.co.uk/

Internet Universities

This web site is here to help you make sense of the revolution in education that is taking place on the internet. It is a great source of information on courses and course descriptions that are being taught on the internet, as well as at all the colleges and universities, although many of the colleges and universities listed are American.

http://www.caso.com/

Learning Store

A UK-based site, here they stock over 1000 different educational software packages so you should be able to find something to help with your studies.

http://www.learningstore.co.uk

Learning Tutorials

Arts and crafts, sport and leisure, travel, technology and health are among the topics covered here and you can find tutorials on anything from shining your shoes to soothing a teething baby or restructuring your business. You can also e-mail the information to a friend.

http://www.learn2.com

McGraw-Hill

McGraw-Hill offer people online learning, and here at their site you can learn all about the different courses on offer. McGraw-Hill online learning offers you quality course information and expert instruction using state-of-the-art technology on the web. Online learning allows you to study where you want and when you want, to study at your own pace, and to interact with instructors via e-mail and discussion groups.

http://www.mhonlinelearning.com/

National Grid for Learning
A government site designed to provide a focal point for education on the web.

http://www.ngfl.gov.uk/ngfl/

Open University
The OU is primarily a British site but it has pioneered a system of study – OU-supported open learning – which brings its courses and other study materials within the reach of the entire population of the European Union, Switzerland, Gibraltar and Slovenia. Also available are a growing number of courses worldwide on the internet.

http://www.open.ac.uk/frames.html

SAM Learning
This site offers information on all major exams, broken down by subject and then topic. It offers explanations and sample questions – with drag and drop so you can complete the answers – to help you revise.

http://www.samlearning.co.uk/

School Zone
Schoolzone was set up by a group of enthusiastic teachers and parents in Oxford, who could see the need for safe, differentiated internet material which teachers, students and parents can access easily, without anyone trying to sell them anything or exploit anyone in any way. Here you will find all the potentially useful sites sorted into subject groupings.

http://www.schoolzone.co.uk/

Student UK

A site for the student with news, features, information on entertainment and general advice on student life.

http://www.studentuk.com

Student World

Designed for students and staff at colleges and universities, you'll find a range of information here from advice on money to news, culture and reference information. Good links to other related sites.

http://www.student-world.co.uk/

Universities and Colleges Admission Service for the UK

Anyone looking for higher education courses can find full information on the UCAS web site, including contact numbers, course searches and other information about degree, HND and other courses.

http://www.ucas.com

Virtual School

Revision courses in GCSE and A level subjects, with material sent by e-mail and tuition done online. At the moment, there is no online ordering, although this may change.

http://www.virtualschool.co.uk

Virtual Student

For both students and graduates, this site contains magazine-style articles, information and advice on careers and student life in general, with hyperlinks to other related sites of interest.

http://www.virtualstudent.co.uk/

EMPLOYMENT

See also Business

Big Blue Dog

Established by the *Evening Standard*, you can log into an e-mail service to receive details of jobs that match your requirements. There's also online CV composition.

http://www.bigbluedog.com

Career Solutions

At this site 'discover what you really want to do and how to get somebody to pay you to do it'. Career Solutions contains lots of useful information and provides clear steps to getting what you want in the job market. The site also points out other free sources of career advice and advises you of what to do if you lose your job.

http://www.careersolutions.co.uk/

CV Search

Employers compose the CV they want to receive from their ideal job candidate and CV Search will match it as closely as possible with those it has on its books.

http://www.cvsearch.net/

E-mum

This is a database of jobs that would suit someone trying to juggle a career with a growing family, plus articles on health, minders and other subjects of interest to the modern working mother.

http://www.e-mum/com/

Hot Jobs

This site lists technical jobs in different career channels worldwide. It is very user-friendly and easier to search than most. Browse and find yourself a new job!

http://www.hotjobs.com/

JobServe

Every day, IT recruitment agencies from all over the UK and Europe send details of their latest requirements to JobServe. The details are entered into a database; a neatly formatted list is then generated and sent out, overnight, by e-mail to anyone who wants it. JobServe is based in the UK but over ten per cent of the vacancies advertised are overseas, including Australia, Austria, Belgium, Denmark, France, Germany, Hong Kong, Indonesia, Italy, Luxembourg, Netherlands, New Zealand, Norway, Russia, Saudi Arabia, Singapore, South Africa, Spain, Sweden, Switzerland and USA.

http://www.jobserve.com/

International Guild of Butlers

This site is aimed at people who are in the profession or are thinking of making a move into it. The guild is dedicated to improving and promoting the interests and reputation of its members and the butling profession. The guild also offers a free advisory service to its members, employers of butlers and members of the public on any matter related to butlering.

http://www.butlersguild.com/

Innovative Cruise Services

This is the web site of the longest-established Cruise Job Consultancy. All their information is factual and constantly updated. The staff are professionals who have worked in the cruise industry for many years. The company is wholly committed to give the best possible chance of helping you get a position and more importantly identify the right job for your capabilities.

http://www.cruiseservices.co.uk/content.html

Jobsite

Created in 1995, Jobsite is the longest-established multi-sector internet recruitment platform in the UK. Jobsite attracts hundreds of thousands of candidates every month from all industry sectors including sales, marketing, management, accountancy, secretarial and administration, as well as IT, telecommunications and engineering.

Jobsite provides both job hunters and recruiters with the most powerful range of internet recruitment services in the world.

http://www.jobsite.co.uk/

Milkround

Interesting and useful site providing details for graduates looking for work. Quick to access, with a database to store your CV and send it to companies.

http://www.milkround.com

Monster.com

Monster.com is one of the leading global online networks for careers, connecting the most progressive companies with the most qualified, career-minded individuals. Features include resumé management, a personal job search agent, a careers network, chats and message boards, privacy options, expert advice on job-seeking and career management and free newsletters.

http://www.monster.com/

http://www.monster.co.uk

Overseas Job Express

This online version of the newspaper for overseas job seekers offers a multitude of excellent resources and advice which is regularly updated. Only OJE gives you vacancies that are genuinely open to non-citizens of your target country. The site has hundreds of fresh jobs online and over 1,500 in every issue of the paper. It gives you all the tools you need to help you get a job abroad.

http://www.overseasjobs.com/

People Bank

Ideal for both employers and job-seekers, there's a wide range of jobs listed here for anyone in the employment market.

http://www.peoplebank.com/

Price Jamieson

If you are looking for positions in the media, marketing and communications, then the Price Jamieson site is for you. You can easily browse international listings here that are updated on a weekly basis.

http://www.pricejam.com

Reed Employment

An effective site in which you can store employment opportunity details and link your requirements to specific jobs. Regular e-mail updates.

http://www.reed.com

Review Computer Recruitment

Review was formed in 1990 and is a specialist agency in the computer personnel recruitment industry. The company specialises in the growing markets of internet technologies, UNIX, relational databases, server networks, PC/Windows, client server and object-orientated design areas. It deals with all aspects of technical recruitment.

http://www.review.co.uk/index.htm

The Riley Guide

This site is a directory of job-hunting resources from around the world. It contains tips on how to use them but is a little awkward to browse. The Riley Guide is a very useful site but you will need to be patient!

http://www.dbm.com/jobguide/

SHL Online

SHL is a world leader in the objective assessment of people, jobs and organisational context. This site is therefore useful to the individual who is applying for a graduate appointment or who has been asked to take assessment tests. This site will show you examples of tests, offer hints and tips and tell you what employers will be looking for.

http://www.shlgroup.com/

Top Jobs

This site offers job opportunities with exclusive employers in specific US locations and also parts of Europe. You are able to register with Top Job and receive an e-mail service which automatically notifies you of all jobs that fit your criteria as soon as they become available.

http://www.topjobs.net/

Virtual Careers Library

This comprehensive site, which is part of the King's College London Careers Service, directs you to many resources. The topics covered include career choice, further study, and job-hunting resources, professional bodies and trade associations, and employer web sites.

http://www.kcl.ac.uk/kis/college/careers/links/links.htm

Work in America

If you are looking for work in America, this free site is the place to start your search. America's Job Bank has links to more than 1800 US State Employment Service Offices and 100,000 vacancies.

http://www.ajb.dni.us

Work in the UK

If you are looking for work in the UK, you can search for British jobs at the Jobsearch site. It covers a wide spectrum of fields and is a good starting point.

http://www.jobsearch.co.uk

World Careers Network

This site is aimed at university students looking for resources to help them find a job after university. Once you have registered, you will have access to a guide on how to get on, together with many resources such as employers in-depth, news and market research, briefing books for each employer, contacts worldwide and lots more.

http://www.wcn.co.uk/

ENTERTAINMENT

See also Children, Dance, Film and Television, Fun, Music, Radio and Broadcasting, Theatre

Aloud

The site gives details of events that are being held throughout the year. You can even book tickets online here.

http://www.aloud.com

Broadcast Network

Plenty of RealAudio feeds to keep you up to date with what is happening in the world of entertainment. Listen to all the latest news, reviews and interviews. The site features books, business, music, movies and much more.

http://www.broadcast.com/

Event Selector

A really useful site if you want to find out what is going on in the world of entertainment. There are listings for cinema, theatre and events for adults and children.

http://www.eventselector.co.uk

Legoland

This site includes all kinds of information on Legoland in Berkshire, including maps and information on opening times and what you can find at the park. The most interesting aspect is that you can buy your tickets online and by-pass the queue. They can be sent to you or collected at the gate.

http://www.legoland.co.uk

Strange Magazine

This is the web site for the American magazine *Strange*. It contains a bizarre collection of tales, myths and other stories from around the world. The web site includes new material never published in the printed magazine, plus features from back issues. Though most of the current magazine is not on this site, you can subscribe to the magazine from the site.

http://www.strangemag.com/

Ticketmaster

Book all your seats for plays, shows, rock concerts, exhibitions and sporting events being held all over the UK from this one site. You can also buy tickets for shows in America, Australia and Canada online using the appropriate Ticketmaster sites.

http://www.ticketmaster.com

http://www.ticketmaster.com.au

http://www.ticketmaster.co.uk/

Time Magazine

This is the offical site of the US-based magazine *Time*. The site itself is free and has the same good stories as the printed magazine. There are lots of subjects covered, such as movies, health, news, politics and more. The site also boasts a good range of links to each story.

http://www.pathfinder.com

Time Out

With everything you need to know about what is going on in the entertainment world in London, *Time Out* magazine has become something of a byword. This is its web site, which offers the same depth and quality of entertainment information for those in London.

http://www.timeout.com

Yack

Pay regular visits to this site to find out when and where online events and celebrity chats are taking place.

http://www.yack.com/

ENVIRONMENT

See also Politics

Abandoned Missile Base VR Tour

This presentation will take you on a full tour of a decommissioned, abandoned underground missile complex. The site was opened many years ago by explorers and vandals, and in fact the technology therein was nearly obsolete by the time the bases were completed in 1963, so there's little 'secret' about it beyond the location of the sites revealed here.

http://www.xvt.com/users/kevink/silo/

Environmental Atlas

The Environmental Atlas is an internet-based tool for researching worldwide environmental policy. It uses a standard set of criteria to categorise environmental conditions and policies and offers quick access to information about a single country as well as comparisons between countries. An excellent resource for people concerned with the enviroment.

http://www.rri.org/envatlas/

Environmental News

The Environmental News Network collects the news concerning our world and contains facts, essays, radio shows and a calendar of events. Everything available on the site deals with the environment, and with all the details in one place this is an essential visit for the environmentalist. You will find that the factual information is often seasonally related.

http://www.enn.com/

Environmental Organisation Directory

Directory of primary production and green-issue sites in focus order.

http://www.webdirectory.com

Environmental Sites on the Internet

Here you will find an enormous amount of information on every aspect of the world environment, greenhouse gases, oil spills, acid rain, electric vehicles, land care in Australia and much more.

http://www.lib.kth.se/~lg/envsite.htm

Environmental Sources

Here is a large directory of pressure groups, government organisations and magazines plus a large information section including some interesting miscellaneous entries as well as features on pollution and transport. This site is a useful resource for anyone intrested in improving and protecting the enviroment.

http://www2.eng.cam.ac.uk/~tpl/env.html

The EnviroWeb

You should be able to find out about any environmental issue here. The EnviroWeb claims to be the largest online environmental information service anywhere.

http://envirolink.org

Friends of the Earth

The largest international network of environmental groups in the world, Friends of the Earth is represented in 58 countries and is one of the leading environmental pressure groups in the UK. Friends of the Earth is a charity which commissions detailed research and provides extensive information and educational materials. If you care about what happens to our planet, the Friends of the Earth web site will inform you of lots of interesting, if sometimes alarming, facts and figures. You will find the site up to date on all green issues, such as the debate on the production and consumption of genetically modified food. Enter your postcode to view the pollution records of local factories and discover what chemicals they currently emit.

http://www.foe.co.uk

The Green Guide

Here you will find lots and lots of advice pages for eco-friendly living. The site will eventually feature directories of green products and services in Britain, Ireland, America, Canada and Australia.

http://www.aim-irl.com/greenguide/

Greenpeace International

This site gives you the low-down on all current campaign events. Whether you want to know more about Greenpeace itself or what they are up to, check out this official site. You can also find out how to join Greenpeace or make a donation.

http://www.greenpeace.org

Ozone Depletion

This site offers you the answers to all your questions about the ozone layer. It covers everything from 'What is the ozone layer and why is it important?' to 'What can we do to help protect the ozone layer?' The site is very clear and helps ordinary people understand the problems and concerns associated with this topic.

http://www.geocities.com/RainForest/Vines/4030/

The Pew Center on Global Climate Change

This is the web site for the American centre where the aim is to raise awareness of climatic changes, and provide guidance on what steps companies and individuals can take to reduce greenhouse gas emissions that have led to global warming.

http://www.pewclimate.org/

Planet Ark News

If you take an interest in environmental issues and you like to keep up to date with what is happening in the world, this site is worth visiting regularly. Planet Ark gives you the daily environmental news from Reuters, the London press agency.

http://www.planetark.org/new/worldnews.html

The Urban Wildlife Garden Site

This site is dedicated to the promotion of organic techniques which attract wildlife and endeavour to live with nature. Their aim is to encourage the biodiversity of nature in urban communities, creating an oasis of sites for wildlife of all kinds. It is hoped that this site will grow and both become a useful resource to those dedicated wildlife gardeners and educate those surfers who favour crazy paving.

http://www.geocities.com/RainForest/4645/index.html

FASHION

See also Beauty and Hair

American Mall

The American Mall web site is based in the Bahamas with distribution centres in Europe. They import and export American and European designer clothing, cosmetics and household items all at discounted prices. Both the site and online ordering facilities is available in four languages: English French, German and Spanish.

http://www.americanmall.co.uk/

Catwalk Coverage

Here you can preview the latest collections online from all the world's best fashion designers, find out about *haute couture* in Paris, or read the features on ready-to-wear collections. You can discover who is showing on the catwalks and search the online database for up-to-date information about your favourite designer. The site also features online fashion TV which shows non-stop fashion clips from a variety of designers.

http://www.worldmedia.fr/fashion/catwalk/

Cosmopolitan

Cosmopolitan offers monthly features with copious illustrations. It includes fashion news, updates from the catwalks and current style debates. A magazine not to be missed by the fashion devotee.

http://www.cosmomag.com/

Designers Direct

This site is an American mail-order clothes service offering DKNY, Hilfiger, Calvin Klein, Levi's, Polo clothes and accessories which they then deliver all around the world. Currently the site offers over 400 items in almost 20,000 sizes and colours.

http://www.designersdirect.com

Designer Outlet

This site was created to provide a new way to shop for designer overstocks on the web. It offers the finest quality overstock goods from the top designers and manufacturers at greatly reduced prices. By selling over the web, the company avoids incurring high overhead costs, and the savings are passed on.

http://www.designeroutlet.com/

Elle International

This site contains snippets from all 27 international editions of the glossy magazine *Elle*.

http://www.elle.com

Fashion Net

This site contains so many fashion links that by the time you have looked at all of them, the new season's collections will be uploading!

http://www.fashion.net

Firstview Collections Online

If you want to see what is in this year in fashion then why not sign up and subscribe for the Firstview service? Once you have subscribed you will be able to preview thousands of photos of the world's top designers' most recent collections – straight from Milan, Paris, New York and London.

http://www.firstview.com/

Ghost

Nothing to do with things that go bump in the night, this site offers you the collections of this designer label, including catwalk pictures of the current and latest collections.

http://www.ghost.ltd.uk

Landsend

This is the site for the well-known leisurewear retail outlet and offers online product selection. For women, there's a personal model service into which you key your details (hair colour, complexion, figure, etc.) so they can offer a selection of clothes to suit you.

http://www.landsend.com

Levi's Europe

This is an interactive site for the great jeans company featuring their TV ads and a brochure to help you choose the style and cut that's right for you. Once you've decided on a pair you can see them in glorious QuickTime video and find out where to buy them in Europe with a European storefinder. You can even buy the music for the adverts here as well.

http://www.eu.levi.com/index.html

Paul Smith Fashion

Paul Smith's mission has always been to make his shops the individualistic antidote to retail uniformity. The Paul Smith web site is the same! Check it out to see his latest fashion creations and one very well-designed web site.

http://www.paulsmith.co.uk

Platform Diva

Whether you love them or loathe them, maybe the long history of the platform shoe will convince you that they, indeed, will always be around. Strap on your platforms and teeter through the styles of the 1600s, 1930s, 1970s and 1990s at this site. You can test your platform knowledge by taking the online quiz.

http://www.geocities.com/FashionAvenue/1495/

Vogue

If you are interested in fashion, then you should regularly check out the Vogue site. It gives daily tips and past and present fashion features. It also has a brilliant search tool that can be used if you want to see what you can get for your money. Find out what the high street stores have in stock, as well as what the top designers are offering.

http://www.vogue.co.uk/

Women's Wire: Style

This site offers you a diverse selection of regularly updated features examining current trends in fashion and beauty. It is down to earth in its recommendations, and never takes itself too seriously – a refreshing change from some sites. It simply provides accessible advice and information for women for whom style is an interest rather than an obsession.

http://www.womenswire.com/style/

Yves Saint Laurent

A lavish site from the French designer Yves Saint Laurent that enables you to take a front-row seat at the catwalk shows. It is just goes to show you how expensive the designs must be because the site does not even try to sell you any of the clothes! Ever heard the expression: 'If you need to ask the price, you can't afford it?'

http://www.yslonline.com/va/index.html

FILMS, TELEVISION, VIDEO AND DVD

See also Entertainment, Fun and Music

Ain't It Cool News

Check out this film site for all the latest insider movie news.

http://www.aint-it-cool-news.com/

All Movie Guide

This directory of the movies comes complete with reviews and synopses, so you can find out all there is to know about your favourite films. As you can imagine, the site is huge but do not be put off by this as it is very easy to navigate your way around and pinpoint relevant information, such as plots, reviews, biographies, etc. It is available in six different languages: French, German, Italian, Spanish, English and Portuguese.

http://www.allmovie.com

Black Star

Online store for video and DVD purchases delivered free anywhere in the UK.

http://www.blackstar.co.uk/

British Broadcasting Corporation

BBC Online provides a huge number of services, bringing information, entertainment and education from the BBC to the web. The BBC home page acts as both a gateway to all their online content and a frequently updated guide to the key programmes and stories of the day. There are individual sites for all the major entertainment and education programmes on the BBC.

http://www.bbc.co.uk

Drew's Scripts-O-Rama

Are you wondering how you can find film scripts on the internet? Perhaps not, but if you are now interested in gaining access to the scripts of your favourite films, look no further than this site. Drew has done all the hard work for you by finding the necessary links to over 500 scripts and it is all free of charge.

http://www.script-o-rama.com/

DVD

This site is the best source of DVDs on the internet, including Region 1 discs from America which cannot be obtained in the UK.

http://www.play247.com

Empire

This is the web site for the video and film magazine where you will find news, competitions, features, cinema and video releases and links to movie-related sites.

http://www.empireonline.co.uk

The Greatest Films

This site is a true labour of love designed by an amateur film buff. It contains a list of the 100 greatest films (see if you agree). For most of the films listed there is a long description and plot synopsis. Worth a look just to see if you agree with the choice.

http://www.filmsite.org/

Hollywood Reporter

Want to know the latest Tinseltown gossip? For daily reviews and previews, plus a look at the showbiz directory, check out the Hollywood Reporter site.

http://www.hollywoodreporter.com

Internet Movie Database

A very comprehensive database that should not be missed by any movie-lover. It has information on more than 100,000 movies and a million actors. When you have found your favourite movie, you can watch full 'filmographies' of the entire cast and crew.

http://www.imdb.com

James Bond

Here you will find a fans' page about the most successful British agent. James Bond 007 is known throughout the world and this site contains everything you will ever need to know. You can find out about the actors who have played James Bond, the villains, the films with reviews, find out about all the gadgets used by Bond, and of course all the lovely Bond Girls.

http://www.geocities.com/Hollywood/5727/ mi6_headquarters.html

Mr Showbiz

If you want to know what is going on in the world of the movies, check this out. It provides movie reviews, features, orbituaries, news, and a lot of celebrity biographies. The TV section is only suitable for Americans but the film information is worth a look.

http://www.mrshowbiz.com/

The Oscars

Interested in the Academy Awards? Have you ever wondered what else the Academy does? If so, then this site is for you. It has information about the public exhibitions and events, the Student Academy Awards, the annual screenwriting competition, all publications, plus the world-class research library and film archive.

http://www.oscar.com

Popcorn

This site features comprehensive searchable listings of what's on at cinemas nationwide throughout the United Kingdom. It also has the entire low-down on the movie industry, with all the glitz, glamour and gossip. The site itself features film reviews, hundreds of pictures, video trailers, audio interviews with major stars, and a personalised e-mail alert.

http://www.popcorn.co.uk

Screen It! Entertainment Reviews for Parents

Despite the title, the site does not tell you how good a film is. Instead, it takes a moral stance and simply rates the film on various scales. Find out whether a film is suitable for viewing by children (and for that matter, by some adults too!) because of the degree of inclusion of alcohol and drugs, disrespectful and bad attitudes, sex and nudity, profanity, smoking and tense family scenes.

http://www.screenit.com/search_movies.html

Showbizwire

For the latest showbiz news on the celebrities to all the film, theatre, television, music and video productions, Showbizwire gets its information from around 50 major sources.

http://www.showbizwire.com

Silents Majority

Do not bother to adjust the volume when watching the films discussed at this site! You will find that the first page steers you to current feature stories, but go beyond this and see that the site links areas on the stars and the technology. There are also some regional showings of the old classics.

http://www.mdle.com/ClassicFilms/

Sky Broadcasting Corporation

This site gives you details of all Sky channels and much more. Find out about the world of entertainment here.

http://www.sky.co.uk/

Star Wars

A directory for any sites related to Star Wars, with information on every conceivable aspect of the films.

http://www.starwarsnet.com/

Tomb Town

This site is a virtual 3D world. TombTown is the only 3D interactive virtual reality cemetery on the web where you actually visit a 'real' cemetery. You experience the cemetery by wandering about, looking at tombstones, listening to birds chirp and crickets sing, and by visiting residents. Famous personalities such as Marilyn Monroe, Plato, Bela Lugosi, Doc Holliday and Jerry Garcia. Also available is the chance to register your own plot for a small fee.

http://www.tombtown.com/

FINANCE AND INSURANCE

See also Banking

Accountant's Home Page

The Accountant's Home Page is a series of pages dedicated to collecting and making available internet resources of interest to accountants. Here you can access an information database with resources on e-commerce, tax law, and the accounting, manufacturing, construction and service industries.

http://www.computercpa.com/

Bloomberg

Bloomberg is organised into three primary channels: markets, money and life. The markets channel offers comprehensive coverage of worldwide financial markets. The money channel features audio and video interviews with market experts as well as articles from the award-winning *Bloomberg Personal* magazine. The life channel covers wine, cigar and art industries, sports, weather and worldwide real estate listing. Bloomberg has sites in Australia, Germany, Italy, Japan, Latin America and the UK.

http://www.bloomberg.co.uk

Carlton

This site offers financial news, investment information and general financial information for anyone in the business sector.

http://www.carltonplc.co.uk

Charcolon

Part of the UK's largest independent mortgage broker, the online wizard at this site helps you to find the best deal for your particular circumstances.

http://www.charcolonline.co.uk

Company Sleuth

Here Company Sleuth offers you the chance to gain a legal inside look at your investments, competitors, partners and clients. Company Sleuth's have the ability to stake out and track the publicly traded companies you choose. They will even send you daily reports, via e-mail, on their business activities, financial moves, internet dealings and legal actions.

http://www.companysleuth.com/

CNBC

Financial-market news, tickers, charts and analysis are to be found on this site which offers vital information for the private sector.

http://www.cnbc.com

Dow Jones

This site brings together an expanded collection of news, information, resources and services. You can also personalise the features that make them relevant to your specific business interests. This is a free site, offering information and resources selected by *Wall Street Journal* editors for any business question. For those times when deeper research is required, the site provides access to premium services and pay-per-view information that's all easily and effectively organised and presented to help you find precisely what you need.

http://www.dowjones.com

E-mail Tax

An advice site run by professional accountants who will calculate your self-assessment tax bill for you.

http://www.emailtax.co.uk/

Eagle Star

The major insurance company sells insurance online as well as offering information and answering any of your questions on insurance.

http://www.eaglestardirect.co.uk

Egg

Although a relative newcomer, Egg has quickly established itself as one of the major players in internet financial services. Loans, savings, accounts, investments and all other major banking services are available at this well-rounded site. It also has links to approximately 150 retail-outlet sites.

http://www.egg.com

Fantasy Stock Broker

Fantasy Stock Market promotes investment education to individuals through active participation and competition which is enhanced by an interactive and easy-to-use web site. Players who sign up are given $100,000 in fantasy money to trade stocks and mutual funds listed on the New York, Nasdaq, American and other US stock exchanges. Fantasy Stock Market will then track the portfolio and rank them against other players.

http://www.fantasystockmarket.com/

Finance News

This site from CNN provides you with all the financial news you could ever need. The site contains stock quotes, market numbers, top news and financial help. Here you can find everything financial from important information for business travellers to the latest stories involving small businesses.

http://cnnfn.com/

Financial Message Boards

If you want to find out information about a company or discuss the future prospects of the company and share information about it with others, this is a good place to look for information or share your information. This board is not connected in any way with the companies listed, and any messages are solely the opinion and responsibility of the poster.

http://messages.yahoo.com/yahoo/
business_and_finance/stocks/index.html

Financial Times

The online version of the UK newspaper, the *Financial Times*, which is the first source of reference in City banking circles.

http://www.ft.com

Find Information

Designed to give you all kinds of financial information, here you'll find a financial information net directory, as well as guidance on investments, insurance, savings, loans and other financial advice.

http://www.find.co.uk

Fool.com

A site devoted to investors, there is detailed information, discussions and portfolios.

http://www.fool.com

FTSE International

More commonly known as the Footsie, this company exists to provide a database of world stock-market indices.

http://www.ftse.com/

Inland Revenue

The official site of the Inland Revenue where you can find the answers to all your tax-related questions.

http://www.inlandrevenue.gov.uk/home.htm

Insurance Reassurance

If you have just received an insurance quote and want a second opinion, you may be able to get one from the Insurance News Network before you sign up. Site discussions cover life, car and home insurance. It includes news items about the industry, company ratings and profiles, and insurance explanations.

http://www.insure.com/

Interactive Investor

The ultimate goal of Interactive Investor is to provide you with all the information you need to make an investment decision by providing the best available information on current investment and the best tools to monitor and manage investments effectively. On their site they provide performance and price information for stocks as well as collective investments such as unit trusts, investment trusts, ISAs and pensions.

http://www.iii.co.uk/

ISAs, PEPs and TESSAs

This is Richard Branson's guide to the new ISAs, as well as PEPs and TESSAs for those who already hold them.

http://www.virgin-direct.co.uk

Investment Checklist

InvestorWeb provides this information service for beginner investors to help them learn what to look out for when accepting investment advice. The internet has no shortage of free advice and much of it is worth what you pay for it. The information is offered to stimulate your thinking, and hopefully to help you avoid making some of the more common mistakes.

http://www.investorweb.com/Begin.asp

London Stock Exchange

The web site of one of the largest stock exchanges in the world.

http://www.londonstockex.co.uk/

Moneygator

A site on which you can see comparisons of credit-car use including credit ratings and other information.

http://www.moneygator.com

Money Extra

Money Extra is a leading UK personal finance web site and aims is to give you fast and easy access to the best financial products and services using independent and impartial comparisons. The services are provided free of charge because they receive sponsorship revenues. The company specialises in financial services e-commerce and the provision of electronic information and transaction services for the life, pensions, investment and mortgage-lending markets. They is also an International section.

http://www.moneyextra.co.uk

National Savings

Recently revamped, this Government-backed personal savings specialist is moving into the world of e-commerce. The site allows users to check for any unpaid Prenium prizes, and offers details on 280,000 unpaid prizes. Other features include a savings selector, a savings calculator and information on products and tax rates.

http://www.nationalsavings.co.uk

Screen Trade

This is an online insurance broker where you can compare prices and policies according to your insurance needs, and even buy online.

http://www.screentrade.co.uk

Silicon Investor

At Techstocks.com investors can read up on timely performance data and other useful statistics on technology companies of all sizes. There is also a chat forum, where active investors can share their views and get advice about the prospects for specific companies and the technology sector itself. Silicon Investor claims to be the world's largest financial discussion site.

http://www.techstocks.com

Simpler Pensions

Established by the National Association of Pension Funds Limited, this is part of its efforts to simplify the company pension schemes.

http://www.simplerpensions.org.uk/

Wall Street Journal Interactive

WSJ.com is the online edition of the *Wall Street Journal*. It not only contains the same information as the printed version but also has charts and data archives that really make it worth looking at. Anyone wanting to find out about investing on the stock market would do well to invest in this.

http://www.wsj.com

UK Invest

Excellent information site for investors and money-related subjects.

http://www.uk-invest.com

FLOWERS

Flowers Direct

Next-day delivery anywhere in the UK is offered from Flowers Direct, where you can choose from a range of prices and arrangements.

http://www.flowersdirectuk.co.uk/

Interflora

Fleurop-Interflora is the world's biggest online flower shop. This worldwide flower-ordering organisation will get your message and flowers to that special person within hours of receiving your order. Just have your credit card number and the delivery details ready when you log on to this site!

http://www.interflora.com

Teleflorist

With same-day or next-day floral deliveries, this is a nicely laid-out site with a good range and easy to use. No excuses there then!

http://www.teleflorist.co.uk

Virtual Florist

At this site they offer you a chance to send a virtual flower bouquet:

a floral image by e-mail that is easy, fun and totally free! You can also send a real bouquet from their reliable and secure internet site. You can select and send a floral image with a personalised message. There are plenty of tasteful arrangements and space to compose a short poem to accompany them.

http://www.virtualflorist.com/

FOOD

See also Beer, Cookery, Food, Wine

Bread Recipes
A vast selection of recipes for breads of all kinds, including muffins, tea breads and other yeast bakes. It's an American site, so all the recipes are in cup measures and there's quite a lot of extra information about who wrote the recipes and what people thought of them, but a good source of recipes, nonetheless.

http://www.breadrecipe.com/

Chocoholic's Delight
Chocoholism is an issue that should be addressed. So for all you chocholics out there, get some help. Do not waste any more time – get online for lots of information and mouthwatering recipes!

http://www.godiva.com

Clearspring
Dedicated to vegetarian foods from around the world, this site offers a catalogue of goods that are available by mail order from London. There is also a database of interesting and unusual recipes.

http://www.clearspring.co.uk/

Dine Online
This independent UK dining and travel e-zine offers a selection of British and foreign food reviews. The informative articles recommend and review specific worldwide venues as well as cover broader food

issues. There is also an equally good but smaller section of wine reviews and suggestions for the perfect meal.

http://www.dine-online.co.uk/welcome.html

Epicurious Food

This massive site contains everything you could possibly want to know about all things edible. There are informative sections on drinking and food etiquette, together with a helpful food dictionary. The cooking classes offer illustrated step-by-step recipes that will take you gently through the creation of some exotic dishes, while the gourmet section reveals the secret to creating more complex culinary works of art.

http://food.epicurious.com/

Food Lines

This site provides sound, reliable food and nutritional information. Food enthusiasts can also obtain information about food-related trade shows, festivals, events and contests held around the world, and search the world for recommended restaurants. There are links to other food, nutrition and recipe sites and you can purchase specialty food, nutrition and health products and services from vendors. Try out a food quiz and crossword to see how much you have learned.

http://www.foodlines.com/

The French Hamper Company

View this site for a selection of fabulous French food and drink for every occasion, both business and pleasure. You can choose from a large range of pre-packaged hampers, but the company also caters for special requests all year round. Recipes in French and English are included with your order so that you can make the most of everything you have in your hamper.

http://www.frenchhampers.com/

Global Gourmet

This is an e-zine with articles about food, wine and diet as well as a full archive of previous issues. Global Gourmet has profiles and recommendations of culinary web sites and cookbooks amongst its regular features.

http://www.foodwine.com/

Greengrocer

Run from a houseboat in Sydney Harbour, this company delivers fruit and vegetables locally and has been a major success. The idea has caught on and you can now find similar services elsewhere. In all parts of the US, there is Netgrocer which uses FedEx for delivery of goods; and in certain parts of the UK, Tesco has its own internet order and delivery service.

http://www.greengrocer.com.au

http://www.netgrocer.com

http://www.tesco.co.uk

Iceland

The first major UK food retailer to ban GM foods from its own-brand range is also the first to offer an organic range of vegetables at the same price as their ordinary ranges – plus all the other ready-made meals and foodstuffs from their freezer. Let's hope others follow suit. Order online for next-day delivery.

http://www.iceland.co.uk

Mail a Meal

Dedicated to sending free food postcards, you can say it with food by mailing a meal to your friends from this mouth-watering site. Say 'sorry' with some chocolates, say 'I love you' with a romantic candlelit dinner, or say 'get well soon' with a bowl of soup.

http://www.mailameal.com/

Menu Master

All you need to do to access the information on this site is to key in your location and you will get a list of all the local restaurants and take-aways in the area. Very useful if you are travelling around and do not know the area.

http://www.menumaster.co.uk

My Meals

You can enter any special dietary requirements you have into this site and it will make a selection of recipes suitable specifically for you. Particularly useful for those with a food allergy.

http://www.my-meals.com

Organics Direct

An easy-to-navigate site, if a little dreary. You can buy organic foods, wine, clothing and bedding online for fairly quick delivery.

http://www.organicsdirect.com

Organic Food and Wine

Organic food and wine on sale online.

http://www.iorganic.com

Real Meat

Ethically produced meat and poultry on sale online with a minimum order quantity.

http://www.realmeat.co.uk

Sainsbury's

The major UK food retailer now has its own web site offering an excellent range of quality foods to order online for next-day delivery.

http://www.sainsburys.co.uk

Schwartz

This site from the UK's major producer of herbs and spices is full of information regarding the products they offer, recipes using their herbs and spices and a section on everything you could need to know about the your favourite herbs and spices. There is even a section on special offers where you can buy related goods, although this is only open to UK residents.

http://www.schwartz.co.uk

Simply Food
For everyone who loves eating and drinking, this site contains food facts, recipes, information on UK restaurants, shopping and wine tasting. Check it out for any food-related topics.

http://www.simplyfood.co.uk

Speciality Foods
Exactly what you would expect, this site is an entry-point to small, specialist UK sites offering unusual foods from organic meat to home-made pickles and vegetarian Parmesan cheese.

http://www.speciality-foods.com

Tesco
One of the first of the major UK food retailers to expand into the online shopping market, Tesco offers good online ordering and delivery in a two-hour window, although not to the whole of the UK at present. You have to have a Clubcard and be over 18 to order by credit card.

http://www.tesco.com

Thorntons
This site is the Thorntons online store where you can purchase gifts and special treats from a selection of their delicious confectionery. Simply fill your shopping basket and place your order, together with a free personal message which can be sent with any gift. Also here is a great kids' area of pages called The Children's Natural Discovery Site with information on gemstones, dinosaurs, fossils, nature and, of course, chocolate.

http://www.thorntons.co.uk

TuDocs

As with many subjects there is a proliferation of recipe and cooking sites on the web. TuDocs is a virtual library which holds tens of thousands of recipes from across the globe, most of which may be accessed free. The site covers almost anything you could ever wish to consume: beverages, cheese, desserts, diabetic recipes, ethnic foods, seafood, spices and vegetarian food, plus it has information on chefs, food groups and more. TuDocs is a directory that has been designed to speed you to the exact recipe or cooking information you want. You can also get an idea of what you might expect from the cooking sites.

http://www.tudocs.com/

Veggie Heaven

Veggie Heaven is *the* place where you can find over 230 of the tastiest vegetarian and vegan recipes, the leading UK vegetarian restaurant guide, amazing facts and figures – and lots more. Created by Rosamond Richardson, one of the UK's most innovative vegetarian cookery writers.

http://www.veggieheaven.com/

Waitrose Direct

Waitrose is the food section of the John Lewis Partnership and sells a vast range of high-quality foods. Investigate its Direct web site for online purchases.

http://www.waitrose.com

Worldwide Hampers

Worldwide Hampers, as the name suggests, will deliver their products anywhere. You will see that the site is presented as a mini-shopping centre, with a food hall, wine store, flower shop and gift shop. You can even buy a hamper for your pets. There is also a post office where you can enter your details to be eligible for product updates and member discounts. You might even receive a mystery gift if your name is pulled out of the hat in the bi-weekly prize draw.

http://www.worldwide-hampers.com/

FUN

See also Children's, Entertainment, Hobbies

Anagrams

At this site you can use the free generator, the anagram genius, to see what anagrams can be made out of your name. You can also use the anagram archive to search those elusive words that are stopping you from finishing that crossword you started at breakfast.

http://www.anagramgenius.com/

Astro Star

Once you have subscribed to Astro Star, they will e-mail you with information on all kinds of freebies from food and games to computer products and gifts.

http://www.astrostar.com

The Avenger's Handbook

If you want to get even with someone, or if you are just looking for some good laughs, then this site is for you. It contains revenge schemes, tactics, ideas, tips and guidance that would scare or pester most offenders into surrender. What it does not do is take any responsibility for your actions! This is nothing to do with the TV show!

http://www.ekran.no/html/revenge/

Disney

For everything about Disney with a style and quality you come to expect of this mega institution.

http://www.disney.co.uk

Dragons

If you want a central source with hyperlinks to a whole range of dragon images and other dragon-related information, you can start your search here.

http://www.draconian.com

Dream Emporium

This site contains a wide range of topics to do with dreams and their interpretation. The topics include how to interpret your dreams; keeping a dream journal; nightmares; sleep disorders such as sleep walking, sleep talking, sleep paralysis and night terrors; lucid dreams; dream symbols; helping children with their nightmares.

http://www.dreamemporium.com/

Fantasy Animation

Devoted to Japanese animation, this site offers lots of pictures of all the weird and wonderful creations – including, of course, Pokémon – plus game-play tips and a message board.

http://www.fantasyanime.com

Fortean Times

Fortean Times is a monthly magazine of news, reviews and research on strange phenomena and experiences, curiosities, prodigies and portents. This site contains highlights and news from the printed publication.

http://www.forteantimes.com

Funny

Want a good laugh? Then go to this online comedy directory with links to other 'funny' sites on the web.

http://www.funny.co.uk/

Guide to US Theme Parks

This theme park guide gives park-by-park advice on how to avoid the crowds and which attractions to ride on first. Read up on how to ride the attractions in order to achieve maximum thrills. You can also get the latest from insiders about up-and-coming US park mergers and future rides.

http://www.screamscape.com

Hamster Dance
Just visit and you'll see!

http://www.hamsterdance.com

Humor Database
This site was started as a high-school science project but the project proved to be so successful, a company bought it! You can find thousands of jokes here, all of which have been rated. You can search for jokes by content, keyword, author or by humour number. Humor Database has links to other similar sites too.

http://www.humordatabase.com/

Humour Net
HumourNet is a mailing list for jokes, humorous stories, and entertaining anecdotes. List members send in humorous contributions, which are periodically collected into collages. The collages then are mailed out to the list on a less-than-regular basis – usually once a month. You can subscribe for free or just read the acrhives.

http://www.humournet.com/

HumorScope
Have you found that your horoscopes are getting too boring or too cynical for you? Check your stars out at HumorScope. The readings are changed daily and, according to the author, are scientifically worked out by spinning a carrot. The author also sends out the daily humorscope to you in your e-mail if you would rather recieve it there instead of on the web.

http://www.humorscope.com/

Infamous Exploding Whale
There has been a story floating around the net for years about a beached whale that was blown up (exploded, not inflated) for lack of a better way to be rid of it. Many people thought it was an urban legend – but it is true! See for yourself exactly what happened at this site – if you are not too squeamish.

http://www.perp.com/whale/

Insect Recipes

You could try out these recipes – if you feel so inclined! Recipes include Rootworm Beetle Dip, Banana Worm Bread and Chocolate Chirpie Chip Cookies made with that singularly important ingredient – crickets.

http://www.ent.iastate.edu/Misc/InsectsAsFood.html

Joke Wallpaper

If you are getting bored looking at the patterns that came with your operating system, you'll find many new ones to choose from at this site. You can download free images for either Windows or Mac.

http://www.jokewallpaper.com

Kissogram

Do you want to send someone a kissogram? Why not send them something slightly different over the net? For a very tacky joke, send an animated kiss or a pouting drag queen or even – well, why don't you see for yourself? There are plenty to choose from!

http://www.kissogram.com.au

Nutty Sites

A fun and non-commercial site with dancing hamsters, lizards and cows as well as magic tricks. A real antidote to a rainy day.

http://www.nuttysites.com

Peeping Tom

Fancy peeping through some of the net's many cameras? They are watching many different people and events 24 hours a day, seven days a week. However, beware: you could end up watching life instead of getting on with it!

http://www.coolbase.com/peepingtom/

Strange Laws

From the obscure to the ridiculous, the Strange Laws web site has them all! Some of them still apply but most simply give an insight into bygone days.

http://www.wj.net/rborek/strange.html

Superstition

If you have ever wondered about all the different superstitions, then this site is for you. Here you will find a list of different superstitions and what you are meant to do to get rid of your bad luck.

http://members.aol.com/JuliannaA/scary.html

They Killed Kenny

Comedy Central's South Park reached cult-worship status overnight. If you can't get enough of it, or want to know more about this bizarre show, then check out its web site. The site includes special events, the South Park booster club and a chat room.

http://southpark.comedycentral.com/southpark/

UK National Lottery

This site contains everything you need to know about the UK lottery. It will not give you the winning numbers to subsequent draws (what a shame!) but you can access previous ones together with numerical analysis and statistics. This may help you put a strategy together – it may be far easier simply to pick six numbers at random and hope for the best!

http://lottery.merseyworld.com

Urban Myths

An Urban Myth is a form of legend. It is a bizarre story that is told time and time again. The people then begin to believe it is true and continue to pass it on. This site is the most extensive collection of these tall tales. If you visit this site, you can see how many times you have been duped!

http://www.Urbanmyths.com

Useless Knowledge

This site contains lots of useless facts, useless quotes – everything on it is useless actually, but it is such a good read!

http://www.uselessknowledge.com/

Wacky Uses

An American site that will give you hours of fun finding out some amazing uses for ordinary things you have lying around the house.

http://www.wackyuses.com

The Weekly

The Weekly is a funny mag of made-up things that is published each Monday. It does not contain true news stories but it is a very entertaining read if you want something to make you smile.

http://www.theweekly.co.uk/

Wow Go

A site for teenage girls, this offers puzzles, general life information and girly matters. A safe site at the time of writing for blossoming hormones.

http://www.wowgo.com

Yuk Yuk

Check out the comics at this site.

http://www.yukyuk.com

Yahoo Games

This site allows you to play classic games such as chess, bridge and backgammon with other people around the world. It is a free service which does not require any special software. A standard web browser and an internet connection are all you need and then it simply takes a moment to register in order to obtain your log-on name. Once you have done this, you can enter a game at the site and have hours of fun!

http://play.yahoo.com

GAMBLING

Blues

This is a betting store which is worth investigating. There's a cashback on your first bet.

http://www.bluesq.com

Casino CoCo

Here you will find access to a real casino that is situated on Saint Marten in the Caribbean. You can play a varity of games – some for real money and others just for fun. The best thing, though, is there is no dress code for this casino.

http://www.casinococo.com

The Casino Network

The Casino Network helps you plan everything you may need for a break to make some money. From this site you are able to reserve your hotel rooms, search around for casinos and find a world of links to gambling-related web sites.

http://www.casino-network.com

DorCino

This site is a virtual casino where you can gamble as much and as often as you wish – and the only thing wasted will be your time, as winnings or losses are virtual, too. Before using the site though first you will have to register. Once that is done if you're successful you can even make it to the monthly top ten list of winners.

http://www.dorcino.com/dorcino2/

Geisha Lounge

Another online casino where you can try your luck at a variety of games of chance.

http://www.geishalounge.com

Internet Video Poker

This site will enable you to play poker online and for free. Every time you win a hand you accrue more points to your total. There is one drawback of this site, though, and that is it is very, very addictive.

http://www.sancho.com/poker

Ladbrokes

Ladbrokes is the world's largest betting shop and from this site you can bet online on all kinds of activities from football to horse racing, as well as finding out all the latest news and form details.

http://www.bet.co.uk

Sporting Bets Online

This is a betting shop which is open online 24 hours a day, bringing you the latest prices and betting opportunities on the world's leading sporting events as they happen. The coverage includes soccer, cricket, golf, tennis, horse racing and rugby (Union and League), NFL, baseball, basketball, hockey and college sports. It is also the first fully regulated online British sports bookmaker to bring you tax-free betting from the British Isles.

http://www.sportingbet.com/

Sporting Life

All sorts of sports news and information are features here as well as racing timetables and online betting information, as you would expect from the site set up by the well-known magazine of the same name.

http://www.sporting-life.com

Virtual Vegas

This site is a virtual casino where you can play games for free. You register before you start so that you can become eligible to win prizes. Do not worry if you cannot play a particular game, all the games have a link to the rules. There are also tips from the experts for the more advanced blackjack players.

http://www.virtualvegas.com

GAMES

All Game Guide
This site allows game players quick access to news and reviews, hints and tips, screenshots and downloads of games, and is easy to navigate considering its size. It includes games from the past, the present and hints on what the future holds.

http://www.allgame.com/

Crime Scene
This site features fictional crime cases. It is a unique combination of interactive storytelling and gaming. Choose a level of participation and become a case detective or a case viewer. You can then examine the evidence and share your tips, leads and observations. The current case is updated each week with items such as: evidence, photos, coroner's reports, witness interviews and surveillance videos.

http://www.crimescene.com/

DI Illusions
A source of computer and video games and the latest news on this fastest-moving area of the market. This site also houses a European online auction.

http://www.axl.com

Free Games
A list of links to sites with free games available to download.

http://www.freegames2000.com/

Future Gamer
For weekly news on games, Future Gamer has it all. Receive it via e-mail or read it on the web.

http://www.futuregamer.com/

Game FAQs

Are you frustrated with the new game you have just bought because you cannot get past the first screen? Do you feel like returning it or even throwing it out because you are totally fed up with it? Do not let your frustration get the better of you because help is at hand at this site. You'll find cheats and walk-throughs to hundreds of games designed for both PC and games consoles.

http://www.gamefaqs.com/

Games Direct

Discounts and a good range of stock as well as information and sales for PC games of all kinds.

http://www.gamsdirect.co.uk

Games Domain

This is a comprehensive British-based games site that provides news, reviews, freebies, chat and a contacts and resources list. It is one of the few sites that really makes good use of its user contributions.

http://www.gamesdomain.co.uk/

Games Net

Second-hand games and PCs at what this family-run company claim are among the lowest prices available.

http://www.games-net.co.uk

Game Online

This is a PC and console online gaming magazine. It is UK-based and updated daily with news, reviews, tips, voting and forums.

http://www.game-online.com/

Game Spot

Game Spot states: 'the best, the worst, the coolest, the hottest – if it's new in computer gaming, you'll find it here!' Apart from news and reviews, it contains a designer diary section, beta centre and 3D model gallery to enhance your gaming experience and blow your mind (not to mention your computer!). With an almost exhaustive amount of information across all platforms, it has everything you will possibly need to do this.

http://www.gamespot.com/

Happy Puppy

This could be renamed Huge Dog considering the size of this long-established game site. It contains an enormous amount of varied information for game players of all persuasions and platforms. From tips and cheats to downloadable demos, this site has it all.

http://happypuppy.com/

Hot Games

This is an online magazine with a sharp edge and a great sense of humour. Subscribe to their e-mail service, Cool News, to receive all the latest news and information on the games world.

http://www.hotgames.com/

Jamba

Self-styled as offering big games, big prizes and lots of fun, this site offers you games such as Armageddon and Catchphrase which you can play once you register on the site.

http://www.jamba.co.uk

Nintendo

Mailings, competitions, recommendations, news, awards and lots of links feature on this game site.

http://www.nintendodirect.co.uk

PC Game Finder

This is a specialised search engine indexing everything the web has to offer for over 3500 PC games. Look up a game to get all of the facts, files and links that you may ever need. The site gives you direct access to the latest reviews, demos, patches, cheats and much more. In order to carry out a search, look up a game by title, by company, by A–Z, or by browsing over 150 detailed categories. You can also check GameScoop to see what's new every 24 hours.

http://www.pcgame.com/

PlayStation

The PlayStation site features all kinds of information on games, discounts, competitions and offers – everything you might want to know about your PlayStation games and console.

http://www.playstationdirect.co.uk

Software First

PlayStation, Nintendo, Dreamcast and Gameboy games are all stocked on this site, together with books, videos and CDs.

http://www.softwarefirst.co.uk/

Total Games Network

This site is actually updated throughout the day, which means that you will always have the latest information at your fingertips, or as it comes hot off the press! Total Games Network provides news, previews, features, reviews and hints and tips on games created for all consoles and PCs. It is informative and well written and definitely a site that gaming experts should check out regularly.

http://www.totalgames.net/

GARDENING

See also Environment, Nature

Baby Bio

Baby Bio is one of the major UK producers of plant foods and pest-control products. The site offers advertising of its own products, of course, but also useful question-and-answer information on plant care and coping with plant and gardening problems.

http://www.bio.uk.co

British Gardening Online

Find out about plants, gardens and gardening events in the UK, search the web or discuss gardening topics.

http://www.oxalis.co.uk

E-garden

Sensible and straightforward advice, with sources for gardening products and supplies are offered on this site, including features from TV gardeners Richard Jackson and Geoff Hodge.

http://www.e-garden.co.uk

Garden Experts

The *Expert Gardener* magazine now has this site which is part of a larger web site on all aspects of gardening, including news, features and a chat room. Once you register, you can access information about the magazine, get gardening advice or buy gardening products.

http://www.igarden.co.uk

Garden Guides

This site is a great resource for gardeners everywhere with articles, guide sheets and tips for all things gardening-related, such as planting hardy perennials, composting and arranging beds. Great stuff, with a free newsletter posted to your inbox every week if you wish to subscribe.

http://www.gardenguides.com/

Garden Products

This site offers a good range of garden products and accessories for sale, with an efficient search engine to help you navigate through the stocks. There is normally a charge for delivery unless you happen to live in London.

http://www.capital-gardens.co.uk

Garden Web

Although a US-based site, so some of the information is of regional relevance, there is also quite a lot of useful information for all gardeners, including planting, plant care and pest control.

http://www.gardenweb.com

Gardening Encyclopedia

You will find an illustrated gardening encyclopedia, problem-solver section containing the answers to 700 horticultural ailments, and a guide to other sites at gardening.com to help the novice and the expert alike.

http://www.gardening.com

Gardening UK

With plant of the month, articles, information and details of events and supplies, this site offers much to interest the keen gardener.

http://www.gardening-uk.com

Herb FAQs

Although this site is presented in a rather disappointing way, it is well organised and hence is easy to use. It consists of a collection of advice about herbs from the newsgroup alt.Folklore.herbs. The herbs are broken down by use – medicinal, culinary, etc. – and listed by name.

http://www.sunsite.unc.edu/herbmed/faqs/herbfaqs.html

Horticultural Index

All aspects of horticulture are covered in this wide-ranging index, including products, colleges, nurseries, shows and equipment.

http://www.ukexnet.co.uk/hort/index.htm

Internet Garden

The Internet Garden has been designed to provide a useful starting point for gardening enthusiasts in search of quality information that is quick and easy to access. It has a search facility and links to other useful sites as well.

http://www.internetgarden.co.uk

Roses

A fascinating site with articles of all sorts for rose fans as well as all kinds of roses on sale. Easy to find your way around and an excellent site for rose gardeners.

http://www.roses.co.uk

Royal Botanic Garden, Edinburgh, Scotland

The Royal Botanic Garden Edinburgh was founded in the seventeenth century on an area the size of a tennis court. It now extends to 31 hectares (at Inverleith in Edinburgh), incorporates specialist gardens at three very different locations in Scotland (Younger, Logan and Dawyck; 50ha, 12ha and 25ha), and is one of the world's finest botanical gardens. Check out the site for all the latest news and information on education, events, publications and research as well as links to other sites and associated organisations.

http://www.rbge.org.uk

Shrubs for your Garden

Online sales of shrubs, perennials, turf, etc. for your garden. A good range with competitive prices and quick delivery.

http://www.shrubsdirect.com

Topiary

An amazing selection of topiary and garden products available to order. Grow them yourself or let Noah's Ark do it for you.

http://noahsarktopiary.com

GAY AND LESBIAN

Gender and Sexuality

This site publishes texts which address gender and gay studies studies, with a particular focus on discussions of sex, gender, sexual identity and sexuality in cultural practices. You will see that the broad-ranging set of links to essays includes eclectic titles as well as the more conventional topics.

http://eserver.org/gender/

OutRage!

OutRage! campaigns on behalf of the gay and lesbian community with the aim of eliminating homophobia. It is a forum for non-violent protest, which uses imaginative, witty and shocking tactics to provoke debate and promote awareness.

http://www.outrage.cygnet.co.uk/

Pink Passport

This site aims to be the number one guide to the best gay and lesbian hotels, clubs, bars, restaurants, gyms and saunas around the world. It certainly is extensive and very impressive.

http://www.pinkpassport.com/

Stonewall

Stonewall is the national civil rights group working for legal equality and social justice for lesbians, gay men and bisexuals. The web site provides a series of free fact sheets covering all issues facing the gay and lesbian community. There is also information about ongoing campaigns, as well as general advice. A mailing list is available for those who want to keep up-to-date with Stonewall's activities.

http://www.stonewall.org.uk/

Straight Answers

This site is a guide on how to answer questions about gay life and change anti-gay attitudes. Although written with a gay audience in mind, Straight Answers is open to anybody. This US-based site has been extremely well conceived.

http://www.sipu.com/sa/index.html

GENEALOGY

Access Genealogy

With advice for those starting out and a huge database of records, you can sift facts and figures to your heart's content.

http://www.accessgenealogy.com/

Ancestors.co.uk

This is the web site of Ancestors Ltd. They can research family trees worldwide and investigate house history, company history and intestacies, plus missing persons and adopted children. They also design and manufacture merchandise for the heritage market. They have full, secure online ordering facilities to enable you to purchase from their range of products and services.

http://www.ancestors.co.uk

Everton's Genealogical Helper

A very good site, especially for the beginner, there's access here to a vast database of information to help you track down your ancestors.

http://www.everton.com/

Genealogy

This site is dedicated to bringing the best and the most comprehensive resources and services on the web. It is the place to go whether you are a beginner or an experienced genealogical researcher.

http://www.genealogy.com

Ultimate Family Tree

If you want to trace your family tree, then this site is for you. The Ultimate Family Tree provides a variety of searches to help you get the most out of the site, together with a glossary of genealogical terms and abbreviations. This is essential because you will come across current legal terms, as well as those that are archaic or now obsolete!

http://www.uftree.com

GEOGRAPHY

See also Travel and Holidays

Chinese Language

A dictionary of Chinese characters on the first site and, at the second, the chance to have your name transliterated into Chinese.

http:www.chinalanguage.com/CCDICT/index.html

http:www.chinalanguage.com/cgi-bin/name.pl

Flags of all Countries

The site gives large and small pictures of the flags of every nation in the world. You can also click on the flags to see a map of the country plus other useful information.

http://www.wave.net/upg/immigration/flags.html

How Far Is It?

This site will find the latitude and longitude of any two places and then calculate the 'as-the-crow-flies' distance between them. It then displays them for you on a map.

http://www.indo.com/distance/

Lycos Mapfinder

Simply key in a postcode and Lycos will find you a street map that you can print out.

http://www.lycos.co.uk/webguides

Mapquest

This award-winning web site can help you get to where you need to be each day. By simply typing in a starting point and destination, or even just a city and state, you can get driving directions, create customised maps, view nearby businesses and points of interest, and plan trips away.

http://www.mapquest.com

Map World

This company produce maps and globes of every kind which you can order on the site. They have an e-mail catalogue and e-mailing list and when you input the details of the sort of material you want, they will provide information and pictures on what is available, including full specifications and prices.

http://www.mapworld.com

Multimap

Excellent online atlas for the UK including postcodes, London street names with links to world atlas. You can search by name or on the outline of the country.

http://www.multimap.com

National Geographic

Full of incredible photos, like the magazine, this web site is one you should not miss. Updated each month with new reports from foreign countries and archaeological digs, the site contains online forums where you can contribute to debates. The site also has an impressive archives section where you can look at the highlights from all the years' back issues.

http://www.nationalgeographic.com

National Geographic Maps

The National Geographic Map Machine is without a doubt the best resource for online maps. The source enables you to choose any destination on the globe and view a political or physical map of the region. You can even see it from above for a real bird's eye view! There is also the Map Machine Atlas containing country maps, facts, flags and profiles.

http://plasma.nationalgeographic.com/mapmachine/

Refugees

You can access information about the plight of refugees from around the world at the site of the United Nations High Commission for Refugees. Read first-hand accounts of people forced to flee persecution and up-to-date news on worldwide conflicts. For holding discussions in the classroom, the site includes a guide for teachers on the subject. It certainly brings home the awful reality of life.

http://www.unhcr.ch/

Volcanoes of the World

This site offers a geographical breakdown of all known volcanoes – and there are more of them than you might think! More often than not they are docile and the kind of destruction that is always depicted in films is not likely to be seen. However, you will find the photo library of this site fascinating as it contains some fairly scary images of Mount St Helens.

http://vulcan.wr.usgs.gov/Volcanoes/

The Web of Culture

The Web of Culture seeks to educate the web community on the topic of effective cross-cultural communications in the global marketplace. Here you can learn more on their goal to provide accurate and timely business and cultural information.

http://www.webofculture.com/

WebCam Central

This site hosts a listing and some previews of fixed cameras bringing pictures from dozens of countries around the world, from Brazil to Russia and the United States.

http://www.camcentral.com/

The World Fact Book

The CIA have produced this extensive guide which is an excellent resource full of information on the world's countries. Information includes cultural, political, economic and geographic topics plus some very good maps.

http://www.odci.gov/cia/publications/factbook/index.html

GIFTS

Drinks Direct

For gifts for any occasion – champagne, wine, hampers, flowers, chocolates – have a look at this site. They'll send your gift beautifully wrapped with a message of your choice.

http://www.drinks-direct.co.uk

Gift Store

Chocolates, flowers, games, cards, ties, cufflinks and other gift items delivered direct on the day you choose.

http://www.giftstore.co.uk

Hot Box

Gadgets and gifts whatever your budget, this is the place to find something for the man who has everything.

http://www.hotbox.co.uk

Present Picker

If you are stuck for gift ideas for the person who has everything, then help is at hand at the present-picker site. From this site you can use a gift wizard which will ask you some simple questions, then provide a list of gifts from various companies and links to their web pages where you can purchase the gift of your choice.

http://presentpicker.com/ppp/

Scottish Gifts
Scotch Corner, the retail outlet, also has this web site on which you can find anything and everything Scottish.

http://www.scotch-corner.co.uk

Star Names
How's this for romantic? You can name a star for your loved one and have it recorded in the Cosmic Library for all time.

http://www.starnames.co.uk/

GOVERNMENT AND POLITICS

See also Environment

All Politics
This site is devoted just to news about politics brought to you by CNN and *Time* magazine and supplies you with the latest political news from inside America. You can take part in a quick poll or research events through in-depth special reports and Congressional quarterly articles.

http://cnn.com/ALLPOLITICS/

Amnesty International
Amnesty International crusades for human rights all over the world and this is its official web site. Find out here about the injustices it is fighting and see what you can do to help.

http://www.amnesty.org

CCTA Government Information

If you need to find any UK Government authority, then look no further – just open this huge directory.

http://www.open.gov.uk

Central Intelligence Agency

If you want to know more about the CIA, then this is the site for you. It gives all sorts of facts, such as details of the CIA's role in international affairs and its history.

http://www.odci.gov

The Commonwealth

This is the web site of the Commonwealth, the unique family of 54 nations around the world. It is also the official web site of the Commonwealth Secretariat in London. Here you will find information about member countries, Commonwealth activities and projects. Also explore the rest of the site to access details of their programmes and activities, read their latest releases, features, reports or publications, to find out more about their upcoming events and to see who their partners are.

http://www.thecommonwealth.org

Conspiracies

Conspiracy theories seem to pop up all over the place. Are they true? Check out these sites to see what certain people may or may not be up to!

http://www.conspire.com/

http://www.mt.net/~watcher/

The Euro

This is the European Commission's internet site dedicated exclusively to the Euro, whether you are a citizen interested in your future currency or a specialist working on technical preparations for the changeover. The site is regularly updated with applicable documents as they become available, and also provides access to an electronic version of *Infeuro*, the Commission's own newsletter on the Euro, plus other sites with useful information on the single currency. The site is available in 11 languages

http://europa.eu.int/euro/html/entry.html

Europarl

This site is the home of the European parliament so if you have wondered what news laws are being passed that may affect you, or what are the most current news and activities, then this is the place to see. It is available in a variety of different European languages.

http://www.europarl.eu.int

The European Telework Development

The ETD site aims to construct a European network of national web sites for each participating country. Some of these are ones that already exist and with which the ETD has agreed to co-operate; others are new ones directly supported by the ETD. Each web site should contain the following: relevant national information important to the country concerned; and also selected European and ETD information in the local language. Some countries have provided their national pages in their own language: Bulgaria, Czechoslovakia, Denmark, France, Germany, Greece, Hungary, Italy, Latvia, Poland, Portugal, Russia, Spain, and Switzerland in German.

http://www.eto.org.uk/

FBI FOIA Reading Room

This site contains FBI documents that have been released as part of the Freedom of Information Act. You will find that there are files on some celebrities such as Marilyn Monroe, and you can even read documents about the British monarchy.

http://www.foia.fbi.gov

FedWorld

If you want to locate any US federal Government documents, contacts or servers, use the FedWorld government site.

http://www.fedworld.gov

Freedom of Information

The US Government passed the Freedom of Information Act in an attempt to be more open with its public. As a result, anyone who is interested in requesting documents from US Government agencies can do so. How to use the Freedom of Information Act explains what kind of information can be accessed, how to make requests and what the cost may be.

http://www.gwu.edu/~nsarchive/nsa/foia_how_use.html

The Gallup Organisation

For over 60 years, the Gallup Organisation has been the world leader in the measurement and analysis of people's attitudes, opinions and behaviour. Check out the site if you wish to take part in any of its opinion polls or fill out the questionnaires. You can see the results of past surveys or go to the Gallup bookstore to purchase books written by Gallup researchers and consultants. Access is also provided at this site to Gallup clients who are receiving research results and consulting services by means of a secure extranet web site.

http://www.gallup.com

InfoWar

If you are interested in warfare issues and in finding out what is going on, this site is for you. It has information on hacking activity, industrial espionage, terrorism and military propaganda.

http://www.infowar.com

Intelligence International

This site is for a magazine produced with the same name. The magazine is the world's leading independent source of political and strategic intelligence so expect the same from the web site. During the 64 years of its existence *Intelligence International* has built up an unrivalled network of intelligence sources covering almost every country in the world. It is this network that has enabled the magazine to be the first again and again with vital news – long before the mainstream press and electronic media.

http://www.intelligence-net.com/asp/index.asp

International Security Organization

The Organization for Security and Co-operation in Europe (OSCE) is a security organisation of 55 participating states which span the geographical area from Vancouver to Vladivostok. It is the primary instrument for early warning, conflict prevention, crisis management and post-conflict rehabilitation. The OSCE approach to security is comprehensive and co-operative. It deals with a wide range of security issues, including arms control, preventive diplomacy, confidence and security-building measures, human rights, election monitoring and economic and environmental security. Here you can find out all about them and their latest projects and concerns.

http://www.osce.org/

Jane's IntelWeb

Jane's is the leading unclassified information provider for military, government and commercial organisations worldwide on the subjects of defence/geopolitics, transportation and law enforcement. You can get brief updates of everything that is occurring in these sectors.

http://intelweb.janes.com

NATO

At this site you can find out all about the North Atlantic Treaty Organisation, founded in 1949, soon after the Second World War. Also available is all the information on projects that are currently being carried out by NATO.

http://www.nato.int/

National Security Agency

This is the site of America's most secret service. Here is also the home of the American National Cryptologic Museum containing documents on the Cuban Missile Crisis and probably more secrets than even the most hardened conspiracy theorist could imagine. A high-technology organisation, NSA is on the frontiers of communications and data processing. It is also one of the most important centres of foreign-language analysis and research within the American Government.

http://www.nsa.gov

Palestinian National Authority

The official Palestinian site giving details and reports of the area over the internet, including regular updates on the settlement process.

http://www.pna.net

Secret Services

This site contains brief introductions to the operations of the real-life James Bonds – MI5 and MI6 in Britain and the CIA and National Security Agency in the US. Also available is a short history of espionage.

http://www2.active.ch/~mwuest/s_services/
secret_services.htm

United Nations

This is where you can find out all about the United Nations and how it helps countries in the world. There is a lot of information about current activities, news and international law and plenty of geo-political information.

http://www.un.org

United Nations Cyberschool Bus

This site is aimed at children who wish to learn more about the world and about the UN. It is split into various sections, which include a discussion area and an interactive database called InfoNation, which contains up-to-date information about most countries in the world, if not all. A good place to start is the virtual tour of the UN, an online introduction to the UN and its work.

http://www.un.org/Pubs/CyberSchoolBus/

The US National Archives

Their mission is 'to ensure ready access to essential evidence that documents the rights of American citizens, the actions of federal officials, and the national experience'. The Exhibit Hall Online contains such things as the police report on Lincoln's assassination. An interesting site to peruse.

http://www.nara.gov/

The White House

Go on a tour of the White House or air your views on any political matter using the White House's official suggestion form. Do not expect your questions to be answered by the president himself, but you never know: someone in there might be taking heed of what you are saying!

`http://www.whitehouse.gov`

GRAPHICS

Animated Gifs of Michael Shaikun

This is a good site to obtain more and more graphics for your own web page designs. Not only are there animated gifs here but there are collections of icons, backgrounds, text – anything you need to make your web page load more slowly!

`http://gifs.net/files/`

Clip Art

If you have a presentation to make, you can always make documents and overhead transparencies clearer and easier on the eye by adding clip art. Use these sites to find exactly what pictures you want.

`http://www.clipart.com`

`http://www.clipartconnection.com`

HEALTH

See also Beauty and Hair, Parenting

Anxiety Disorders

Millions of people suffer from anxiety disorders and the majority are never diagnosed. To find out about each known anxiety disorder, check out the National Institute of Mental Health's Anxiety Disorders Education Program. The site is in English and Spanish and contains a section for health professionals.

`http://www.nimh.nih.gov/anxiety/`

Biorhythms Site

The principle behind biorhythms is that our lives are affected by three primary cycles: physical, emotional and intellectual. These cycles start at a mid-point when we are born, then go up and down at different rates throughout our life. It is believed that people can improve the quality of their lives by monitoring their biorhythms and acting accordingly. This site enables you to create your own biorhythm chart to conduct your own investigation into this theory.

http://www.facade.com/attraction/biorhythm/

British Geriatrics Society

This is the official web site of the British Geriatrics Society. The purpose of the site is to make available information which is of use to its members, or anyone with an interest in geriatric medicine, gerontology and the care of the elderly. It has links to related sites.

http://www.bgs.org.uk/

Care Homes

A database site containing information on nursing homes and residential care homes in the UK.

http://www.carehomes.co.uk/index.htm

The Center for the Study of Autism

This is one of the most complex developmental problems of childhood. It will affect about 4.5 per 10,000 births. The Center for the Study of Autism provides overview materials in four languages, together with resources for autism and for all the related syndromes.

http://www.autism.org

The Contemporary Exercise Company Personal Fitness

The CECO web site offers personal fitness trainers and services in all the major cities in the UK. CECO trainers can both come to your home, office or gym and guide and motivate you through your programme designed to increase your fitness, or on the web site you will find specialised fitness solutions. Find out your current fitness and get a customised analysis, hints and tips on specific exercises and lots more.

http://www.ceco.co.uk/

Culpeper

The Culpeper name is known throughout the world for high-quality information and goods on herbs, and this web site offers information on and sales of herbs and herb products for medicine and cooking, as well as seeds and books. A very well-organised and pleasant site.

http://www.culpeper.co.uk

Cyber Psychologist

This is psychoanalysis online. Modern psychological technology offers proven solutions to many common problems. The site has a question-and-answer forum, information on depression, stress, phobias, anxiety and addictive behaviours. You can also find advice on how to improve your relationships and get help with career and work issues.

http://www.cyberpsych.com/main.html

Cyberdiet

This well-organised and informative site offers tips on how to reach an ideal weight and how to maintain it through exercise and diet. You can also have a nutritional profile created that calculates your ideal body weight.

http://www.cyberdiet.com/

Depression Analysis

Put together by New York University, this short, multiple-choice test is machine-graded. Only you will know the results, so why not find out a bit more about yourself.

http://www.med.nyu.edu/Psych/screens/depres.html

Good Health Directory

Information on a range of complementary health issues and therapies, with links to other useful health-related sites.

http://www.goodhealthdirectory.com

Headaches

The American Medical Association provides a two-pronged site dealing with headaches, which is well worth checking out. The migraine information centre covers all types of headaches, including information on how to tell them apart together with their possible treatments. Physicians can find details of the latest research, together with a literature review.

http://www.ama-assn.org/special/migraine/

Health and Fitness

This site is American so unless you live in America you may have problems with the gym locator. Nonetheless, the site has plenty for anyone who is into working out to get a fitter and better-looking body. Here they will design a customised fitness programme based on what you tell them, and they have different fitness recipes for you to enable a balanced diet as well as also an online fitness test. There are also very good reports on different aspects of fitness and lots of links.

http://www.healthfitnessnetwork.com

Health and Fitness Network

For anyone wanting to know more about how they can keep fit and healthy – and do it safely and correctly – this is the site to check out. It has over 900 links to other sites, too.

http://www.healthfitnessnetwork.com

Health Gate

Health Gate states that it is committed to providing you with health information you can trust. Consumer health and medical information at Health Gate is brought to you from several reliable sources. They contract freelance health and medical writers to write new and informative articles about health issues facing consumers today. Many of their writers have advanced degrees in health-related fields or work in the health-care professions.

http://www.healthgate.com

Health World Online

The most comprehensive global health network on the internet. Although it is US-based, it is global for two reasons: because of the global nature of internet delivery, and because it integrates both alternative and conventional health information.

http://www.altmed.net/

Healthlinks USA

Although most of the links are to US sites, this is nonetheless a very useful starting point for finding out information on anything to do with health, as it has links to thousands of health-related sites.

http://www.healthlinksusa.com/

Home of Reflexology

The ancient healing art of reflexology has been known to man for many thousands of years. It was first practised by the early Indian, Chinese and Egyptian peoples who observed that congestion or tension in any part of the foot mirrors congestion or tension in a corresponding part of the body. The Home of Reflexology provides details of reflexology organisations, together with information on reflexology and other reflexology related links.

http://www.reflexology.org/

Homeopaths UK

With both an online pharmacy for homeopathic products and a directory of homeopaths in the UK, this site is an interesting one for those involved with alternative medicine.

http://www.homeopath.co.uk

Homeopathy Home

This site provides comprehensive information and links to every homeopathy resource available. Site sections include a directory of addresses and contacts, reference area, services and supplies over the internet, discussion forums and links to other sites and societies.

http://www.homeopathyhome.com/

How to Love Yourself

They do say that before someone else can love you, you have to love yourself. Discover how to love yourself here.

http://www.for-him.com/THEPATH/howlove.htm

Human Anatomy Online

There are two ways to use this very informative site. The first is by using interactive anatomy, where you choose a body system – such as the skeletal system – then click within it for detailed information on specific parts. The second way is through reading a series of anatomy lessons. It is important to note that both ways will take a while to download due to the size of the application.

http://www.InnerBody.com

Hyperreal Drugs Archive

This site contains articles that provide details of both the pleasures and pitfalls of using recreational drugs. The Hyperreal Drugs Archive also contains links to other similar sites. It must be noted that the information in this archive is provided for educational purposes only.

http://www.hyperreal.org/drugs/

Intelihealth

Explanations on a range of common health problems, together with advice on treatment.

http://www.intelihealth.com

The Interactive Patient

This is a teaching tool for physicians and medical students. The site offers a case with a chief complaint to the user who then has to interact with the patient, requesting additional history, performing a physical examination and reviewing laboratory data and x-rays. After this has been carried out, the user is encouraged to submit a diagnosis and a treatment plan to the system, based on the information obtained. All submitted answers are evaluated and feedback is provided.

http://erowid.org/Physcoactives/Physcoactives.shtml

Internet Mental Health

This is a free encyclopedia of mental health information. Internet Mental Health is for anyone who has an interest in mental health – professionals, carers or patients – who wants to learn more about various psychological problems. The site contains information on each of the 50 most common mental disorders and on each of the 65 most common psychiatric medications. There is even an online diagnostic program that can be used to diagnose anxiety disorders, eating disorders, mood disorders, personality disorders and substance-related disorders, as well as lots of links to other related sites.

http://www.mentalhealth.com/

Internet Health Library

This is where you can find plenty of heatlh and medical information, as well as online health tips. It works very much like a search engine, with both keyword and directory searches available.

http://www.health-library.com/

Medical Dictionary

Everything you need to know about your medial problem or the medication you have been prescribed to alleviate or cure it. The site is very easy to use and does not take long to load. There is also a good links page to other medical sites on the web.

http://www.kemc.edu/n.html

Medicinal and Poisonous Plants Database

Here at this site you will find lots of links to other pages on the internet containing information to help you learn about the medicinal and poisonous properties of various plants. The site is aimed more at people who are studying the plants and the effects but it is also a good place to search if you are interested in learning more.

http://www.wam.umd.edu/~mct/Plants/index.html

Mental Health Information

For regularly updated online articles and links to other relevant web sites, the Mental Health Net is a must. The disorders and treatment section has information on symptoms, treatment and support groups as well as the links. There is also a professional resource section, which includes research journals and links to job advertisements.

http://www.cmhc.com/

The Natural Death Centre

This is a non-profit charitable project which was launched in Britain in 1991 and has three psychotherapists as directors. It aims to support those dying at home and their carers and to help them arrange funerals. It also has as a more general aim of helping improve 'the quality of dying'.

http://www.worldtrans.org/naturaldeath.html

Pharmacy

Advice and medication are both available from this shopping site where you can order from a huge range of branded products including both medicines and other items you would normally buy in a pharmacy.

http://www.pharmacy2u.co.uk

Physical Health

There are four major areas on the site: nutrition, fitness, weight loss and pregnancy. There is a self-analysis section, which is made up of many interactive features designed to help you assess your health and help you improve it. There is information on eating well and working out, together with 'encyclopedias' which are interactive references of hundreds of nutrition and fitness terms. You can use the forums to share and discuss ideas, opinions and solutions about a number of topics concerning personal health as well.

http://www.phys.com

Positive Thinking and Stress Management

This site contains a collection of entertaining and informative free books on stress, stress management, positive thinking, personal development and biofeedback that you can freely download.

http://www.ozemail.com.au/~vital1/free.htm

Quackwatch

This site is concerned with presenting the truth about alternative therapies and questionable theories related to health. It includes a large number of articles on a wide range of topics and is constantly updated. There are links to other sites and a comments page. Questions can be posted and are usually answered very quickly.

http://www.quackwatch.com/

The Site

This web site is your definitive guide to surviving and enjoying life in the 1990s. This site is for everyone, although the British person who needs help and advice through his or her bad spells will benefit from their list of contact addresses and support groups. They have a huge database with over 16,000 organisational records along with dozens of factsheets and features on a wide range of subjects.

http://www.thesite.org.uk

Social Anxiety

This is a light-hearted test that aims to help you identify your social anxieties. It only takes a few minutes and will probably tell you what you already knew, but identifying specific character attributes can be useful if you are selecting a career, for example.

http://www.queendom.com/soc_anx.html

Surgery Door

Information and advice on health topics provided by health experts.

http://www.surgerydoor.co.uk/

Think Natural

In just three and a half months from August to November 1999, Think Natural created and launched what is now the UK's premier web site devoted to natural health and body care. They stock thousands of natural health products in their warehouse in Berkhamsted, Hertfordshire, which you can order online. Think Natural also provides a huge amount of information, including encyclopedia content from

Dorling Kindersley and contributions from their expert journalists and natural health practitioners.

http://www.thinknatural.com/

Vitamins Reference Guide
This site gives a general overview followed by specific information on the vitamins that your body needs in order to function properly. Find out about the importance of each vitamin and what the deficiency symptoms are.

http://www.realtime.net/anr/vitamins.html

You Are What You Eat
Familiarise yourself with the concepts behind nutrition – and you may find you need to change your diet! This brilliant interactive site enables you to compare what you are currently eating with what you should be eating. You can plan your next meal with the food planner, and find out the nutritional value of what you are eating with the online database.

http://library.advanced.org/11163/gather/cgi-bin/wookie.cgi/

HISTORY

See also Children and Youngsters, Genealogy, Government and Politics, Reference, Women's Interest

Anne Frank
If you are interested in the story of Anne Frank, you can see a biography, or read excerpts from her diary in Dutch as well as English. You can even revisit the Anne Frank House in Amsterdam.

http://www.annefrank.nl/

Biography
This site is connected to an American show called *Biography* and it offers a page on at least 15,000 people. The site is easy to use and search for specific information as you can choose from an alphabetical

listing or search for a specific name for short biographical entries. They even include small video clips of broadcast shows.

http://www.biography.com/

The British Monarchy
If you want to know more about the British Royal family, you should visit its official home page. The British Monarchy site gives details of the current members of the House of Windsor. You can find information on each of the palaces and when they can be visited. It also explains the lines of succession, as well as giving a concise history of the Royals through the ages.

http://www.royal.gov.uk/

The Commonwealth War Graves Commission
This site for the commission was established in 1917 and its duties are to mark and maintain the graves of members of the forces of the Commonwealth.

http://www.cwgc.org

Discoverer of the New World?
We first thought that Christopher Columbus discovered the New World, then we started to give Leif Eriksson the credit. It now looks like everyone is wrong yet again. What about the Irish monk Brendan the Navigator, who is believed to have landed in Newfoundland and for whom St Brendan's Island is said to be named? Read all about it and decide for yourself.

http://www.castletown.com/brendan.htm

Distinguished Women of Past and Present
Search for biographies of distinguished women by name or by field and you can find out all about the most influential female writers, educators, scientists, heads of state, politicians, civil rights crusaders, artists, entertainers and others.

http://www.distinguishedwomen.com

Earthlore

Earthlore concentrates on recounting tales of ancient cultures and the many legacies of our ancestors. It poses such questions as: 'How are we reflected through our cultural heritage?' and 'What are the historical forces which led us to where we are today?' You can explore the great mysteries of history and perhaps come to understand a little more about the mystery of your self.

http://www.elore.com/elore.htm

Explorers of the World

There are those who dare to challenge the boundaries of space, time, ignorance and science. What kinds of people chose a life of exploration, challenge and discovery? What do you think of the explorers at this site? Which do you admire the most?

http://www.bham.wednet.edu/explore.htm

Exploring Ancient World Cultures

This site gives you the history of the ancient world in 10 short pages. To research or read more, each page contains extensive links.

http://eawc.evansville.edu/

Gallery of Achievers

In the Gallery of Achievers, the focus is on individuals whose accomplishments have helped to shape the twentieth century.

http://www.achievement.org/galleryachieve.html

The Great Chicago Fire

On 8 October 1871 the Great Chicago Fire was started around 9.00 p.m. when Mrs O'Leary's cow kicked over a lantern. However, new analysis of the data suggests that this may not have been the case. Look at maps of the area, newspapers, essays and stereophotographs at this web site and see the evidence for yourself.

http://www.chicagohs.org/fire/

The Great War Web Pages

On this web site you will find articles on various aspects of the First World War. Although the articles available at the moment mainly relate to the British and Empire involvement on the Western Front, Hellfire Corner is dedicated to the memory of all combatants, in all theatres of the war and from all sides.

http://www.fylde.demon.co.uk/welcome.htm

Guardian's Egypt

The goal of the site is to present Egypt in an archaeologically responsible light and create the most complete and inclusive Ancient Egypt web site. The current main feature is the ongoing cyber-journey to Egypt, which was created to allow people to visit the ancient monuments of Egypt from their own computer. Bring one of the wonders of the world into your home by visiting this historically and pictorially packed site, and embark on a virtual journey of Egyptian magic. Who were the famous pharoahs? How do you translate hyroglyphics? Does the curse of the sphinx exist? Find out here. There's a section for children, some archived news stories and a discussion board. This is a definitive chronology of Egyptian history and the site is still developing.

http://guardians.net/egypt/

The History Channel

As with most TV channels, this one also has its own web site. Here you will find a large amount of history-related information, as well as a listings guide and information about the channel itself.

http://www.historychannel.com

History Today

History Today is a monthly general history magazine published in London, England. It covers all types and periods of history, and the web site includes samples of articles taken from the magazine, as well as some additional material. The web site went live in August 1997 and was redesigned in October 1998.

http://www.historytoday.com

Leeds Castle

This is a very good site on Leeds Castle in Kent, England, but it is graphic-intensive and could take a while to load. Once it does though you will be able to look all around the castle and find out about all the different shows and events that are going on there throughout the year. The site also offers excellent travel directions and information on admission prices.

http://www.leeds-castle.co.uk

Native American

If you are interested in Native American history, then this is the place for you. Here you will find heaps of information plus a large collection of links to other sites that can tell you what you need to know. The links are vast and various and lead to tribal home pages, Native American organisations, goverment and educational resources and much more.

http://www.cowboy.net/native/

Reliving History

Relive some of the great historic moments at this imaginative and fact-packed site. Listen to the Queen's coronation or Albert Einstein or Martin Luther King, among many others. Watch short video clips of 'this day in history', play the interactive games and visit the online shop. Although inspired by the American TV channel, there are some fabulous ideas here, so make a visit.

http://www.thehistorychannel.com

Roman History

According to the Romans, every day should be celebrated for one reason or another. Find out which days belonged to whom at this historically fun site. You can discover the significance of your own birthday using the instruction manual linked from the home page. Each day has an accompanying graphic with an explanation of the significance of the day.

http://www.clubs.psu.edu/aegsa/rome/romec.html

Site O

Site O is dedicated to fortifications from all times and from all over the world. It includes lists of members who can be contacted by e-mail (membership is free), a discussion forum, links, information including a downloadable dictionary, and free exchange of information. Essential for anyone interested in castles, the design of Vauban, the Atlantic Wall, the Maginot Line, WW1 bunkers and so on.

http://www.feelit.se/siteo

Spartacus Books

Spartacus is a small educational book publishing company formed by a group of teachers and is committed to providing free resources for the internet community. The books sold here are all to do with history, though the site does contain some good reference pages and lots of good educational links. There are also some online history books which are great for reference.

http://www.spartacus.schoolnet.co.uk/

The Stone Pages

This is the complete guide to the megalithic sites of Europe. It reads and feels like a reference book, with a useful glossary if you're not *au fait* with the terms, a map section, links to other archaeological resources and an online bookshop. Full of pictures (which can be slow to load), it's an excellent reference point for this subject.

http://www.stonepages.com/

Theban Mapping Project

Fascinating research; great for Egyptology.

http://www.kv5.com/intro.html

War Links

For those with a political or military interest, this is a useful research tool offering links to hundreds of war-related sites.

http://links2go.com/topic/War

The War Times Journal

The goal of this site is the quality presentation of articles and archives relating to military history and science. To make it easy to use, the journal is divided into: achives – featuring constantly updated collections of historic dispatches, memoirs and photographs; articles, interviews and commentary about battles, people, technology and tactics; war and games, featuring online board and miniature war-gaming resources and online store.

http://www.wtj.com/

Westminster Abbey

As well as being a functioning Anglican church, Westminster Abbey is also a major tourist attraction where tours, concerts and coronations are held. This site lists the schedules of services and events, gives you a tour around the abbey, offers samples of the organ music played there, and provides the history of the abbey and who is buried there.

http://www.westminster-abbey.org

World History

A huge resource with a truly global range of topics, it's easy to get immersed and forget what you were actually looking for, if you're even remotely interested in history. Topics range from early Chinese civilisation to epistemology (the study of the theory of human knowledge) to the agricultural revolution. Maintained and updated by Washington State University.

http://www.wsu.edu/~dee/WORLD.HTM

World War One

For an extensive account of the Great War, this is the site to look at. Its pages contain information on the people, places, and events that comprised one of the worst calamities of modern history. This is an evolving project and new material is being added on a constant basis. If the topic you are looking for is not here, check for it again at a later date or use the many links to similar sites.

http://www.worldwar1.com

World War One Documents

The World War One document archive contains online documents and photos (all of which can be downloaded) and links to other related sites. Useful research tool.

http://www.library.byu.edu/~rdh/wwi/

Write Like an Egyptian

Nom en Hieroglyphes is a fun site to visit. It allows you to type in your name phonetically and receive the corresponding hieroglyphics. However, the instructions are given in French and English in alternating paragraphs so it is a little confusing. What you must not miss is the Album in English link, which you will find at the bottom of the page. This gives you a tour of the pharaohs.

http://webperso.iut.univ-paris8/~rosmord//nomhiero.html

HOBBIES

See also individual subjects

2Busy Stitching

Learn here all about needlework and its history as well as details such as reference to all the different stitches. Check out the designs and the designers and find links to other needlework sites and chat rooms, plus there's a stitchers' post office, a bulletin board and a game room.

http://www.2busystitching.com/

British Royal Mint

The fascinating story of how Britain's coins have been minted for more than 1000 years. The Mint, a government agency based in South Wales, is responsible for making coins for the UK and 100 other countries. All the information is available here. There is even a coin club which you can join if you wish.

http://www.royalmint.com/

Coin Universe

Have you ever wondered how much that the coin found in the bottom of the drawer could be worth? You can find out here. Coin collectors around the world can find out about prices, a collectors' auction and a vast links page to other coin sites.

http://www.coin-universe.com/index.html/

The Comics Page

If you are a fan of any comic then you are going to find it here on the Comics Page. See how reading a comic on the site compares to reading the real thing – you might decide that the site is good for reference purposes only.

http://www.comics-page.com

Country Walks

Created by the Ministry of Agriculture, Fisheries and Food, this interesting site gives you a vast selection of country walks throughout the UK, with details of what you will find along the route, and maps so you don't get lost!

http://www.countrywalks.org.uk/

Diamond Cutters

A site specifically created for gem wholesalers, Diamond Cutters is a good read for anyone wishing to know more about this stone. It has a concise tutorial on diamonds, which will leave you knowing just as much as the experts do when you have read it. Also well worth checking out are the sections on the history and science behind this gem. Read it and dream!

http://www.diamondcutters.com/

Kasparov Chess

Created by world champion Gary Kasparov, this is an excellent site for anyone interested in the game, and includes online games as well as news, lessons and information.

http://www.kasparovchess.com/

Learn to Juggle

Simple step-by-step animated advice on how to juggle, and links to other instructions sites once you have mastered the basics.

http://www.vivanet.com/~stevemd/juggle1.html

Photography Information

Fed up with cutting the heads off all your subjects? Do you always have your finger over the lens just as you take the picture? If so, then Kodak's Photography Information Menu is just for you, containing an online tutorial and a guide to better pictures with an informative introduction to photography and covers everything to do with the lens, from what is in front of it to what is behind it, as well as the workings of a dark room.

http://www.kodak.com/us/en/nav/takingpics.shtml

Royal Mail

For stamp collectors throughout the world, this site offers information and sales of British stamps for collectors. There's a wide range of things you can buy, although it could be easier to navigate.

http://www.royalmail.co.uk/athome

Stamp Universe

Stamp collectors should check out this site. As well as containing information on stamps, it also contains pages with links, chat rooms, calendars and a collectors' auction.

http://www.stampworld.com/index.html/

Stanley Gibbons

One of the best-known names in stamp collecting offers one of the best sites on the web for those interested in philately. Stamps, albums and everything else the stamp collector could need are available to buy online.

http://www.stanleygibbons.com

The Webville and Hypertext Railroad Company

This is not a real railroad but a collection of information and links for railroad enthusiasts. The most interesting stuff is in the main yard section. Here you can find out what railroad signals mean, see diagrams of real railroad yards, and even read railroad ghost stories.

http://www.spikesys.com/webville.html

INTERNET

See also Computers and Software, Reference, Search Engines

1,001 Best Internet Tips

If you need help, here you have it. The internet doesn't come with a manual but you're in luck: *PC Computing*'s exclusive guide to the 1,001 best web tips gives you the top net speed-up tricks, undocumented secrets and loads of insider information. This site is guaranteed to make you an instant internet expert.

http://www.zdnet.com/pccomp/besttips/

4 the Net

All kinds of useful information and services for your surfing activities: free e-mail, a guest book, web tools, statistics and lots more.

http://www.4thenet.co.uk

Easy News

Easy News automatically decodes and indexes the binary files found in UseNet (newsgroups). If a binary file is posted to any newsgroup, Easy News will catalogue it into an easy-to-navigate thumbnail index. They browse through all the newsgroups to bring you the newsgroups that contain binary files such as AVIs, MPEGs, MP3s, ZIPs and JPEGs. The unfortunate part is that you have to subscribe to this service, though if you do download a lot of binaries files from the newsgroups, then it is worth it.

http://www.easynews.com

Internet Help Desk

This is a free guide which is designed to help both beginners and advanced internet users. It has guides to e-mail, 'netiquette' and browsers.

http://w3.one.net/~alward/

Learn the Net

Learn the Net is a web-based tutorial for internet novices and a continuing source of educational and technical assistance for all users. It was originally created as a publication of Paradesa Media. The English site went online in April 1996, followed by the French, German, Spanish and Italian editions. It has subsequently become a publication of Michael Lerner Productions.

http://www.learnthenet.com/english/index.html

Microsoft Internet Guide

If you are new to the net then this site is a great starting point for you. The site is clearly written with loads of advice for everyone. It starts with an explanation of the basics of using the internet and takes you right through to how to create your own web site.

http://www.microsoft.com/insider/internet/default.htm

NetLingo

This site will be very helpful for anyone new to using e-mail and internet chat or who gets confused with all the jargon, as it provides an online dictionary of internet terminology. The site is well organised, with new terms at the front of the site, and even a downloadable dictionary.

http://www.netlingo.com/

Webopedia

If you find new jargon you cannot understand, go to this site for good definitions and explanations of the latest web-related terminology.

http://www.webopedia.com

What Is?

This site offers the quickest way to get reliable definitions for internet, computer and telecommunications jargon.

http://www.whatis.com

INTERNET PROTECTION

The Adult Check System

This adult verification system is the largest of its kind in the world. It has been designed to prevent minors from accessing information of an adult nature. There are over 45,000 participating sites and the service is available in seven languages, including Chinese and Japanese.

http://www.adultcheck.com/

The Adult Pass

Created by internet specialists as a response to US government censorship, this verification service restricts minors from accessing adult-oriented sites. You must have a valid credit card number to be verified as an adult.

http://www.adultpass.com/

Cyber Patrol

Parents around the world have come to trust Cyber Patrol as one of the most effective tools to protect children online. Cyber Patrol is a good way to manage children's computer use and safety on the internet. You can create different filtering criteria for your children according to their age and needs; supervise your children's internet access; regulate time spent online; and protect your child from sites you determine to be objectionable. Children have the opportunity to explore the internet safely and have a positive learning experience. At the site you can download a trial version of the software for use at home, work or school.

http://www.cyberpatrol.com/

Family Internet

Discover web sites for the family to enjoy together or individually, including software to control web site access.

http://familyinternet.about.com/

Internet Lifeguard

This site offers you a collection of tips and resources for safer internet surfing. It includes a library of filtering software, a parent/child agreement and online basics.

http://www.safesurf.com/lifegard.htm

Internet Watch Federation

The IWF was launched to address the problem of illegal material on the internet, with particular reference to child pornography. All users of the internet are encouraged to report potentially illegal material. Note, though, that the IWF is concerned with the law, not personal taste or morality, and can only act on material that could be prosecuted under UK legislation.

http://www.iwf.org.uk/

Kid Safety

An easy-to-follow tutorial for kids on internet safety with step-by-step instructions on how children should behave online.

http://www.ou.edu/oupd/kidsafe/inet.htm

Net Nanny

Net Nanny filtering software for your PC protects children from the dangers from the internet from standard e-mail, chat programs and newsgroups. Net Nanny offers you the necessary tools to ensure safety and peace of mind while on your PC and allows you not to worry about access to inappropriate material, to prevent the threat of cyber strangers and deny the misuse of personal information. You can download a trial version of the software from their site.

http://www.netnanny.com/

The Recreational Software Advisory Council

The RSAC is an independent, non-profit organisation based in Washington, DC that empowers the public, especially parents, to make informed decisions about electronic media by means of an open, objective content-advisory system. The RSAC system provides consumers with information about the level of sex, nudity, violence and offensive language (vulgar or hate-motivated) in software games and web sites. Here at their site you can find out about them and how they work, their rating system and how to use it, and register your own web site to be rated.

`http://www.icra.org`

Surfer Beware

It is widely assumed that unless you explicitly give away personal information, your anonymity remains when you surf the web. Unfortunately this is not true and to find out just how much information you are giving away, visit Surfer Beware: Personal Privacy and the Internet. The site has been put together by the Electronic Privacy Information Centre and is well worth checking out before you decide to visit those sites of an adult nature!

`http://www.epic.org/reports/surfer-beware.html`

LAW

ACAS

The Advisory, Conciliation and Arbitration Service mediates in industrial disputes and promotes good employer-employee relations. Its site offers general information, press releases, local offices and a booklist.

`http://www.acas.org.uk/`

Active Most Wanted and Criminal Investigations

This site is a compendium of fugitive listings. Check out the FBI's top ten most wanted on the war criminal directory. The site also has information on the US State Department's Anti-terrorism Unit.

`http://www.activemostwanted.com`

Advertising Law Internet Site

This site has been established by a US law firm which specialises in US advertising law, consumer protection, anti-trust and trade association law. They have a long history of assisting clients regarding advertising and marketing law issues. The site has links to other internet advertising, marketing and consumer law sites. From time to time, links to articles, press releases and other related materials are added.

http://www.advertisinglaw.com/home.html

Consumer Law

Many consumer organisations offer consumers assistance by providing guidance on how to resolve disputes without the need to hire a lawyer or to initiate a legal proceeding. Although most organisations will not take action on behalf of individual consumers, they may provide you with contact information, education activities or publications. This site contains links to these organisations. It is mainly American but it does contain some useful international links.

http://consumer.findlaw.com/congen/index.html

Bentham Archive of British Law

This site has been produced to appeal to a wide range of people, from lay people with legal problems or interests, to students, right up to practitioners. It is a resource for research and a guide to help those seeking legal help. Therefore it must be remembered that the role of the site is limited to providing information on how to get good legal advice and to provide the background information you might need to make the most of that advice once you get it. The site is constantly changing and evolving.

http://www.ndirect.co.uk/~law/bentham.htm

Dumb Law

It may not be surprising that much of this site is US information about stupid laws that should have found their way off the statue books of various countries. It's a sobering thought that in some cases the law really is an ass!

http://www.dumblaws.com/

Find Law

This is one of the leading web portals focused on law and government. It provides access to a growing online library of legal resources for legal professionals, consumers and small businesses. At this site you will find lots of different features such as web search utilities, cases and codes, legal news and more.

http://www.findlaw.com

Law Net

The Law Net site offers lots of information on law to internet users and is sponsored by attorneys and vendors of legal services and products in America. It is a good resource for searching for specific laws and attorneys who specialise in specific areas of law, There is also an online forum available for the discussion of legal issues. This site is one of the longest-running sites dedicated to law so it has an exhaustive array of resources.

http://www.law.net

The 'Lectric Law Library

The library's goal is to allow you to find and access law-related information and products that you want or need – easily and free. There is a lot of material for legal professionals, business people and formal and informal students of the law, but mostly the site has things that just about everyone could find interesting or helpful at some stage.

http://www.lectlaw.com/

Legal Pad Junior

This site provides kids and teens with an area in which they can express themselves using either message boards, chats or newsletters produced by adults for kids. Legal Pad For Kids hosts Kids Who Care for kids aged 6–12 and 2B Heard for kids aged 13–17. It is designed to encourage positive attitudes and active participation in learning how the law and good character affect our lives both today and in the future.

http//:www.legalpadjr.com/

Organised Crime

This site contains all the information that you need to find out about organised crime. This site will fascinate conspiracy lovers, worry the fearful and leave law-abiding citizens wondering what's gone wrong.

http://www.alternatives.com/crime/

Police Officers Directory

A directory containing more than 1500 police bureaux, together with law libraries and special operations branches. You can also use it to find out what investigative tools are used in the process of solving any crime, and information on wanted criminals and hate-groups.

http://www.officer.com

MOTORCYCLES

See also Motoring, Sport

Aprilia

This site from the manufacturer of scooters and motorcycles offers photos and a technical chart for each model. Also available on the site is racing information and news in Italian, German, Spanish, Dutch and English.

http://www.aprilia.com/

Bike Net

A motorcycling e-zine mostly dedicated to road use rather than racing, the range and speed of the news here is excellent, and the site is a must for all motorcyclists. They say they 'have brought together the world's top suppliers of bikes and gear to help you find what you need' and as a result, you will find that the site contains a large and extensive classified advertisement section.

http://www.bikenet.com/

BMF Riderspace

This is the web site of the British Motorcyclists' Federation, Britain's largest rider group. The organisation states that its job is 'to protect and promote the road-riders' interests so no matter what you ride, there is bound to be something here for you'.

http://www.bmf.co.uk/

Ducati

There is a lot to see and do at this web site for the Ducati make of motorcycle. On the site you will find exclusive shots from their model range, technical designs, model year previews and more. You can also search all over Europe for your local dealer by selecting your country from the map. The site is also available in Italian.

http://www.ducati.com/

Harley Davidson

The site has been created to provide a forum for enthusiasts so that they are able to chat to Harley Davidson directly and find out what it means to be part of the Harley family. Whether you are a Harley rider, future Harley owner, or just want to experience the Harley lifestyle and culture, check out this site, which also includes an archive of Harley photographs and videos.

http://www.hd-stamford.com/

Honda

Find out about Honda's range of motorcycles and get information about the Honda Rider's Club here. For a chance to see all touring, off-road, racing, sport, and custom motorcycles, plus scooters and all-terrain vehicles, check out this site.

http://www.hondamotorcycle.com/index.html

Isle of Man TT

The Isle of Man TT has truly become a festival of motorcycle sport, with over 40,000 fans travelling to the island for those two special weeks every year. This site contains a photo gallery and gives details of the various social events, races and results, news and the history of the TT races. Rider Steve Hislop also provides the site with an excellent guide to the course.

http://www.iomtt.com/

Kawasaki

Motorcycles as well as jet-ski watercraft, all-terrain vehicles (ATVs), utility vehicles, and portable generators are just some of the unique consumer products that have made the Kawasaki brand a household name around the world. Learn more about Kawasaki by checking out this site. Here you can find information on the history of Kawasaki and its products, view industry links, get free brochures and copies of the *Good Times* magazine, or find out about job vacancies within Kawasaki.

http://www.kawasaki.com/

Motorcycle Consumer News

The idea of this site is to introduce *Motorcycle Consumer News* magazine to people by showing them sample articles and departments from the monthly print-version of the magazine. On the site you will find features worth bookmarking for future reference, such as an events calendar which is updated monthly and the used bike value guide. If you like what you find here, consider subscribing to the magazine. It is an American magazine but it does ship worldwide.

http://www.mcnews.com/mcn.htm

Motorcycle Safety Foundation

This organisation is American so all the information concerning courses are for the Americas. However, the site also contains a lot of information that is applicable to motorcyclists all around the world. For example, it has sections concerning protective clothing, riding safety and helmet information.

http://www.msf-usa.org/

Motorcycle Web Index

If you are looking for information on motorcycles, then this is one place for you to start. Here you will find links to many different sites on motorcycling covering magazines, movies, dealers, fan pages, safety and insurance, with links newsgroups and mailing lists.

http://www.sepnet.com/cycle/index.htm

Motorcycle World

Is this 'the world's number one motor cycle web site'? Find out for yourself by checking out the generous mix of racing results, news, features and the latest product information.

http://www.motorcycleworld.co.uk/

Suzuki

It all started in 1930 when Suzuki developed the first cotton loom works in Japan. In 1940 Suzuki put an engine on to a bicycle and thus developed the motorcycle principle. Since then Suzuki has been at the forefront of design and technology in the worlds of two-wheel racing, commuting and off-road. Find out more about the company and its products, which include automobiles and marine 'mean' machines too!

US: http://www.suzuki.com/

UK: http://www.suzuki.co.uk/

Triumph

At the official site, check out Triumph's classic, sports and touring ranges as well as details of accessories, clothing and dealers. Go on a tour of the Triumph factory, which is situated on the outskirts of Hinckley in Leicestershire. Find out what the Riders' Association of Triumph has to offer. RAT is the worldwide club for owners of modern Triumphs and is run by the factory, from the factory. It is a direct link to Triumph and offers a range of services including a quality colour magazine, a package of exclusive discount arrangements and an extensive international events programme.

http://www.triumph.co.uk/

Used Motorcycle Evaluation Guide

This is a web page that contains a very good resource for the second-hand bike buyer. The document contains practically everything you need to look out for when buying a used motorcycle, with pictures, parts-based breakdowns and links. This is an American-based site.

http://www.clarity.net/~adam/buying-bike.html

Used Motorcycle Guide Online

This is a UK-based guide which provides reports on Honda, Kawasaki, Suzuki and Yamaha motorcycles and contains information on motorcycle faults, data, comments and UK prices.

http://umgweb.com/

Yamaha

The Yamaha Motor Corporation began operating in 1955. It is a major part of the entire Yamaha group but is a separately managed business entity from the Yamaha Corporation. The Yamaha Motor Corporation produces not only motorcycles but also snow mobiles, golf carts, outboard engines and water vehicles. Yamaha is the second largest manufacturer of motorcycles in the world and at this site you can get information on all its models.

http://www.yama-motor.com

http://www.yama-motor.co.uk

MOTORING

See also Motorcycles, Sport

AA

With everything from hotel and insurance recommendations to warnings of road works and information on fuel prices, the AA site aims to help you get the best out of your motoring.

http://www.theaa.co.uk

Audi

The official site in German or English lists everything you may want to know about Audi cars and the Audi company.

`http://www.audi.com`

Auto Bytel

This site makes buying a car easy in America, Sweden, Canada and the UK. Here they give you point-and-click access to as much information as you want in order to make your car-buying decision. Once you're ready to buy, you specify the make, model and other relevant information for the car or truck you wish to purchase. You submit this information online. Then they connect you to the Autobytel.com manager at an accredited dealership near you. The manager finds you exactly what you asked for and offers it to you at a low price. You go to the dealership, and if you like what you see, you buy the vehicle at the agreed price.

`http://www.autobytel.com/`

Auto Trader

Britain's biggest showroom for new and used cars plus information on insurance, finance and other related topics. There are also helping-hand features, advertising, a buyers' guide and bookshop. If you want to find a dealer, get an insurance quote, hire or lease a car, you'll also find help here.

`http://www.autotrader.co.uk`

Automotive Advice

If you have got a problem with your car, van or truck, Dave Benoit, a certified auto mechanic with over 25 years' experience, may be able to help you. However, Dave is American, and therefore may be unable to give advice on certain models. It is worth giving him a try though.

`http://members.home.net/daveandlois/`

Bennetts

This is a site for the motorbike enthusiast as it offers information on biking events, insurance, product prices, security devices, news, tips and special offers.

http://www.bennetts.co.uk

BMW

The official web site of BMW is available in either German or English. Like many other car companies, you can find out about all the models in their various ranges as well as the company itself. They have a vast library area where you can download all the information on their models. The site serves BMW cars and motorcycles.

http://www.bmw.com

Carnoisseur

Very modern, blokey site for a company selling alloy wheels, flash accessories for cars with special offers, online ordering and details of shops throughout the UK. Almost trade prices.

http://www.carnoisseur.com

Carsource

If you want to buy a new or used car, need information on dealers, what's new on the market or insurance, take a look at this site. There's also a useful search service so that you can find exactly what you want.

http://www.carsource.co.uk

Car Talk

This excellent magazine-style site featuring model reports gives answers to problems and advice on car maintenance. Go to the good 'carma' zone too where you can either help others or share your problems. On a light-hearted note, why not find out if you are you a good match for your car? If you turn out to be incompatible you can then see which cars their 'car-o-scope' recommends for you.

http://cartalk.cars.com/

Cars DIY

This web site has been developed with the car DIY enthusiast in mind. As you browse, you will hopefully gain more knowledge and understanding of the car and how it works. They have tried to cover as much on the topic as possible without going into ridiculous amounts of detail, but if you have specific problems, you can send them the information and they will help you to rectify the problem as quickly and cheaply as possible.

http://www.carsdiy.co.uk/

Chevrolet

At this site you again will find all the information you will ever need about the Chevrolet range and the dealers in the group in America. Here is also a link available to GM motors, the company that owns the Chevrolet group. One good feature of the site is the pages detailing all their current special offers.

http://www.chevrolet.com

Classic Car Directory

This is a superb resource for classic car enthusiasts. With an A–Z listing of all classic car companies and clubs, plus a parts and services directory, price guide, and diary of events around the UK, everything is covered.

http://www.classic-car-directory.com/

Classic Car World

From the publishers of *Classic Cars*, *Classic Car Weekly* and *Practical Classics*, this excellent site offers all the news and features from these magazines plus cars for sale and chat areas for enthusiasts. Classic Car World is split into four major areas: cars, events, auctions and marketplace. Each is colour-coded for easier navigation to let you know at all times where you are on the site.

http://www.classiccarsworld.co.uk/

Classic Motor Monthly

This is the web version of the newspaper for all classic car enthusiasts. The site gives all the news and a selection of features, coupled with an archive, hints and tips and details of veteran, vintage and classic automobile events, plus spares and services.

http://www.classicmotor.co.uk/

Ford

This is the offical web site of the famous Ford motor company. From this site you can access countries' own individual web sites around the world, everywhere they sell Ford cars, by using the find-your-dealer feature. You can also find out all the information you want about the Ford motor company itself from cars to careers, design and technology. Also available is information on the other car manufacturers within the Ford group: Volvo, Mazda, Lincoln, Mercury, Jaguar and Aston Martin.

http://www.ford.com

Honda

The Honda web site includes information both about the company and its range of cars.

http://www.honda.com

Mercedes–Benz

This is the offical site of the German car manufacturer where you will find all the information you need about Mercedes cars.

http://www.Mercedes–Benz.com

MG Enthusiasts

You can tell by this site alone that there are lots of proud MG owners out there and if you are one of them, or you would like to know what makes this car so appealing to so many, look no further. The site contains every conceivable detail on every MG ever made, and lists of cars for sale in countries all around the world. You will also find details of worldwide clubs and services here too. The site is hosted in the UK, but for faster access from America and Canada you can try the American site.

http://www.mgcars.org.uk/

No Risk: Used Car Buying

Thinking of buying a used car? If so, then you would do well to check out this site first. It tells you what to look out for so that you can give those dodgy dealers and their cars a miss!

http://www.goodasnew.com

Opel / Vauxhall

For anyone interested in Opel cars and services, this is their offical web site, full of information. Here you can take a compact, informative tour of the complete Opel showroom or choose quick access to your country's national site. Also available is a route planner which gives you the best directions to your destination, and improved links point the way to just the information you want.

http://www.opel.com/

Peugeot

Peugeot's official site, this one is written in French but is available in English as well. Pages list all the models and options available for the Peugeot range in the relevant country. Also available are fun things like screensavers and wallpaper for you to download for your computer.

http://www.peugeot.com/

Piaggio

For over 50 years Piaggio have been making scooters. Whether you are into scooter nostalgia or simply want a run-around that is able to weave its way through the rush-hour traffic, find out everything about the Vespa scooter here.

http://www.piaggio.com

Porsche

From the main site you choose either a site in English on an EU server or American server, or the site in German. Also available is a virtual in-depth tour of the facory or you can even locate your local Porsche club anywhere in the world.

http://www.porsche.com

Rolls Royce and Bentley

This is a very good and informative site from the manufacturers of one of the most exclusive hand-built cars in the world. The site has two sides: one that deals with only Rolls Royce and the other which is Bentley cars.

http://www.rolls-royceandbentley.co.uk/home.html

Scions of Lucas

This is an index of comprehensive British car marque web sites. From the site you can see that there is a large, vibrant group of British car enthusiasts drawn from all over the world and that the major interest is vintage cars. The site contains links to all British car manufacturers as well.

http://www.team.net/sol/solwebs.html

The Speedtrap Registry

This is the site if you are planning a tour in your car and do not want to be caught speeding. The site lists speedtraps all over the world, though because it is run by an American there is a bias towards the states of America. You can use their form to add any speedtraps that are not listed and even find out about unmarked police vehicles in your area, the scanners available for the motorist and if they are legal where you live.

http://www.speedtrap.com/

Swift

The Swift Group is one of the world's leading manufacturers of touring caravans and both coach-built and hi-top motor homes. This is essentially a corporate web site, but you can use it to browse Swift's current range of vehicles and to request a full brochure.

http://www.swiftleisure.co.uk/

Toyota

At the offical site of Toyota you can use the international directory to get the worldwide listing of Toyota sites. If you were to link to the Toyota Motor Corporation in Japan, you could take a tour of the virtual factory, or pass the time at their automobile museum and catch up on all the latest news and information about Japan's leading car company.

http://www.toyota.com

Volkswagen

The site default is German but click on the little ball with the Union flag on it for an English version of the site. Here there are links to all the country-specific sites in the world dealing with Volkswagen cars.

http://www2.vw-online.de/international/english/index_2.htm

Volvo

From the offical site you can access information and dealers around the world for all the machines that Volvo make. Here you can find information on anything from cars, trucks, buses, to plant machinery and marine and aero engines that are produced by Volvo.

http://www.volvo.com

Woman Motorists

Whatever some people say, women drivers are, in fact, safer than men! Although this site is designed specifically for the female driver, it would be of interest to anyone since it is designed to contain information on all kinds of related topics from buying or selling a car through to general car maintenance, all explained in straightforward language. The site is also very easy to navigate. One very good part of the site is the safety section, which is full of useful information.

http://www.womanmotorist.com/

MUSEUMS AND GALLERIES

See also Art and Culture, Entertainment

24-hour Museum
The 24-hour Museum is the UK gateway to museums, galleries and heritage attractions. It is quality controlled, which means that only museums and galleries registered with the Museums and Galleries Commission – or non profit-making galleries, historic houses and heritage attractions – are included on this site.

http://www.24hourmuseum.org.uk

The British Museum
British Museum press, gifts, shopping and the British Museum traveller are the main sections on this site, which aims to support and build the reputation of the museum throughout the world. Online ordering of gifts and replicas is included, as well as what's new at the museum, and details of its tour programme.

http://www.britishmuseum.co.uk

Central Intelligence Museum
This site contains pictures and details of different types of spy equipment. The objects shown on this site have been made according to technical descriptions and/or schematic drawings of equipment allegedly produced by the Central Intelligence Agency's Office of Technical Services. The site is neither endorsed by nor associated with the Central Intelligence Agency of the United States of America!

http://www.acmenet.net/~dna

The Louvre
This is the online site of the world-famous Louvre Museum in Paris. At this site you can take a look at the collections they have on show, read the history of the Louvre and you can even take a virtual tour of the museum. There is all the information you need at this site to make your visit easy. You can even purchase your entry tickets online. The site itself is available in French, English, Spanish and Japanese.

http://mistral.culture.fr/louvre/louvrea.htm

Museums Around the World

This site is a directory of web services connected with museums around the world. The museums listed are categorised by country/continent.

http://www.icom.org/vlmp/world.html

The Natural History Museum

This is the official site of the Natural History Museum in London, England. The site contains science galleries, museum history, details of services and scientific research, visitor information and links to hosted sites. It is well worth a visit to this site, especially if you are planning a visit to the museum itself.

http://www.nhm.ac.uk/

The Science Museum

Visitor information, exhibition details, collections, research and commercial information are all included on this fascinating site, which features some QuickTime movies and online experiments.

http://www.nmsi.ac.uk/

The Victoria and Albert Museum

Collections, education and research, what's on, membership, art library, features, views and newsroom are all elements of this excellent site created by the London fine-art museum. Their various collections include prints, china and glass, costumes, metalwork and sculpture. The site also gives details of opening hours and general information about the museum.

http://www.vam.ac.uk

MUSIC

See also Entertainment, Fun, Films, Television, Video and DVD, Radio and Broadcasting

All Music Guide

A huge music database in which you will find most of the popular genres. Despite its large size, it gives sufficient critiques, is well researched and is comprehensive, making it easy to use. On the site you will find biographies, keyword crosslinks, reviews and ratings, together with an online ordering service.

http://www.allmusic.com

Alternative Addict

If alternative rock is your kind of music, then this is the site for you. It has monthly news and reviews, the majority of which are on the alternative rock music scene.

http://www.addict.com

Audio Review

If you want to know more than the manufacturers are telling you about the latest audio equipment, check it out here. All audio equipment has been reviewed by end users on this site. However, it must be remembered that some opinions can be quite extreme! Once you have taken this into account, verify what you have read by looking at the links page.

http://www.audioreview.com

Audiostreet

This is an online sales site for music, DVDs, games, CDs and gifts, as well as a source of music news, charts and information. Prices include VAT and free delivery in the UK.

http://www.audiostreet.co.uk

A–UK

Calling itself the Useful Knowledge Company, you can use this site to order guides on learning to play a range of musical instruments.

http://www.a–uk.co.uk/

CD Now

CD Now offers approximately 500,000 CDs, cassettes, vinyl albums, music videos, laserdiscs, DVDs, movies, T-shirts, mini-discs and other music-related items. Clips are available to listen to or watch using both Real Player and mpeg files. CD Now also ships worldwide and has various bases over Europe to make the delivery time quicker. The site is available in the following languages: English, French, Dutch, Japanese, Portuguese, Spanish, Italian and German.

http://www.cdnow.com

Classical MIDI Archives

Search this database of over 2500 MIDI files of mostly classical music. Software for playing MIDI files is also available. Download up to 100 MIDI files per day from here.

http://www.prs.net/midi.html

Classical Net

Classical Net provides a point of entry into a wide array of information files about classical music – over 4200 files at Classical Net and over 2500 links to other classical music web sites. The site also includes a repertoire list, reviews and articles, a CD-buying guide and a database of composers.

http://www.classical.net/

Crotchet Music Store

A site dedicated to classical music, jazz, film soundtracks and world music, and for over 40 years it has been successfully mailing sounds around the world. It has a main classical department and nine specialist departments: baroque, chamber, historical, jazz, modern, orchestral, soundtracks, vocal and Warner.

http://www.crotchet.co.uk/

The Dailywav

Every week day this site brings you yet another TV or film sound sample that you can listen to or download. It will even do the occasional 'grab bag' at the weekend. So now there is no excuse for driving everyone crazy by playing the same tune!

http://www.dailywav.com

Dotmusic

Check out this site for up-to-the-minute music news, UK charts, reviews, interviews and gossip.

http://www.dotmusic.com/

Dusty Grooves

For all lovers of soul, jazz, funk, Brazil and Latin music, Dusty Grooves has it all on vinyl and CD.

http://www.dustygroove.com

Freebase Internet Magazine

Get all the reviews, charts and gig guides at this site, where you can check out audio samples of up-and-coming, currently unsigned bands and read features such as reviews, charts and gig guides. You can even visit the chill room and make your thoughts and comments known to others.

http://www.freebase.com/

Harmony Central

Harmony Central is an attempt to bring together many of the music-related items that can be found on the internet. The site hopes to make it much easier for musicians to find useful things quickly and easily, as well as provide some useful services. There are plenty of links here to equipment, software, bands, as well as ads for musicians and a good auction service.

http://www.harmony-central.com

HMV Music Store

The web site for the high-street music store, you can buy CDs, videos and PC games direct from HMV.

http://www.hmv.co.uk

Live Concerts

If you have missed gigs that you really would have liked to have gone to, this site is for you. It offers live and archived webcasts of concerts, covering all kinds of music, so you can see your favourite singer or band perform 'live' after all! You can also visit the listening post to hear an exclusive album before it is officially released and talk about it all in the 24-hour chat room.

http://www.liveconcerts.com/

Moving Music

Moving Music specialises in superb-quality, low-cost, mail-order music cassettes and CDs, special interest videos, children's videos and feature films. Worldwide delivery, with an excellent reputation.

http://www.movingmusic.co.uk/

Music for Free

Here you'll find hours of music and all for free. Don't scoff at the bands listed in its archives. They may seem obscure today but you will end up knowing some of them very well quite soon.

http://www.mp3.com

MTV

The MTV site is certainly not as fast-paced as the TV programme – in fact it is slow – but that is not surprising considering the size of its content. It holds a huge amount of information and has plenty of chat rooms. So have patience with it and check out the A–Z of bands, news, charts, video clips, interviews and reviews.

http://www.mtv.com/

Music at 101
This site offers music, videos, games and books at discount prices, as well as reviews, information on new releases and recommendations. Over 450,000 CDs available.

http://www.101cd.com

Musicnewswire
If you want to know what is happening on the music scene, this site will give you all the information you need.

http://www.musicnewswire.com

New Musical Express
This well-respected musical paper has its own web site where you can read articles and find all sorts of information on what is going on in the music business.

http://www.nme.com

OperaGlass
This fine resource is an opera information server. Here you can get detailed information, including performance histories, synopses, libretti, discographies, pictures and more on any of a small but rapidly growing number of operas. It also has a fair-sized list of links for international opera listings.

http://rick.stanford.edu/opera/main.html/

Opera Schedule Server
The Opera Schedule Server has been set up to serve opera-lovers in the internet community. There is a constant demand for information about the schedules of different opera companies, and this server will try to satisfy that demand. Search by city, title, artist or composer.

http://www.fsz.bme.hu/opera/main.html

Opera Schedules, Houses, Festivals, Reviews and Links
This site is now working in partnership with Opera America. You can get venue/booking/season details for over 500 opera houses and

festivals, schedules for thousands of singers and powerful opera-performance search tools. There are mouse-sensitive maps, reviews from leading newspapers, hundreds of links to opera resources and timelines of composers and works. Available in five languages.

http://operabase.com/

Second Sounds
If you have been trying to get hold of that CD you wished you had bought years ago, it could be on the database of this online store.

http://www.secondsounds.com

Ultimate Band List
If a band is not on the list of the Ultimate Band List site, it does not exist! For links to all your favourite bands, look no further.

http://www.ubl.com/

Virtual Opera House
A light-hearted introduction to opera. Meet the singers, composers and conductors, listen to some sound clips, read some synopses and anecdotes – and perhaps by the end of the performance you may be curious enough to venture closer to real opera.

http://users.lia.net/dlever/main.asp

NATURE AND THE EARTH

See also Animals, Environment, Travel

Australian Botanical Gardens
Even if you never get the chance to visit, you will know everything about the Botanical Gardens at Canberra by the time you finish looking at this site. The site includes information on all flora and fauna projects right through to fire procedures! Although the site is not that well ordered, nature lovers will find it is really worth wading through.

http://www.anbg.gov.au

Earthquakes

The activities of the British Geological Survey's (BGS) Global Seismology and Geomagnetism Group (GSGG) cover a broad spectrum of research and information services concerned with earthquakes and man-made seismic disturbances. This site will tell you everything you may want to know about earthquakes. Find out what causes earthquakes and where they strike. See what devastation that they leave behind.

http://www.gsrg.nmh.ac.uk/

The Electronic Zoo

This is a directory of fauna information which is guaranteed to have what you are looking for. It just takes a while to find it!

http://netvet.wustl.edu/e-zoo.htm

The Mineral Gallery

Explore rocks and minerals at this site, which includes both pictures and detailed information, as well as the chance to purchase rock specimens.

http://mineral.galleries.com/default.htm

Myst@Rain Forests

This site is all about the most important ecosystems in the world, the rain forests. From breathtaking pictures of the Amazon to the island tropics everywhere, Myst@Rain Forests brings it to you. It is an educational web site that provides information about saving and protecting the earth and the rain forest inhabitants.

http://www.geocities.com/RainForest/Vines/1009/

Volcano World

At this site you can ask a volcanologist anything about volcanoes that you want. Check out any current eruptions and see what it is like to be at the crater's edge.

http://volcano.und.nodak.edu/

NEW AGE

See also Astrology, Health

Alexander Technique

A brief description of the technique, with information on courses in the UK, Ireland and Spain, plus links to related sites.

http://www.homepageeircom.net/~alexandertechnique

Cassandra Eason

New age site by the well-known author contains information on customs and superstitions, details of current festivals, psychic experiences and magical rituals. A reader-friendly site that is informative and contains actual experiences to give beginners an overview of divination and other related topics without being weird.

http://www.cassandraeason.co.uk

Conscious Net

A US-based site with stacks of information, articles, book reviews and features on a range of New Age subjects, sometimes with a political bias but interesting nonetheless.

http://www.consciousnet.com

Crystalinks

An online encyclopedia of information on everything from aboriginal spirituality to werewolves. Entries are fairly brief but informative.

http://www.crystalinks.com

Feng Shui Society

Talk to the consultants at the Feng Shui Society and find out how to live in harmony with the energies around you.

http://www.fengshuisociety.org.uk/

Goddesses

Goddess site of the organisation celebrating the goddess in all her forms. Open to men and women, it offers a calendar of goddesses of every day of the year, with information on their focus.

http://www.fellowshipofisis.com

New Age

Another US-based site, but a good starting point for New Age research in that it has an extensive web-links index for mind, body and spirit topics, as well as articles and a catalogue of products.

http://www.accessnewage.com

Palmistry

An excellent site if you are interested in palmistry, with new and updated information to download.

http://www.edcampbell.com

The Palmistry Center

Home-study courses on palmistry are available from this web site created by the Palmistry Center of Quebec.

http://www.palmistry.com

Spellbound

Magic and esoteric products for those with an interest in New Age topics. A very attractive site for those with an interest in magic. Lots of articles to read and products for sale.

http://www.spellbound-online.co.uk

NEWS

BBC News Online

From its TV, radio and world services, this site provides access to all the BBC's news services.

http://www.bbc.co.uk/news

CNN

This is a huge web site from the American news giant. You can find in-depth information on most current international and American stories, as well as a good archive area. There are many categories to choose from, such as weather, stocks and sports scores. You can also use the clipping service to track companies or other topics in the news.

http://customnews.cnn.com/cnews/pna_auth.welcome

CNN Interactive

CNN Interactive is updated 24 hours a day, seven days a week, so you have the latest US and world news and other related topics at your fingertips.

http://www.cnn.com/

Crayon

Crayon is a tool for managing news sources on the internet and the web. You can create a customised news page that contains only the daily information you are most interested in. In fact your paper is not updated at all, it is the information that your paper has links to which is updated daily. All you do is click to retrieve the story. It is fun to create and useful to use.

http://www.crayon.net/

Drudge Report

Look here and get sensational news hot off the net and not off the press! Drudge is well known for leaking stories by free bulletin and beating all the major press at releasing the headlines! You can also find many of the best news sources on the net through the top page of this site.

http://www.drudgereport.com

The Guardian

The online version of the UK daily newspaper.

http://www.guardian.co.uk

Megastar

An online newspaper with up-to-date news and sports reports. Select your areas of interest from the contents list and read the latest news from around the world.

`http://www.megastar.co.uk`

The Mirror

These two sites relate to the sister *Daily Mirror* and *Sunday Mirror* UK newspapers.

`http://www.mirror.co.uk`

`http://www.sundaymirror.co.uk`

MSNBC

This is the home of the American news giant MSNBC. Because it is American there is a bias towards American news but there are international news stories as well. Before you use this site you will need to download a small piece of software for the news menu but it works well once that has been done.

`http://www.msnbc.com/`

News Trawler

Database search for news stories featured in various newspapers and magazines and found by country or topic.

`http://www.newstrawler.com/nt/nt_home.html`

One World

Many think this is the best newspaper on the web.

`http://www.oneworld.net`

Sky News

For all the latest news and current affairs, check out this site for 24-hour news coverage from around the world.

`http://www.skynews.co.uk/`

The Smoking Gun

See what makes the celebrities shameful. The Smoking Gun brings you exclusive documents that cannot be found anywhere else on the web, using material obtained from government and law enforcement sources, via Freedom of Information requests, and from court files.

http://www.thesmokinggun.com/

Sports News

This web site is brought to you from CNN as a joint venture with the magazine *Sports Illustrated*. It has all the news and scores for over a dozen sports as well as in-depth coverage of events, fantasy games, discussion areas and complete team and player statistics.

http://www.cnnsi.com/

The Telegraph

All the latest news and information from the web site of the UK national daily broadsheet.

http://www.telegraph.co.uk

The Times

If you want to read *The Times* and *The Sunday Times* newspapers, why not read them on the net? The internet editions are updated daily at about 2 a.m. London time with virtually the complete content of the printed edition. There are direct links to all the sections and there is also easy access to back issues and those challenging crosswords!

http://www.the-times.co.uk

http://www.sunday-times.co.uk

The Voice of America

You can listen to audio clips or read the text of international, regional and US news in 52 languages to an estimated weekly audience of 83 million. It is 'on the air' 24 hours a day, seven days a week, and has been tailored to provide news and information to each region of the world during its prime listening hours.

http://www.voa.gov

USA Today

This site gives you all the day's news, sport, money, life and weather in the USA.

`http://www.usatoday.com`

ORGANISATIONS AND CHARITIES

Age Concern

Age Concern cares about all older people and believes that later life should be fulfilling and enjoyable. The British-based organisation provides a number of its fact sheets online, with topics ranging from going on holiday to organising a funeral. Also gives contact information and details of various courses for the over-50s. Works closely with partner organisations around the world.

`http://www.ace.org.uk/`

Consumer's Association

This site includes a list of all the companies who have joined its Which? Web Trader Scheme for consumer protection and gives details of the protection it offers anyone who has suffered a problem with a registered trader.

`http://www.which.net/webtrader/wt5.html`

Hunger Site at the UN

Information on world hunger plus one click on the site (per person, per day) means that a sponsor will pay for a meal for a starving person.

`http://www.thehungersite.com`

NCH Action for Children

NCH Action for Children improves the lives of Britain's most vulnerable children and young people by providing a diverse and innovative range of services for them and their families, and campaigning on their behalf. Find out exactly what they do at this site.

`http://www.nchafc.org.uk`

Neighbourhood Watch

Useful tips on beating crime, together with all the information you need if you are already a Neighbourhood Watch member or would like to set up a scheme.

http://www.nwatch.org.uk/

PARENTING

See also Divorce, Health

Adoption

This site contains useful help, information and guidance on all aspects of adoption. It is home to the world's largest online searchable registry of hopeful adoptive parents. The registry allows birth mothers to find adoptive parents with specific characteristics. On the other hand, if you are searching for a lost birth relative, the Reunion Registry is there to help. The person you are searching for might already be looking for you. Just register and add your details.

http://www.adoption.com

All for UK Mums

Online British magazine offering advice and information for mothers present and future. Also available are chats, debates and tales of parenthood. The company that runs this site for mums also runs a site for dads.

http://www.ukmums.co.uk/

http://www.ukdads.co.uk/

Baby Names

The perfect site to help you name the new addition to your family. Here you will find the most extensive, ethnically diverse names database online. You can search the database by name or meaning, or go to one of their unique names lists.

http://www.babynames.com/

Baby Time

This site is an internet resource for pregnancy, birth and childcare. Here you will find everything you need – from the first signs of pregnancy to what to pack in your labour bag – to help you have a well-informed pregnancy. Be sure to check their comprehensive list of pregnancy terms as well.

`http://www.clicked.com/babytime/`

Babyworld

This is a 'webazine' (online magazine) which is full of practical advice for new parents. The site covers everything from trying to conceive to what to do once the baby has arrived.

`http://www.babyworld.co.uk/`

Child Care

This site is for anyone who is involved in looking after children or looking for childcare in the UK. It is full of useful information with advice for parents, suggestions for children's activities, useful addresses and a directory of childcare agencies in the London area.

`http://www.childcare-info.co.uk/`

Childnet International

This is a British charity organisation that helps children all over the world, especially in poorer countries and regions. It hopes to help these children learn more about life and their studies, using the internet as a work tool. There are many projects going on and you will find out all about them and about the charity here. You can even make a donation to them online if you wish. It also has some good links for parents worried about their child using the internet. The site is available in German, Spanish, English and French.

`http://www.childnet-int.org/`

Generation Gap

If you are a parent, you have probably visited that gap more than once with your teenager. For an insight into your adolescent's state of mind, visit Spank! The Magazine of Youth Culture. Find out what worries them (school bullying, exams, etc.) and about the things that bother you (body-piercing). It's an essential read for every parent.

http://www.spankmag.com

Gingerbread

Gingerbread is the leading support organisation for lone-parent families in England and Wales. Its site is a valuable resource which provides information about the organisation, including how it can help you and how you can help it. A reply service enables you to locate the Gingerbread group nearest your home.

http://www.gingerbread.org.uk/

Idea Box

All sorts of ideas and activities for toddlers and kids to keep them occupied are available here. The guides are very easy for parents, teachers and children to understand and complete. Grown-ups may also find things here they had forgotten since they themselves were young. Great for playgroup holidays.

http://www.theideabox.com/

Kids Health

Kids Health, sponsored by the Nemours Foundation, is a good place to get some help and advice on children's health. Parents can find information on safety and infections, and children can find an explanation of feelings and a games room. The site also contains an area for paediatricians and other health-care professionals.

http://kidshealth.org/index2.html

Moms Network Exchange

This site is full of resources for mothers who are working from home. It is a good place to share tips, ideas, seek advice and communicate with other home-working mothers. The site includes things such as a business survival kit, products and services resources, a classified section and more.

http://www.momsnetwork.com/

National Centre for Fathering

The NCFF provides helpful information on all aspects of fathering. For men who are about to become fathers, the site consists of humorous scenarios to complement its down-to-earth, practical advice. For people who have not been in contact with their fathers for a while, the site also includes suggestions for getting back in touch.

http://www.fathers.com/

National Centre for Missing and Exploited Children

The NCMEC spearheads efforts to locate and recover missing children and raises public awareness about ways to prevent child abduction, molestation and sexual exploitation. It is a private, non-profit-making organisation and this is its official site. It is good for parents to be aware that it exists, and it is the place for anyone to contact if they can be of help with any leads.

http://www.missingkids.org

Pampers Parenting Institute

The Pampers Parenting Institute provides a forum for child health and development experts to give parents information, guidance and support in caring for their infants and toddlers. In an effort to inspire the loyalty of Pampers customers by providing this valuable resource, the information is presented in a way that is cross-cultural, sensitive and appropriate to the diversity of families everywhere.

http://www.pampers.com/index.html

Parent Soup

This site contains regularly updated articles, advice pages and discussion boards. Good online advice and support for all parents.

http://www.parentsoup.com/

Parents Place

This site is a not your normal web site as it allows parents to connect, communicate and celebrate the adventures of child-rearing through the use of bulletin boards and chats. You can find your speciality here whether you are interested in talking about women's health, child development, your daily pet peeves, school work, discipline or family-related politics.

http://www.parentsplace.com/

UK Parents

This is a general meeting place where you can find information, exchange experiences and chat with other mothers at the same stage of pregnancy or with children about the same age as your own.

http://www.ukparents.co.uk

PERSONAL DEVELOPMENT

Dream Life

A personal development web site with online classes by worldwide experts. A good way to improve your life skills without having to attend expensive seminars.

http://www.dreamlife.com

PREGNANCY AND CHILDBIRTH

See also Health, Parenting

Babyonline

Lots of useful tips and information on diet, diseases, development and more, can be found in this baby resource. It contains well-written features that cover everything and take you through all of the stages. Find out about pregnancy, childbearing, and rearing babies and toddlers.

http://www.babyonline.com/

Online Birth Center

If you're pregnant, planning a pregnancy, or know someone who is, you will find lots of interesting information on this American site. Do remember, though, that things are not always treated the same way in the UK. Here you can learn about pregnancy, birth, home birth, midwifery and breastfeeding. You'll also find a variety of general health resources, including alternatives to the Western approach to medicine.

http://www.efn.org/~djz/birth/birthindex.html

Pregnancy Calendar

Once you have a baby on the way, visit the Olen Interactive Pregnancy Calendar. Enter the approximate day of conception (the site has instructions for estimating it) and get a customised calendar that gives a day-by-day account of your baby's development. If you know someone who has a baby on the way, why not create a calendar for them? You will also be able to pick up parenting tips and links to other information sites as well as talk to other people in various chat groups.

http://www.pregnancycalendar.com

Ultrasound Procedures and Pregnancy

For parents-to-be who want to know more about the ultrasound procedure, the Obstetric Ultrasound Page is the site to visit. It gives a complete explanation of the procedure, why it is used and what can be learned from it. There is also an ultrasound gallery showing foetuses at various stages of development.

http://www.ob-ultrasound.net

PROPERTY

08004 Homes

More than 70,000 properties are advertised on this site, with a database of mortgages and finance, regular news and features related to the property market, such as house-buying advice and neighbourhood guides.

http://www.08004homes.com

Buy-to-let

All sorts of advice on raising finance, the best type of property to buy and how to renovate and furnish properties for letting.

http://www.buy-to-let.com

Finding a Home

A huge range of properties from a collection of agents with a search facility which is very much area-based. If you find something you like, you can then e-mail the relevant agent from the site.

http://www.assertahome.com

House Web

House Web is a comprehensive resource for buying, selling, renting and exchanging properties. It includes guides and extensive links to other property-related web sites. House Web also contains a glossary of terms used in the property market, e.g. APR (annual percentage rate), disbursements, and MIG (mortgage indemnity guarantee).

http://www.houseweb.co.uk

Loot

Property to let and buy throughout the UK, including student accommodation. Largely London-based but does include other parts of the UK as well.

http://www.loot.com

Property Auctions

This is an internet property auction site for the UK. There are other sites covering Australia, Hong Kong, Scandinavia and the US. If you have a property to sell, using this facility enables you to reach thousands of buyers – not only in the UK but worldwide! If you are looking for a property to buy, you can receive free catalogues of properties within your desired area by e-mail.

http://www.propertyfind.co.uk

Property Broker

An excellent database for those wanting to buy or sell their home, you can view properties without registering, or you can advertise your own property, including a photograph, for a reasonable fee.

http://www.propertybroker.co.uk

Property Sight

Details from a large number of estate agents are included on this site and are updated daily. Key in your requirements by region and specific details to see a range of appropriate properties. You can then contact the relevant agent.

http://www.property-sight.co.uk

Under One Roof

This site does just what is promises, bringing property information from estate agents together with information on everything from mortgages and finance to removal firms under one roof.

http://www.underoneroof.co.uk

Up My Street

Up My Street is the first web site for Europe that helps you pick and probe at the latest published statistics about where you live today, or might live tomorrow. It also carries direct links to a wide variety of useful local services.

http://www.upmystreet.com/

RADIO AND BROADCASTING

Broadcast.com

The Broadcast.com web sites offer a large and comprehensive selection of programming, including sports, talk and music radio, television, business events, full-length CDs, news, commentary and full-length audio books, serving an average of over 1.1 million unique users per day. The site broadcasts on the internet 24 hours a day, seven days a week.

http://www.broadcast.com

BRS Radio Directory
A comprehensive directory of international radio stations on the web.

http://www.radio-directory.com

Imagine Radio
Do you ever wish you could change the music that is played on the radio? If so, then tune into this site. You can now have you very own radio station and decide what is played on it!

http://www.imagineradio.com

Net Radio
Net Radio is an internet-based online music source that provides more than 120 unique music channels. You can listen to music that has been programmed and also purchase the music that you hear on this site. In addition to this, Net Radio provides dozens of audio information channels from country music vews and jazz notes to sports and celebrity news.

http://www.netradio.net

Online Broadcast Guide
The broadcast site offers you a large and comprehensive selection of live programmes, including sports, talk and music radio, television, business events, full-length CDs, news, commentary and full-length audio books. The site broadcasts on the internet 24 hours a day, seven days a week, and its programming includes live continuous broadcasts of over 410 radio stations and networks, 49 television stations and cable networks, game broadcasts and other programming of over 450 college and professional sports teams.

http://www.sportslive.net/

Radio Now

This site gives you a list of almost 300 radio stations in the UK with their frequencies.

http://listen.at/RadioNow

REFERENCE

See also Books and individual subjects

Abacus

The abacus is a calculator, the earliest known use of which is about 500BC in Babylonia, although the abacus as we know it today appeared about 1300AD in China. However, it was the Japanese in Korea who began to make serious use of the Chinese abacus in about 1600AD and to continue its evolution. Addition, subtraction, division and multiplication can be performed on a standard abacus, which is still in use today by shopkeepers in Asia and in 'Chinatowns' worldwide. Its use is also taught in certain schools in Japan and the US. In fact, it is used to teach mathematics to blind children in situations where a sighted person would use pencil and paper. This site offers instructions on the use of the abacus.

http://www.ee.ryerson.ca/~elf/abacus

The Active Mind

This excellent site offers theories and information on the more earthly mysteries, such as the lost city of Atlantis, Nostradamus, Stonehenge and Bigfoot.

http://www.activemind.com/

Altavista Translations

At this site (with two possible addresses), translate text between English and French, German, Italian, Portuguese and Spanish. It is fast and you can even use it to translate web pages.

http://babelfish.altavista.digital.com

http://www.globalink.com

Bartlett's Familiar Quotations
This site is a searchable database of pre-twentieth-century quotations. It also contains chronological and alphabetical listings of hundreds of major contributors.

http://www.bartleby.com/qq/

Biographical Dictionary
This is a free, general-purpose source of biographical information on more than 27,000 notable men and women. It is searchable by name, year of birth or death, positions held, professions, literary and artistic works, achievements and other keywords.

http://www.s9.com/biography

Brewer's Dictionary of Phrase and Fable
This classic work of reference has been described as 'a browser's joy'. The dictionary is extensively cross-referenced, which makes it ideal for the hypertext environment of the internet. This first hypertext edition is taken from Dr Brewer's substantially revised and extended edition of 1894. Either browse or search this site, it is both useful and very appealing.

http://www.bibliomania.com/Reference/PhraseAndFable/index/html

Calculators Online
Calculator.com gives you free access to online calculators that help you to solve problems and answer questions in the home, office and school. There are calculators for finance, business, science, cooking, hobbies and health. Whether you want to solve problems, satisfy your curiosity or just have fun, there are calculators to suit every need.

http://www.calculator.com

Central and Eastern European Languages
If on your travels you are heading for an Eastern European country, then this site is a must – unless you already speak the language. Here you will find basic phrases and pronunciation in 14 different lanuages.

http://www.cusd.claremont.edu/~tkroll/EastEur/index.html

Dead People Server

If you are wondering whether a famous actor, musician, film star or politician is still alive, look here to see if their name is listed!

`http://dpsinfo.com/`

Department of Trade and Industry

Important information for all UK businesses from the Department of Trade and Industry. Most DTi documents can be downloaded.

`http:www.dti.gov.uk`

Dictionary

A web dictionary both in English and foreign languages with advice on correct grammar and style.

`http://www.dictionary.com`

Dictionary of English Slang

A unique dictionary of slang and colloquialisms used in the UK, which is updated every month. It is both useful for the student who has been taught textbook English, and for anyone who finds themselves wondering what the latest terms being used actually mean – wicked!

`http://www.peevish.co.uk/slang`

Encyclopedia

Encyclopedia.com is one of the internet's premier free encyclopedias. This site offers you an extraordinary amount of information. There are more than 14,000 articles from the third edition of *The Concise Columbia Electronic Encyclopedia*, which have been assembled to provide free, quick and useful information on almost any topic. The entries are short, so you can check facts quickly, though each one has extensive cross-references.

`http://encyclopedia.com/`

Encyclopedia Britannica Online

The Encyclopedia Britannica is the world's most comprehensive reference product and has been since its first publication in 1768.

Encyclopedia Britannica Online includes the complete encyclopedia as well as *Merriam-Webster's Collegiate Dictionary* and the *Britannica Book of the Year*. You will also find an internet directory with more than 130,000 links to web sites that have been selected, rated and reviewed by Britannica editors.

http://www.eb.com

Encyclopedia Mythica

This is an encyclopedia on mythology, folklore, legends and more. It contains over 5100 definitions of gods and goddesses, supernatural beings, legendary creatures and monsters from all over the world. The site has a search facility that allows you to locate key subjects and the bibliography lists the sources consulted. You can even make your own contributions and the site is fairly regularly updated.

http://www.pantheon.org/mythica/

Essay-writing

An essay can have many purposes, but the basic structure is the same. You may be writing an essay to argue for a particular point of view or to explain the steps necessary to complete a task. This site gives you the steps to guide you on how to construct your essay.

http://members.tripod.com/~lklivingston/essay/

Eyewitness

The Eyewitness Encyclopedia offers all the content of Dorling Kindersley's acclaimed Eyewitness Guides on the internet. Eyewitness Encyclopedia is designed to make it quick and easy to find exactly what you want. A powerful search engine and interactive page spreads offer access to images and text to cut and paste as required, providing an invaluable resource of information and explanation for users of all ages. With over two million words and 6500 pages, Eyewitness Online offers the ultimate online study resource.

http://eyewitness.dk.com/

Foreign Dictionary

A site that will not only allow you to look up the meaning of the word you are looking for, but will also allow you to translate it into different languages. A good site if you are planning to travel abroad.

http://www.dictionary.com/others/

How To

The answers to as many 'how to?' questions as you can think of are here on this site – well, almost.

http://www.how2hq.com

International Dialling Codes

Look up international dialling codes in a telephone directory, or check them out at this site. You will find a list of dialling codes for most countries in the world.

http://www.eventsworldwide.com/I–codes.htm

Knowhere

Whether you are thinking of moving or want to visit another area of the UK on holiday, this site will give you the low-down on the town or area of your choice.

http://www.knowhere.co.uk

Languages

For anything you need to know about languages – from dictionaries to tuition – this site is a starting point listing a huge range of internet sources from lessons to dictionaries.

http://www.june29.com/HLP/

Language Translator

This site is handy for people who correspond with others around the world. Here you can copy some text and translate it to a foreign language. Also you can even translate foreign language web pages by placing the address in the web page address box.

http://translator.go.com/

List of Lists

This is one of the largest directories of special-interest group e-mail lists (also known as listservs) available on the internet. To submit updates for the description of an existing mailing lists or to add a new entry for the list, you can use the list submission form. This list is the SF-lovers' mailing list and you are able to search for a list by subject or content.

`http://catalog.com/vivian`

Liszt

A directory of mailing lists, newsgroups, chat lines to browse and find those of interest to you.

`http://www.liszt.com/`

Mega Converter

Mega Converter.com is an ever-growing set of weights, measures and units conversion/calculation modules which allow users to discover things like how many seconds old they are, the difference between a gallon in the USA and a gallon in the UK, how many nanometers to an inch, and much more. For just about anything you can think of, Mega Converter can show you its equivalent. There are a ton (that's 4,540,000 carats) of modules available now and many more on the way.

`http://www.megaconverter.com`

Merriam–Webster Online Dictionary

Search Merriam-Webster Online for the word you need defining. You will find that the site is quick to respond and the definitions are concise and helpful. However, it must be remembered that it does have a bias towards American spelling and usage.

`http://www.m-w.com/`

One Look

There are a number of good dictionaries on the internet, and people who use dictionaries regularly tend to have a favourite. This page is intended to make the process of finding the right dictionary quick and painless. The purpose is to encourage people to use internet glossaries and dictionaries by searching over 500 dictionaries at the same time for the word you seek. The One Look dictionaries page provides two approaches to finding definitions for a word. You can either search the site indexes for the word you seek or link directly to a dictionary page.

http://www.onelook.com/

Postcodes Online
Whether you have an address but not the postcode or know the postcode but not the address, you need look no further than this site. It consists of Royal Mail's postcode-finder and address-finder services.

http://www.royalmail.co.uk/paf/

Public Record Office
The Public Record Office and Family Records Centre offer an online catalogue of files as well as useful information related to records that can be ordered up for providing on a specific date to save time doing the research when you go there.

http://publicrecord.com

The Quotations Page
This page was originally developed as a catalogue of quotation resources on the internet; it has since evolved into a large-scale quotation site with many original resources. It now consists of many thousands of quotations and is updated daily. It is searchable and you will find that that site users are also invited to contribute their own favourite quotations.

http://www.starlingtech.com/quotes/

Reference Desk
A huge site offering a compilation of reference sources from dictionaries and phone books to information on government and religion.

http://www.refdesk.com/

Resources for Writers

At this site you can learn more about grammar and punctuation.

http://owl.english.purdue.edu/writers/by-topic.html

Roget's Thesaurus

Now you can browse the thesaurus through the six broad categories into which Mr Roget classified the entire vocabulary of the English language, or you can browse through the alphabetical index of headwords.

http://www.thesaurus.com

Royal and Noble Genealogical Data

At this site find genealogical data for the British Royal Family and just about all the European Royals. It is worth visiting the site on a regular basis because the data is not static but is being constantly updated. You will also find links to other related sites.

http://www.dcs.hull.ac.uk/public/genealogy/

Scoot

This site is an internet version of the *Yellow Pages*, although the latter has its own site as well. It contains a free directory of all businesses and gives you other information such as local cinema listings. To use Scoot, simply enter the type of business being searched for together with the area or location, then press the Scoot button. After a few seconds, you will have a list of all the services in your area, including all telephone numbers and addresses.

http://www.scoot.co.uk

Sign Language Dictionary

This is a site on which you can learn all you need to do sign language. All you have to do is to watch the sign language gestures and learn!

http://dww.deafworldweb.org/asl/

Spelling Test

At this site you can test yourself and learn some techniques to improve your spelling.

http://www.sentex.net/~mmcadams/spelling.html

Telephone Directories on the Web

Telephone Directories on the Web is a really comprehensive and useful index of online phone books. It has links to *Yellow Pages*, *White Pages*, business directories, e-mail addresses and fax listings from all around the world.

http://www.teldir.com/

Time 100

This is where *Time* magazine features the people who are considered to be the most influential of the twentieth century. Categories of influence include leaders and revolutionaries, artists and entertainers, and scientists and thinkers.

http://www.pathfinder.com/time/time100/

UK Dialling Codes

If you need to know the dialling code for any city or town in the UK, look it up here.

http://www.brainstorm.co.uk/utils/std-codes.html

UK Legal Resources

This site is the portal to legal resources in the UK and Ireland. It is regularly updated and you will find that it has been split into four areas. It gives details of free legal information to individuals and also to companies. There is information for solicitors and barristers plus information from the current issue of the *International Newsletter for Lawyers*.

http://www.venables.co.uk/legal/

UK Passports

All the information you require to find out how to obtain a passport, qualifications, visa details and so on.

http://www.open.gov.uk/ukpass/ukpass.htm

UK State

This site is a mass of information on all aspects of the legislation and government of the UK, with all kinds of useful reference material that relates to you, your home and your business.

http://www.ukstate.com

What's In Your Name?

Some people believe that your name is extremely important because it has a powerful influence on your life. Apart from being the way you identify yourself and how others identify you, an insight into its influence will give you a greater opportunity to enjoy the successes you are capable of achieving. If you want to see what your name says about you, visit this web site. An interesting read.

http://www.kabalarians.com/gkh/your.htm

World Clock

At this site you can select among several selections of cities in the world to locate the time. There are two different views: full will display all the cities/places known to the world clock; standard will show the large/important cities all over the world. Then there is a number of continental versions, each showing all cities for a particular continent for more in-depth view. There are versions for Africa, North/Latin America, South America, Asia, Europe and Australia and the Pacific Islands.

http://www.timeanddate.com/worldclock/

World's Bank Holidays

Do you find yourself trying to contact somebody abroad but cannot get in touch with them? Do you find yourself travelling half-way around the world to do business when the company you are visiting has closed for the week? Ensure that this does not continue to happen by looking up worldwide bank holidays and feast days here.

http://www.national-holidays.com/

Worldwide Words

This site is an archive of words and phrases that have not yet reached most dictionaries. There are indexes of topical words, weird words and turns of phrase. Find out where words and phrases come from as well as what they mean, and why they are the way they are now.

http://www.quinion.demon.co.uk/words/

RELATIONSHIPS

See also Entertainment, Fun

Care Zone

This is an information resource site for parents and children who have been affected by divorce. It provides contact addresses and extensive recommended reading lists. It is aimed at helping people break through the isolation and vulnerability they may feel after separation or divorce. It provides a means of trying to understand and accept all that has happened in a positive and forward-looking way.

http://www.dudley-gateway.co.uk/cz/czindex.htm

Divorce Central

This is a useful site full of resources for people who are divorced or in the process of divorcing. It contains information, support and discussions on the different issues surrounding divorce.

http://www.divorcecentral.com

Good Vibrations

At Good Vibrations, they believe that sexual pleasure is everyone's birthright, and that access to sexual materials and accurate sex information promotes health and happiness. Their goal is to serve as a resource for quality products and information, to model honest communication about sexuality, and to take every possible opportunity to promote the philosophy that sex is fun and natural.

http://www.goodvibes.com/

Match

A leader in online personals, match-making and dating, this site offers a fun and safe environment to meet other single people and has a privacy guarantee. It caters for straight or gay men and women who are looking for romantic relationships or just a casual date. You have to pay to register, but a free trial is on offer if you are not convinced that it will be of use to you.

http://www.match.com/

Matchmaker

This is the leading online community enabling connections between people with similar interests and needs. If you are looking for a lifetime lover, a weekend workout partner or a local wine connoisseur, Matchmaker is the place to meet all types of people across the world. They have a register of over 2.6 million members from the US, Australia, Brazil, Canada, Ireland, England and Singapore.

http://www.matchmaker.com

Relate

Relate can help you whether or not you are married and whatever your age, race, personal beliefs, sexual orientation or social background. It offers guidance and counselling for those in troubled relationships of any kind and gives contact details for Relate services around Britain and information on what you can expect.

http://www.relate.org.uk

Secret Admirer

A fun, free service, this has already matched up plenty of couples throughout the world. Secret Admirer helps you start a relationship with someone you already know and like, and also offers romantic gifts to help love on its way.

http://www.secretadmirer.com/

RELIGION

About Islam and Muslims

This British-based resource gives information about the different aspects of Islam. An English translation of the Koran has been included, together with an interesting series of articles on popular misconceptions about Islam.

http://www.unn.ac.uk/societies/islamic/

The Bible Gateway

The Bible Gateway is a front page of a script that would create HTML versions of Bible chapters. Not only will it display the page but it will display the page in one of the following languages: German, Swedish, Latin, French, Spanish, Portuguese, Italian, Tagalog, Norwegian.

http://bible.gospelcom.net

Bible Magazine, Internet Edition

This site contains the online version of the *Bible* magazine, although to read the magazine you have to subscribe. However, there is an good database listing of all previous magazines and articles for sale. The site does contain downloadable sample files of the magazine.

http://www.biblemagazine.com/

British Humanist Association

'Humanism is an approach to life based on reason and our common humanity, recognising that moral values are properly founded on human nature and experience alone.' Site gives the association's principles and advice on non-religious ceremonies.

http://www.humanism.org.uk/

Buddhist Information Network

While identified as an Eastern religion, Buddhism has quite a following in the West where its more open-ended teachings appeal to many people. Find all you need to know about the many aspects of the Buddhist faith.

http://www.buddhanet.net/

Catholic Online Saints and Angels

Information on all the Catholic saints, allowing you to scroll through an alphabetical listing or to use the 'saint search' facility. You can also search for answers to your questions about angels.

http://saints.catholic.org/index.shtml

Church of England

The official site of the Church of England gives contact details, news, details of daily services, and articles on the Church's views. Find out about the organisation of the Church of England, its history, liturgy and relations with other denominations.

http://www.cofe.anglican.org/

Cult Information Centre

The Cult Information Centre is an educational charity that provides vital information on mind-control cults. It is a London-based centre, but for security reasons the office location will never be made public. The site includes a guide to detecting cult recruiters and a list of things you should or should not do with regards to communicating with friends or relatives who have joined a cult. The Cult Information Centre also provides a list of contact addresses and web links.

http://www.xenu.net/cic/

Hinduism Online

The Hinduism Online web site is created and maintained by the monks of the Saiva Siddhanta Theological Seminary at Kauai's Hindu monastery on the island of Kauai in the Hawaiian islands. This web site is a public service of Himalayan Academy to make available the timeless truths of the Sanatana Dharma, the Hindu religion, to the people of the world.

http://www.hinduismtoday.kauai.hi.us/ashram/

The Holy See

This is the official site of the Vatican and has been written in six languages. Find out everything about the Vatican City State: its library, secret archives and museums and, of course, the Pope himself.

http://www.vatican.va

Introduction to Hinduism

There are over 700 million Hindus, mainly in Bharat, India and Nepal. Hinduism is referred to as Sanatana Dharma, the eternal faith, and is not strictly a religion. It is based on the practice of Dharma, the code of life. It is quite a complicated faith, however, so have patience as you use this site as a gateway to understanding the Hindu gods!

http://www.geocities.com/RodeoDrive/1415/indexd.html

Jewish Holy Days

This site is a guide to the Jewish high holy days. It contains explanations of the days as well as recipes, prayers and quizzes. It also has an ask-the-rabbi section if you have any other questions that have not already been answered. The site has been split into two areas, one geared for adults and one aimed at children.

http://www.virtualjerusalem.com

Jewish Magazine

This is a major Jewish information resource on the web, containing articles by Jewish authors on Jewish and Israeli topics and the contents of the magazine change monthly. Over 200 articles of varied Jewish interest are in the archive area alone for this site. The site also contains a good links page to all other Jewish sites on the internet, as well as giving you the chance to get your magazine sent to your e-mail address at the beginning of the month.

http://www.jewishmag.co.il/

Maven

This 'Jewish Portal' is a web directory and search engine that covers all aspects of Judaism plus Jewish and Israeli culture. It also includes the option to subscribe to *Maven Announce*, the free, weekly newsletter, and have it sent to your e-mail mailbox.

http://www.maven.co.il/

Nida'ul Islam Internet Magazine

Nida'ul Islam is a bi-monthly magazine published in over 60 pages in both the Arabic and English languages. An independent magazine, it will provide you with news, regular articles on the political sphere, articles on the youth, Islamic economics, women, special reports and other topics of interest.

http://www.islam.org.au/

Patel's Corner Shop

A site displaying Muslim prayer times.

http://www.PatelsCornerShop.com/

Shambhala Sun

This is another religious magazine published on paper each month, from which samples are put on the internet. You can subscribe from this site to the magazine. The magazine is inspired by Buddhism and the world's great contemplative traditions, and the magazine aims to bring compassion and insight to the arts, politics, relationships, social issues, livelihood, and all aspects of life in the modern world.

http://www.shambhalasun.com/

SCIENCE

See also History, Nature and the Earth

4,000 Years of Women in Science
This site comprises of biographies of women who have made a major contribution to scientific thought or discovery.

http://www.astr.ua.edu/4000ws/4000WS.html

About Rainbows
It is a shame that there are no pots of gold at the end of the rainbow, but nevertheless it is still well worth looking out for them. Visit About Rainbows and learn why they occur and how they are formed.

http://www.unidata.ucar.edu/staff/blynds/rnbw.html

Cells Alive!
See for yourself what different cells, viruses, bacteria and crystals look like under very powerful microscopes. Find out about the techniques that are used for cell imaging and research here too.

http://www.cellsalive.com

Chem4Kids
Chemistry is the study of matter and the changes that take place with that matter, and since 'matter' comprises everything we can touch, see, feel or smell, it is an important, albeit often neglected, area of learning for some people. This site is easy to navigate via its site map and search engine, and includes a drop-down glossary for terms. Chem4Kids also includes data on atoms, elements and matter, as well as biographies of famous chemists.

http://www.chem4kids.com/

Classic Science
From its workshops in Nottingham, England, this company manufactures decorative scientific instruments, including telescopes and astrolabes.

http://www.classicscience.co.uk/

Conchologist's Information Network

Everything you ever wanted to know about shells and the mysterious creatures that live inside them can be found here. At this site all levels of interest are covered and there is even a specific children's section. There is also plenty of information about the Conchologist's Information Network organisation as well.

http://coa.acnatsci.org/conchnet

Desert Life

Learn about the desert environment and the unique characteristics that define the beautiful arid and semi-arid landscapes of the American South-west. The site begins with a general introduction to the complex and delicate desert ecosystems, including a discussion of the role humans play in the changing desert environment.

http://www.desertusa.com/life.html

EurekAlert

The latest scientific inventions are featured on this site so you can be the first to break the news about tomorrow's world.

http://www.eurekalert.org

A Guided Tour of the Visible Human

The Visible Human Project consists of some 9,000 digitised sections of the body. The animations and images in this tour demonstrate the planes of section, and how the two-dimensional images provide a unique means of studying the three-dimensional anatomy of the human body.

http://madsci.org/~lynn/VH/

The Heart

From the moment it begins beating until the moment it stops, the human heart works tirelessly. In an average lifetime, the heart actually beats more than two and a half billion times. There has always been an air of mystery surrounding the heart, and even though modern technology has removed much of that mystery, there still remains an air of fascination and curiosity. Explore the heart at this site. Discover the complexities of its development and structure. Follow the blood through the blood vessels. Wander through the web-like body systems. Learn how to monitor your heart's health and ensure that it remains in peak condition. Look back at the history of heart science.

http://www.fi.edu/biosci/heart.html

How Stuff Works

Do you find yourself wondering how things work, or do you need to find out for that school project? If you do, then pay a visit to this site straight away. It contains a huge collection of articles on the numerous technologies and is divided into topics such as engines, around the house and electronics. A new article is added each week. So don't take the appliances you use every day for granted any more!

http://www.howstuffworks.com

How Things Work

If you find yourself wanting to ask someone 'How does this work?' then do so. A physicist at the University of Virginia has designed this site as a call-in program on the web. Simply go to this site and ask it anything. All the questions are archived, so scroll through to find the answers you need.

http://www.rabi.phys.virginia.edu/HTW/

Interactive Frog Dissection

The Interactive Frog Dissection was designed for use in high school biology classrooms as an online tutorial. However, anyone can take part and so if you are not squeamish, why not have a go? The site will help you to learn the anatomy of frogs and give you a better understanding of the anatomy of vertebrate animals in general, including humans.

http://teach.virginia.edu/go/frog

National Science Foundation

The NSF is an independent US Government agency responsible for promoting science and engineering through programmes that invest over $3.3 billion per year in almost 20,000 research and education projects in science and engineering. On their web site is a huge listing of online scientific resources. It should be one of the first places you look for any information needed on scientific problems.

http://www.nsf.gov/

Nova Television

Nova is an American television company that makes science programmes for the US and the world. Men, women and children of all ages explore the science behind the headlines, along the way demystifying science and technology. On its web site you can view written information about all the programmes it has made and the content of these programs, watch small video clips from previous shows and even purchase videos. The site is full of resources for all on a vast range of topics.

http://www.pbs.org/wgbh/nova/

The Periodic Table of the Elements on the Internet

This site includes a detailed version of the periodic table and links to additional information. It is easy to use and there are different ways to view the table, which helps make this a useful reference site for any chemist or student of chemistry.

http://www.chemicalelements.com

Physics Biographies

This site contains biographies of all the great physicists, so if you want to know about Aristotle, Copernicus, Einstein or Newton, look them up here. There is also a comprehensive history of physics, a full list of Nobel Prize winners since 1901 and much more.

http://hermes.astro.washington.edu/scied/
physics/physbio.html

Pretty Strange Patents

This site displays the most bizarre inventions from around the world. The site's descriptions also come with diagrams showing you how the inventions really work – or in some cases don't.

http://soundreach.simplenet.com/psp/

Science, Technology and Medical Biographical Dictionary

This is a useful, searchable index of hundreds of figures from the history of science and technology, linking to brief biographical information. A good reference site for science projects and an interesting read.

http://www.asap.unimelb.edu.au/hstm/hstm_bio.htm

Spy Gadgets

High-tech spy gadgets – a fact not fiction. The Central Intelligence Museum claims to have produced models of actual spy hardware and you can examine them online. They might not be items you can add to your shopping list, but keep dreaming!

http://www.acmenet.net/~dna

Telescope Makers

Ever wanted to build your own telescope but don't know where to begin? Look up the Amateur Telescope Makers' page for help. The site contains sections on design, mechanics and optics and lets you choose the type of telescope you are interested in. Once you have done this, you can see detailed plans to help you on your way to creating your own equipment.

http://www.atmpage.com

SEARCH ENGINES

See also Internet, Reference

Search engines do the hard part of searching the web for you. They all differ in how you input the search criteria and also in their look and content. There are many to choose from, and you will soon find the one that suits you best. The good thing about a lot of the search engines is that they are country-specific. So if you only want to find information in France then you would use the French search engine as well as or instead of searching the whole web.

One thing you have to be careful of when using the search engines is the criteria you use for searching: you need to be very specific otherwise they will come up with a host of irrelevant material. Another thing to watch out for is that they can list sites that may not be suitable for children, although you can counteract this by using filtering software (see page 81). You will find additional search engines in the book listed under their relevant subject category.

About.com
Calling itself 'The Human Internet', this site offers an entry-point to a whole range of linked sites with information from news updates to maps of Finland.

http://www.about.com

All the Web
Claims to be able to reference 200 million web pages.

http://alltheweb.com

Alta Vista
The AltaVista search service helps you find documents on the web. To tell the search service what you are looking for, simply type in key words, phrases or questions in the search box. The search service responds by giving you a list of all the web pages in the index that relate to those topics. The most relevant content will appear at the top of the list.

http://www.altavista.com/

Ask Jeeves
This is a search engine with a difference. If you want information on anything on the net, Ask Jeeves can tell you the answer. You ask a question in plain English and Jeeves will give you the answer. It is a mix of human and automation, and there is no need to mess about with multiple keywords and phrases like with most traditional search engines. Not only that, but Ask Jeeves is linked to major search engines like Yahoo, Alta Vista, Infoseek and Webcrawler and gives you their answers too.

http://www.askjeeves.com/

Cybercafé Search Engine

This is a site for people who need their fix of the internet while away on business or holiday and do not have the luxury of a portable computer. The database at this site contains listings of 1537 cybercafés in 89 countries. You can search for a cybercafé by name or by a city.

http://www.cybercaptive.com

Deja News

This engine is specialised in searching the newsgroups. It is exceptionally good for accessing old articles and for finding the right newsgroup to which to subscribe.

http://www.dejanews.com

Excite

Popular and efficient search engine with reasonable reference index.

http://www.excite.com

GoTo

'Simply type what you are looking for and GoTo it' is what this site offers, so it gives you easy access to sites if you don't know their URL.

http://www.goto.com

Hotbot

This engine is a good and easy-to-use search engine with useful search options. It can also be tuned to your own needs. The site is well known for its accurate and thorough keyword searches.

http://www.hotbot.com

Infoseek

At Infoseek you can search the web, newsgroups, and various web FAQs. The web search is quite fast but there are not that many results as its databse is not as big as many others available.

http://www.infoseek.com

Ixquick

This service uses a slightly different approach in that it searches 14 other search engines and gives you the best options on the subject you are looking for.

http://www.ixquick.com

LookSmart

This is being called the next-generation internet directory. Looksmart organises the web for you like no other as it is three powerful internet tools in one. Explore speeds you through familiar categories to help you pinpoint web sites faster and more easily. Search will search its listings for sites first, then use Alta Vista to find what you want. Personalise allows you to choose your own favourite shopping, software and news sources and will provide you the top links from your own home area based on this information

http://www.looksmart.com

Lycos

This is a search engine that offers the user a customisable keyword search if you require, together with a range of web guides to browse.

http://www.lycos.com

Northern Light

One of the largest catalogues of any search engine, this also includes various other magazines and databases.

http://www.northernlight.com

People Search

AT&T Labs is trialling an advanced web-based directory service site, AnyWhoSM Directory Service, which integrates traditional business and consumer *White* and *Yellow Pages* telephone listings with enhanced, internet-based contact information such as e-mail addresses and web site URLs. Toll-free and fax numbers can also be listed. This is only for the USA at present.

http://anywho.com/aboutus.html

Real Names

This engine is one of the fastest ways to search the web. You can use Real Names addresses in Alta Vista, LookSmart, Inktomi and GO Network. All you need to do is to type a name, brand or company in the RealNames locator box and Real Names service takes you to the exact site, or to a list of companies that match your query.

http://www.centraal.com

Regional Directories

Nearly every country has its own web directory purely for itself. At this site you will find a comprehensive list of country-specific web directories. Not totally exhaustive, but it is a good place to start.

http://www.edirectory.com

Search Engine Watch

This is not a search engine itself but a very good and useful resource about search engines for both beginners and the more experienced. Here you can find out how to use all the popular and largest search engines available on the web. Or if you are trying to get your site listed at the top of the search engine databases, this will tell you all you need to know about how to do that.

http://www.searchenginewatch.com

Webcrawler

This search engine is actually owned by Excite but has its own unique user interface. The search engine itself is mainly directed towards news, so it is a good place to look for stories about what is currently going on in the world.

http://webcrawler.com

UK Plus

This site is a friendly, sensible guide to the web designed to help you find what you want, quickly and easily. Although it concentrates on UK web sites of all kinds, there are also many from all over the world.

http://www.ukplus.co.uk

Yahoo

This site considered the oldest and the biggest search directory of them all. It is very easy to use and it is also available as country-specific. However, this search engine is now turning more into a community rather then just a plain search engine, offering you free e-mail access and free web space now as well. Also available here is the chance to search in other engines for the same keyword if your search fails to bring results.

http://www.yahoo.com

SENIOR CITIZENS

British Geriatrics Society

A world-wide organisation of doctors, scientists and researchers who specialise in geriatric medicine and age-related illness.

http://www.bgs.org.uk/

The Oldie

Richard Ingrams, who for 23 years was the editor of *Private Eye* magazine, launched *The Oldie* magazine in 1992. He founded the magazine because he was alarmed that the media was side-lining good writers and journalists simply because of their age. This humorous magazine provides cartoons, regularly updated articles and ample opportunity to subscribe to the paper version.

http://www.theoldie.co.uk/

Saga

Saga pioneered the idea of providing holidays exclusively for mature travellers some 45 years ago. Today they are the leaders in the field, with offices in Britain, the US and Australia, and they are associated with much more than holidays. Saga provides an increasing range of services for people aged 50 and over, including their acclaimed magazine, as well as financial and insurance services.

http://www.saga.co.uk/

Seniors Information Resource Centre

Don't be put off by the title as this is a fairly useful resource with a broad range of categories for you to explore. It is the only search directory exclusively for the over-50 age group. Not all the sites here are exclusively for the elderly but the best sites are labelled 'senior friendly'.

http://www.seniorssearch.com/

Third Age

The site states that the Third Age is 'a time of life characterised by happiness, freedom and learning. A life stage following youth and preceding old age'. This is 'a web site where like-minded people find intelligent conversations and useful tools'. So, in order to find out what to do in your best years yet, look no further. There are sections devoted to family, health, living, money, news, technology, romance and work. There are also daily jokes, comics, crosswords and word games, as well as regular articles and chats.

http://www.thirdage.com/

SERVICES

British Telecom

This site tells you everything you may need to know about British Telecom, its services and how to get the best out of them. It also includes information on business and share prices.

http://www.bt.com

Buy the Right Services

If you are looking for ways to cut your bills for gas, electricity, mobile phones or water services, come along and browse round this site for good information.

http://www.buy.co.uk

SHOPPING

You'll also find that many specialist sites either have links to sales outlets or you can buy online from those sites, so if you are looking for specialist items, check out the relevant subject pages.

American Priceline

Priceline.com is a revolutionary new buying service where you can save money by naming your own price for the things you need in America. The way that this does it is that you submit a bid for the price you are prepared to pay, and they pass it on to the relevant company. You can name your own price for home mortgages, home equity loans, mortgage refinancing, even new cars and trucks!

http://www.tickets.priceline.com/

Argos

The well-known UK catalogue-based stores sells almost everything from tents to trainers. Browse or search for specific products. There's a useful finder, help guide, order forms and services details.

http://www.argos.co.uk

Auctions

This is not just an auction site but also posts information on auctions through the UK and a search facility so you can track down specific items from auction catalogues.

http://www.thesaurus.co.uk/

Avon

The well-known UK supplier of cosmetic products now has a web site from which you can order its range of cosmetics and associated products. The site has a good range and is easy to navigate. Delivery of the goods takes about five days.

http://www.avon.com

Best of British

Fashion, accessories, interiors, cosmetics, hampers and everything British, which you can purchase online. There are special offers and a good keyword system of searching for the item you want.

http://www.thebestofbritish.com

Bigsave

With a range of over 7000 products and promises of up to 70% discounts off high-street prices, it's not surprising that this is a popular site for products and services from clothes to electrical goods. Online purchasing, direct delivery and full guarantees.

http://www.bigsave.com

Boots

Beauty products and a wide range of other products stocked by the high-street chain and now available online. It also includes pictures of various make-up looks and descriptions of the products needed to achieve them.

http://www.boots.co.uk

Bristol Street

Buying cars online is becoming more popular, so this group of dealers have created their own web site so that you can do just that. An easy-to-navigate site, it still has the dealer link for peace of mind.

http://www.bristolstreet.co.uk/

Carphone Warehouse

This company was established to give impartial advice to help you make the best decision on the phone that is right for your needs. The web site works on the same principle, and adds a special deal online every day.

http://www.carphonewarehouse.com

Catalog Mart
The Catalog Mart is the easiest, fastest and most direct way to receive just about any catalogue offered in the US today. It offers more than 10,000 catalogues in over 800 topics that are free of charge with no obligation. Just choose your product categories and fill out the electronic order form.

http://catalog.savvy.com

CD Direct
This is the place to buy your CD Roms, Playstations, Nintendos and DVDs as well as the CDs, DVDs and games to play on them.

htp://www.cddirect.co.uk

Check a Price
For all kinds of product prices, from CDs to cars, you can key in what you need to buy and the search engine will offer comparative prices from various online sources.

http://www.checkaprice.com

Comet
The electrical retailer has this online sales service for all kinds of kitchen, household, entertainment and personal-care products.

http://www.comet.co.uk

Condom Country
Buy condoms, books and sex aids at this mail-order site. Condom Country believes in personal choice and personal privacy. It provides high-quality products to people all around the world. Customer information is confidential and will never be given to any other organisation for any purpose. The electronic and physical mailing lists only include those people who have specifically asked to be on them.

http://www.condom.com

Contacts Direct
Making savings through low overheads and direct supply, Contacts

Direct can pass those savings on to its customers and supply designer glasses, sunglasses and contact lenses at considerable discounts.

http://www.contacts-direct.co.uk

Daltons Web

Daltons Weekly has been published for many years, listing properties, holidays and other items for sale. Now the magazine is online with good database-search facilities.

http://www.daltons.co.uk

Domestic Appliances

All kinds of electrical goods are on sale here, but the site is especially good for household electrical products such as washing machines, as well as both gas and electric cookers. There is also a good range of telephone equipment.

http://www.qed-uk.com

Early Learning Centre

The direct-sale point for the well-known UK high-street chain selling educational toys is a great site with a good search engine that allows you to find specific items or a general range.

http://www.earlylearningcentre.co.uk

Easy Shop

For all kinds of shopping online, take a look at this site, which offers perfumes, lingerie, tights, swimwear and lots of other products. Delivery is easy and free.

http://www.easyshop.co.uk

Electrical Goods

Photographic and electrical goods at the entertainment end of the market are available for sale online. A very wide range of goods is available at competitive prices.

http://www.unbeatable.co.uk

Exchange and Mart

The site for the well-known magazine in which you can buy everything from cars to can openers, book holidays and find jobs.

http://www.exchangeandmart.co.uk

Fat Face

Another online store, you'll find clothes and accessories for sale on this site, with some useful discounts on offer.

http://www.fatface.co.uk

FragranceNet

FragranceNet is a great way to buy your favourite fragrances because you can make savings of up to 60 per cent off the retail price! Even if you do not have a favourite fragrance, you may be able to decide on a scent by reading the description given. Do you like floral or fruity scents, or do you prefer an oriental, musky note? Whatever your taste, this site will have a fragrance for you.

http://www.fragrancenet.com

FreeShop

FreeShop is the place to subscribe to hundreds of magazines and to try before you buy on the internet. Shoppers can browse through nearly 20 popular-interest categories for access to free samples and risk-free magazine trial issues. The site has a shopping assistant that compares prices across the internet, making it easy to find the best value available.

http://www.freeshop.com

Hamleys

The online site of the well-known toy store in London's Regent Street. You can buy a huge range of toys and collectables to be delivered to your home.

http://www.hamleys.com

Harrods

This is the web site of the world's most famous store. Do we need to say anything else?

http://www.harrods.co.uk

HI-TEC Sports Online

Find a huge collection of sports footwear from the UK-based stockist here for you to buy online. The web site also includes news, sports-related games and Real Video to keep you on the run.

http://www.hi-tecsports.com/

Innovations

Following the success of its mail-order catalogue containing unusual household, DIY, gardening and gift items, this site now offers the online equivalent.

http://www.innovations.co.uk

Jungle

Now familiar to most people because of TV advertising, Jungle offers computer equipment, games, CDs, videos and DVDs for sale online.

http://www.jungle.com

Kays

An easy site to use, this is the online Kays catalogue, which includes fashion, household wares and a whole range of other items for sale. Key in what you want to see, the price, size and colour, and it will give you a list of matching items. Select the ones you want to view and drop your final choices into a shopping bag.

http://www.kaysnet.com

Kit Bag

For all kinds of sports equipment, this site offers a good range for online purchases and free delivery.

http://www.kitbag.co.uk

Last Minute

At this easy-to-use site, snap up the latest bargains in travel, entertainment and holidays. Get help in choosing the perfect gift in the presents section or find short-term accommodation from flats and houses to country mansions and castles. You can even purchase items from auctions. Registration is free and even though you may not always find something to buy, it is definitely worth checking out this site if you are interested in obtaining last-minute flight or concert tickets.

http://www.lastminute.com/

Loot

On this site you can search the advertisements for a whole range of goods from sports equipment to household items. Search for what you want, and they will supply the full details of the advertised products.

http://www.loot.com

Organic Shopping

Organic clothes and bedding as well as food, with a ten-day delivery on clothes, check out this site for all your environmentally friendly needs. The site is easy to navigate although it has no pictures.

http://www.organicsdirect.com

Quote UK

At this site they have developed a revolutionary new way to find the best deals on anything from car insurance to a holiday cruise. The different quotes available are CarQuote, a site which is now supplying around 300 quotes per day; PrintQuote, a service for businesses which provides easy access to the best prices from printers up and down the country; HomeQuote which provides quotes on house insurance; and CreditCardQuote.

http://www.Car.Quote.co.uk

http://www.Print.Quote.co.uk

http://www.Home.Quote.co.uk

http://www.CreditCard.Quote.co.uk

QVC

QVC, The Shopping Channel, prides itself on having an interactive relationship with its customers, listening to what they say, learning what they want and delivering it quickly and efficiently. On their web site you will find all the products offered on the TV show. Ordering online is available or by telephone if you wish. QVC broadcasts in three countries – USA, UK and Germany – so the web sites are available in all three languages.

http://www.qvc.com – USA

http://www.qvcuk.com – UK

http://www.qvc.de/ – Germany

Retail Link

Not so much a site in itself, but a link to the sites of dozens of leading UK high-street shops, offering information on their products and, in many cases, the opportunity to buy online.

http://www.retail.co.uk

Scotch Corner

Set up by a part of Scotch Corner, the high-street store, this site provides information on the correct tartans and everything you could possibly need to know about Scottish highland dress. Some items can be delivered in a few days; other items, such as kilts, are made to order and so take about six weeks.

http://www.highland–dress.co.uk

Shops on the Internet

This is a resource site aimed at advertising and reviewing the sites that are selling on the internet, and giving awards to those that have a good retail environment. Shops on the Net is operated by NetCommerce Ltd, a multi-faceted organisation providing commercial internet services in the United Kingdom and Europe.

http://www.shopsonthenet.com/

ShopSmart

An easy way to find the best shopping sites, ShopSmart offers reviews of over 700 online shopping sites with the facility to compare prices between the different sources.

http://www.shopsmart.com

Sony Online

This site gives news, previews, support and information on Sony's movie and TV merchandise, computing and accessories, music and consumer products. It has an online shop and also a store locator facility. You can even play games online at this site.

http://www.sony.com/

Ticketmaster

Visit this site and you will be able to book all your seats for plays, shows, rock concerts, exhibitions and sporting events being held all over the UK. You are also able to buy tickets for shows in other countries such as America, Australia and Canada online using the appropiate Ticketmaster sites.

http://www.ticketmaster.com

http://www.ticketmaster.au

http://www.ticketmaster.co.uk/

Top Shop

A good range of clothes, especially for the younger set, from the familiar British high-street chain. Payment is by credit card so you have to be over 18.

http://www.tops.co.uk

UK Screentrade

Screentrade offers you the chance for someone to prepare a number of competitive, personalised quotes for you in just a few minutes. Then you can compare prices and cover, and see just what you're getting for your money – you'll probably be surprised how policy features differ. All you do is key in your details once and you're in touch with some of the biggest names in the market. Then you can buy online or over the phone, whichever suits you best.

http://www.screentrade.co.uk/

Value Direct

With a good search system, this is an online store for household appliances such as televisions. Free UK mainland delivery.

http://www.value-direct.co.uk

Vegetarian 'Leather'

Fake leather clothes such as shoes, jackets, gloves and coats for sale online with delivery in about a week. Prices compare favourably with the real thing.

http://www.vegetarian-shoes.co.uk

The Virtual Mall

This is the UK's only real-life internet shopping mall. The site contains links to 120 of the leading high-street and internet shops in one place. The only difference is that this mall is open 24 hours a day, 365 days a year. The site contains four floors at the moment and it is always increasing. Every floor has a mall directory to help you find a specific store, or specific type of store.

http://www.thevirtualmall.co.uk/

Waitrose Direct

Waitrose is the food section of the John Lewis Partnership and sells a vast range of high-quality foods. Investigate its Direct web site for online purchases.

http://www.waitrose.com

Zoom

A rapidly changing site with constant updates on what is latest on the fashion scene, gossip, news and tips.

http://www.zoom.com

SPACE

See also Astronomy

NASA

This official site is full of information on NASA science and technology. If you are interested in the latest news on the space programme, then this site is a must. It is updated daily and always features a lead article on the latest space discovery. It contains links to other interesting NASA sites, such as future shuttle launch dates and details of the space station. You can also experience further sights and sounds by stepping into the NASA multimedia gallery.

http://www.nasa.gov

Space Online

Space Online's web site content is divided into five categories and covers all aspects of space information. The site's categories are: Next Launch targets (when the next major rocket launch is scheduled to depart the planet with a complete launch manifest); Space Today (up-to-the-minute news and top space stories from Florida plus NASA status reports, industry news releases and other timely information); Visit the Space Coast (an electronic journey to Florida's space coast to check out the best places to see a launch and learn more about the space programme in Brevard County; Explore the Archives (recent history of the space programme told in stories, photos, sounds and video culled from Florida Today's library and other sources); United in Space (a complete report on the international space station which is now taking shape in orbit).

http://www.flatoday.com/space/

Star Wars

The official Star Wars site with free club for kids to join, inside news, pictures to print and colour, regular newsletters and interactive scenes. A very classy site.

http://www.starwars.com

UFOs – Fact or Fiction

This site will help you make up your mind as to what is really going on in space with the UFO stories. This site is mainly based upon UFO information but there is a lot of content you would see on the TV series *The X-Files*. Here you can post your views on conspiracies, UFOs and paranormal phenomena and swap information, and buy from their online source for alternative media and paranormal paraphernalia. Books, magazines, aliens in a jar and lots more, browse ParaScope's image gallery, read hundreds of declassified documents on covert operations, abuses of government power and UFOs, and everything you need to use the Freedom of Information Act successfully to obtain government information.

http://www.parascope.com/

SPORTS

ADVENTURE SPORTS

Extreme Explore

This web site is a mecca for all the people who are into extreme sports. The site's content covers an in-depth look at a variety of activities including biking, snowboarding, climbing, watersports and many more. The site asks visitors to share their experiences to make it as interactive as possible.

http://www.explore.com

AMERICAN FOOTBALL

American Football

This site offers informative profiles on each of the thousands of players in the league together with individual club pages. It also offers you stats, a video and a very good news service. With terrific graphics, animations, games, countless surprises and bags of attitude and fun, it will appeal to everyone who is a footie fan.

http://www.nfl.com/

ANGLING

Where to Fish

This site claims to be the world's largest online fishing information service. At this site you will find more than 3,000 pages of daily updated information covering fishing locations in the UK and abroad, both at sea and on land. There is also a wide range of articles covering all aspects of fishing. Users of the site can add their own fishing information.

`http://www.where-to-fish.com/`

ATHLETICS

International Athletics

This is the official site of the IAAF. Here you can find out about all the current news, stats and results. The sport section gives the history, landmarks and required qualities in each event. From legends to the latest scientific advances and last season's major events, this has everything, including video interviews and coaching tips for the budding athlete.

`http://www.iaaf.org/`

Running Tracks

With maps, address, telephone and fax numbers for all the running tracks in the UK, this is an invaluable site for athletes.

`http://www.runtrackdir.com/`

AUSTRALIAN RULES FOOTBALL

Australian Football League

This official site contains everything you could possibly want to know about the Australian Football League with news, views and highlights plus information on forthcoming matches.

`http://www.afl.com.au`

BASKETBALL

National Basketball Association
This is the official site of the NBA. It contains all the information you could possibly want on the game and its teams and players. For the news, history, statistics and schedules plus special features and the online NBA store, look no further.

http://www.nba.com

BASEBALL

The Official Site of Major League Baseball
This site is really for the true baseball fan as it has no glossary or 'idiot's guide'. It is very informative with detailed team sections, history, masses of multimedia and stats. A section for kids offers profiles, interviews and interactive games.

http://www.majorleaguebaseball.com/

BOXING

Boxing.com
The complete low-down on boxing. Find out the schedules, ranking and results and add your own opinions to the site.

http://www.boxing.com

CRICKET

CricInfo
CricInfo provides detailed cricket information, including live scores for international matches free of charge to cricket fans around the world. CricInfo promotes interest in cricket worldwide through building and maintaining the largest and, at times, the most popular cricket database on the internet. It has mirror sites in the UK, the USA, India, Australia and South Africa.

http://www.cricket.org/

Cricket Line

Up-to-date information on current match scores, both international and domestic.

http://www.cricketline.com

CYCLING

Tour de France

Keep up with the 21-day race around France from the comfort of your own home! The site has profiles of the riders, the route, the rules, videos of the race and merchandise for sale. During the race, the site is updated daily.

http://www.letour.com

FOOTBALL

Arsenal

News, results, ticket information, diaries and all kinds of other information about this major UK football club.

http://www.arsenal.co.uk

Football 365

At this site you will find the most comprehensive, exciting and funniest football site on the web. The site is run by football fans who are dedicated to bringing you a view of the game that combines knowledge and passion. They have the latest news, interesting features, opinions, match reports, interviews and football humour, together with plenty of avenues for input.

http://www.football365.co.uk/

Football Nationwide

A wealth of information on football for the enthusiast, plus plenty of links to the financial services of Nationwide, the football sponsor.

http://www.football.nationwide.co.uk

Football News

This is the place for the sporting statistician as it contains every kind of result or table you could think of throughout the range of soccer leagues in the UK.

http://www.footballnews.co.uk

Manchester United Football Club

This site is about England's premier football club, Manchester United. You will find the latest news, information on players, matches, fixtures, results, goals and more.

http://www.manutd.com

Soccer Net

A complete guide to the new season's fixtures and a forum for you to chat to other fans.

http://www.soccernet.com/index.html

Teamtalk

This site is one of the UK's leading independent football news and reports services, producing news, results, statistics and reports on 59 top club and national teams. It also provides up-to-the-minute audio news and match reports for all 59 league teams.

http://www.teamtalk.com/

When Saturday Comes

See for yourself just how good the site really is! For example there is the football pub guide that gives details of top pub venues for important matches, and the famous player alert section where the almost inconspicuous activities of past and present players are noted. You can also add your own views.

http://www.wsc.co.uk/wsc/

GENERAL SPORT

CBS Sportsline

Check out this site for the news, views, fixtures and scores on all US sports. It gives fast facts on the standings, schedules, statistics, teams and players.

http://www.sportsline.com

International Blind Sports Association

This site is available in either English or Spanish and contains a regularly updated news section plus an impressive and wide range of articles and features. Best of all is the colossal database. It has brief profiles and sporting records of hundreds of athletes and clear, accessible guides to 14 disciplines.

http://www.ibsa.es

Sky Sports

This site has a rolling sports news service which gives you all the latest sports news and scores 24 hours a day, seven days a week, 52 weeks a year. Find out what is happening in the world of soccer, cricket, rugby, boxing, golf, tennis, NFL and motor racing.

http://www.skysports.co.uk

Sports Web

An online sports store together with news and information on sports, especially football.

http://www.sportsweb.com

GOLF

Golf Agent

Golf Agent enables internet users to book tee times at a wide range of golf courses. Reservations are all online, using SSL credit card encryption methods for security and ease. When tee times are booked on-line, the golfer's details appear on the club's system as if the person had telephoned the club and they had taken the booking themselves.

http://www.golfagent.com

Golf Europe

Golf Europe is a commercial web site with a mission to be the definitive reference point for European golf on the internet, and to offer golfers a genuinely valuable information resource free of charge. On the site is a course directory containing every club in Britain and Europe. Other sections include an almanac and golf tuition to provide the golfer with a host of valuable reference information.

http://www.golfeurope.com/

Golf Today

Home news, travel, golf questions and answers, this is the site of the premier golf magazine, a mine of information for anyone interested in the sport.

http://www.golftoday.co.uk

Golf Web

A major golf web site, this is committed to providing 'everything golf on the worldwide web'. Golf Web offers something for everyone with an interest in golf, from the latest professional and amateur tournament scores and news to extensive golf course information and an online pro shop. Golf Web's auxiliary sites are Golf Web Japan and Golf Web Europe.

http://www.golfweb.com/

Golf World

A brave name, but this site more than lives up to it. There's exhaustive, up-to-date tour results, plus archived stats and majors sections. But this site excels for the player rather than the spectator, with hundreds of recommended courses from over 30 countries, club-choosing tips, fitness, rules and endless advice. Discover the joys of the Texas wedgie in the dictionary and learn the art of yelling 'Fore!' in Joey West's humour section. And if you're really, really good – or lucky! – you can always join the hole-in-one register.

http://www.worldgolf.com/

Professional Golfers' Association European Tour

This is the official web site of the PGA European golf tour. It gives details of events, players, ranking and sponsors, as well as all the latest news.

http://www.europeantour.com

ICE HOCKEY

National Ice Hockey League

An American site which contains everything you need to know about the National Ice Hockey League. It has non-stop news, photos, video highlights, articles, encyclopedic Winter Olympic details and features ranging from match previews to the features on old players file. They also broadcast live commentary on every league game.

http://www.nhl.com

MOTORSPORT

Autosport

The online site for the premier motor racing magazine. You can subscribe here, or read articles on all aspects of motor racing.

http://www.autosport.com

Motorsport International

Motorsport News International provides news, results, race reports and other information about all types of motorsports – from Formula One and road racing to stock cars, from midgets to rallies, and from dragsters to touring cars – through the internet and through a digest-format mailing list.

http://www.motorsport.com/

Racer

Racer.com is the online news and commentary service of *Racer* magazine. This is a monthly American publication. Stories are augmented by news of the latest motor racing developments, along with an easy-reading summary of important race results and a complete day-by-day listing of all live and taped television motor-sports events for the month.

http://www.racer.com/

RUGBY

International Rugby Football Board

The International Rugby Board (IRB), with its headquarters in Dublin, Ireland, is the world governing and law-making body for the game of rugby union. The board was founded in 1886. This is the official site and contains information about the board and the game itself, together with links to other relevant sites.

http://www.irfb.com

Planet Rugby

The ultimate resource for international rugby union, this site includes ranking, tournaments, an interactive chat room, fixtures and an interesting archive.

http://www.planetrugby.com

Rugby Club

At this site you can find details on every aspect of the playing side of the game: the results, the fixtures and a comprehensive guide to the clubs and their players. The Allied Dunbar League tables are updated within a couple of hours of the end of matches. There is also the subscriber club where supporters can register to be sent pre-match information by e-mail on the club of their choice.

http://www.rugbyclub.co.uk

Rugby Mail

This is a *Daily Mail* site designed to keep sports fans up to date with the latest news on current tournaments and players.

http://www.rugbymail.co.uk/

Rugby Scrum

Up-to-the minute news, results and comments on the international game of rugby union. The site gives information on the tests, tours and tournaments and has links to other similar sites.

http://www.scrum.com

World of Rugby League

Whether you are a fan of rugby league or simply wonder why 26 men should want to play such a rough game, check out this site. Statistics, news and scores are posted on the World of Rugby League site after each game.

http://www.rleague.com

SAILING

International Sailing Federation

With daily news updates, a weekly newsletter and an exhaustive fixture and results service, this official site gives you all need to know about ocean racing. There's thorough coverage of the big races and more than 700 regattas listed in their global calendar, together with lots of features and editorials. With its varied content and fleet of photos, the site is entertaining as well as hugely informative.

http://www.sailing.org/

SKIING AND SNOWSPORTS

GORP Skiing and Snowsports

This page covers all you need for downhill and cross-country skiing, as well as other snow sports such as snowboarding and snowmobiling. The are trail maps of American skiing areas, regional ski area guides, and the all-important equipment pages. A good resource if you are planning a skiing break in America.

http://www.gorp.com/gorp/activity/skiing.htm

Ski Central

This is a search and index site for skiers and snowboarders. Ski Central is designed as the primary gateway for accessing ski and snowsportrelated sites. Use this free service to find information related to these sports quickly and easily on the internet.

http://www.skicentral.com

Winter Sports Foundation

This site is both fun and very informative. The site's home page features an image map of a cartoon winter resort. Click on the area of the map for further information on that sport. Guided by one of the top names, each section features history, news, description and how to get involved. You can send questions to internationals in the resort's town hall or even share stories with other enthusiasts of winter sports.

http://www.wintersports.org/

SNOOKER

Embassy World Snooker

At this site you won't just find information about the World Championships but also details of other ranking tournaments, match reports, a review of last year's season, a hall of fame and player profiles. You can also test your snooker knowledge with a trivia quiz, pick up some tips on trick shots from John Virgo and find out how snooker is televised. A comprehensive and very informative site for all snooker fans.

http://www.embassysnooker.com/

Snooker

With great graphics, good display, interesting information and right up-to-date text, this site has everything for the enthusiast.

http://www.stud.ifi.uio.no/~hermunda/Snooker/

SURFING AND SEASPORTS

Adventure Surf Unlimited

Adventure Surf Unlimited is designed to serve as an introduction to the sport in a exciting holiday package. If you have ever dreamed of the ultimate adventure surf trip but lack the know-how and equipment, then ASU will supply it all for you. It provides all inclusive surf camp/excursions to some of the best surfing in North America.

http://www.adventuresurf.com/

Ocean Blue

This site is dedicated to all aspects of seasports, as well as information about the best beaches in America, and environmental concerns for the oceans of the world. The site is split into three sections: the island earth pages aim to promote the well-being of the planet; the sea sports pages cover the world of ocean-based sports; the best beaches pages are devoted to the beaches of the world but mainly those in America.

http://www.oceanblue.com/

World Surfing

This site is a must for all surfers. It gives links sorted by region, which cover all aspects of the sport. Find out how to forecast waves or where to buy equipment and go on holiday. Read the surf reports or watch the action through the large number of surfcams.

http://www.goan.com/surflink.html

TENNIS

Association of Tennis Professionals Tour Site

This is the official men's tennis tour site. It is attractive and fun, and is much more than just a fund of information. Here you will find up-to-the-minute news, player, tournament and ranking details, or head for the Acerace Quiz for quick-fire trivia questions against the clock, or Pick the Champ where you can back your favourites for forthcoming championships. The site also includes excellent magazine features and a notice board for you to find that doubles partner.

http://www.atptour.com/frameset.asp

International Tennis Federation

Claiming to be the most authoritative database on tennis on the net, there certainly seems to be a vast range of information collected here.

Rules, champions, news, players, results are all covered in this ITF site.

http://www.itftennis.com/

Tennis

From the most recent tournament reports to topical feature articles, this first-rate site leaves few bases uncovered. Though the design may be bland there's latest news, rankings, Grand Slam sections, a free monthly newsletter and endless magazine features. You can improve your skills with the tip of the week, organise that tennis holiday in the travel pages and give your mind and body a workout in the fitness section.

http://www.tennis.com/

WRESTLING

Wrestling
Watch your favourite wrestlers being punched, smacked and thrown around. Then think just how glad you are it is not you in the ring!

http://www.wrestling.com

TECHNOLOGY

See also Astronomy, Computers, Science, Space

Product Review
This site tracks product reviews from a wide variety of consumer magazines and posts the summaries online. Simply enter the product name to receive the information.

http://www.productreviewnet.com/home.html

Wired
This site is the top technology site on the web and is well known for its ground-breaking news stories on the subject of technology. You can even subscribe to its free mailing list, which will then deliver the news to your e-mail account.

http://www.wired.com

THEATRE

See also Entertainment, Films, Television, Video and DVD, Music

Official London Theatre Guide

Plan your trips to see shows in London's West End using this site. You can search by type of performance or by what is new. The site gives descriptions of the shows, including details of how long they last. The only thing you cannot do through the site is book the tickets (go to Ticketmaster, see page 208). However, all the phone numbers you may need are listed here for your use.

http://www.officiallondontheatre.co.uk/

On Broadway

This is 'a site dedicated to the shows, musicals and history of the 'Great White Way'. Visit Jogle's Broadway page to find listings information for on and off-Broadway shows. As well as all this, you will find a useful cabaret hotline, plus a list of Tony award winners and theatre links to give you further information.

http://www.on-broadway.com/

Playbill Online

The magazine for theatre-goers, *Playbill*, is now available online. On the site you will find all the listings for US and international performances, with lots of industry news, events, feature articles and the chance to purchase tickets for London shows. Also available here is the Playbill Online Club. Playbill Online is dedicated to bringing club members the opportunity to receive discount ticket offers, as well as travel and dining discounts and advantages.

http://www1.playbill.com/playbill/

Royal Shakespeare Company

Brilliant site with details of performances, productions and booking.

http://www.rsc.org.uk/

Virtual Library Theatre and Drama

On this site you will find pointers to resources in more than 40 countries around the world for professionals, amateurs, academics and students of all ages to do with theatre and drama. The site itself and its links are updated daily.

http://www.vl–theatre.com/

TRAVEL AND HOLIDAYS

See also Camping and Caravanning, Entertainment, Geography, Museums and Galleries

1001 Villa Holiday Lets

This site is well organised and easy to use as you can search for villas and apartments around the world by the use of keywords or by location. Each listing includes plenty of information and a number of colour photos to help you make your choice. To save time at the site, you can also request the adverts by e-mail.

http://www.1001–villa–holidaylets.com/

A2B Travel

Here you will find everything you need to know about travelling into, around and out of the UK. This comprehensive online travel resource includes flight booking, flight arrival and departure times, a huge hotel finder, car-hire details, traffic reports, plus bus, ferry and train timetables. There are also lots of travel tips to help you on your way.

http://www.a2btravel.com

About Travel

You can go direct to the travel page of About.com to gain entry to a whole range of sites on destinations around the world, including maps and travel and tourist information.

http://www.about.com/travel

Airport Guide

With maps, directions and full details of all the airports in the UK, this is a highly valuable site for the regular traveller or holidaymaker.

http://www.a2bairports.com/

Air Traveller's Handbook

The Air Traveller's Handbook is a summary of useful information for air travellers. It is quite easy to find your way around this site and is well worth checking out. The focus is on obtaining inexpensive air fares, although other topics are also covered. The information in this site applies primarily to US domestic flights, though some information also applies to international flights.

http://www.cis.ohio-state.edu/hypertext/faq/usenet/
travel/air/handbook/top.html

Airport Rental Cars in the US

Do you want to travel in the USA? If so, you will find that this site will steer you in the right direction as it has an interactive guide that enables you to find the best rental rates. Over 90 major airport auto rental companies and franchises at over 100 airports are listed here. Even if you are not going to the States, the tips are relevant for car rental anywhere in the world.

http://www.bnm.com

Air Tickets Direct

Your 24-hour travel agent offers bookable discounted air fares online, with a good search facility.

http://www.airtickets.co.uk

All Hotels

This site contains links to thousands of hotels worldwide. You can search for hotels either by destination or chain, and get the hotel's own description, with photos, plus additional information on the surrounding area.

http://www.all-hotels.com/

Arab Net

The aim of Arab Net is to provide the most comprehensive online resource on the Arab world, primarily dealing with countries in the Middle East and North Africa. There is a general overview of each country together with information on its culture, history, geography, government, business potential and transport facilities. There is also a guide to attractions and sights for the tourist or business traveller.

`http://www.arab.net`

Association of British Travel Agents

'Look before you book' at possibly the best index of UK travel sites you can find – and it gives information on reputable agents only! This site includes a full listing of ABTA members.

`http://www.abtanet.com/`

Aviation Safety Records

If you are scared of flying, then this site may not be the one for you! However, if you wish to find out exactly what goes wrong up in the air, look no further.

`http://www.faa.gov/asafety.htm`

BLVD Europe

This is an arts, culture and events magazine covering most of Europe. It includes a thorough listing of events and exhibitions around Europe, a series of interviews with various European celebrities, and travel-related classified advertisements. A mailing list service is also available.

`http://www.blvd.org/`

British Foreign Office Travel Advice

The consular division of the Foreign and Commonwealth Office produces a range of material intended to advise and inform British citizens travelling abroad. This includes advice to help British travellers avoid trouble, especially threats to their personal safety arising from political unrest, lawlessness, violence, natural disasters, epidemics, anti-British demonstrations and aircraft safety. Get access to the full range of travel advice notices, and a selection of consular information material. In certain circumstances the site may recommend that you contact the local consul.

http://www.fco.gov.uk

Brochurebank

Whether you want to spend all of your time relaxing by a pool or you want to have an action-packed holiday, Brochurebank is likely to have a brochure to suit your interests. Simply select a type of holiday and destination or a travel company and then order any of the free brochures suggested by this site.

http://www.brochurebank.com/

CNN Travel Guide

The CNN Travel Guide is a massive database of the latest global travel news. It also has extraordinarily detailed guides to cities around the world and many in-flight-magazine-style features that make it more reader-friendly.

http://europe.cnn.com/TRAVEL/

Crossing Borders

It may be important to you, or simply of interest, to find out about what a unified Europe means to the United States of America. At the site entitled 'The European Union in the US', you will find an in-depth discussion on the matter. Read about the evolution of the EU, the role the US has played in the process, and the benefits of an EU-US partnership. If politics and economics are not your thing, you can browse *Europe* magazine and catch up on the latest in social and cultural events.

http://www.eurunion.org/

Dangerous Places

The travel guide with a difference! Fielding's Dangerous Places claims to take you to the areas that you simply would not come back from alive. Each country has a synopsis of why it is so dangerous to visit. The guide is also divided into topics such as forbidden places and criminal places to make it easier for you to see exactly where NOT to go on your next holiday.

http://fieldingtravel.com/df/index.htm

Driving In Europe

If during your holiday break or day trip you wish to hire a car to drive in Europe, then this site is just for you. Here you will be able to familiarise yourself with the wordless road signs you will encounter. As well as explaining signs, this site will also tell you about safe travel in Europe and information on the fines you would receive if you were to break the law.

http://www.travlang.com/signs

E-Bookers

The aim of this site is to be Europe's best travel portal and preferred travel retailer on the web. There's lots here to explore and purchase 24 hours a day, seven days a week, including two million discounted flights to destinations throughout the world on over 75 airlines, world-wide hotel booking, car hire and travel insurance, package holidays, special-interest destinations and lots more.

http://www.ebookers.com/

easyJet

This flight operator has been very successful offering no-frills, good-value flights. If you access its web site, you can find news and information on all its services and you can also buy tickets online.

http://www.easyjet.com

English Tourist Board

The gateway to the Visit Britain site, which covers England, Scotland, Wales and Northern Ireland, this site offers views of England and general travel and tourism information.

http://www.travelengland.org.uk/

European National Railways and Timetables

This server provides information about the European Railways, for railway fans as well as for travellers who wish to explore Europe by train. On this site you'll find links to the web servers of the European national railways, to rail fan pages with lots of information on a national railway, and to online timetables and travel planners.

`http://mercurio.iet.unipi.it/home.html`

European Tourist Information Centre

A comprehensive travel database containing just about everything you will need to know. You will find that in addition to country-specific sections, there are general links to sites providing accommodation, rail, underground, airline, weather, currency, language, electricity, telephone, TV and map information.

`http://www.iol.ie/~discover/europe.htm`

Eurostar

Information, timetables and fares on the Eurostar service.

`http://www.eurostar.com/`

Eurotrip

This comprehensive site contains everything you need to know about backpacking your way around Europe. It has useful links, advice and gives tips on cost-effective travel.

`http://www.eurotrip.com/`

Flyer Information

If you are a frequent flyer, you may be interested in the travel listings, events, features and weather information on this site.

`http://www.flyer.co.uk`

Fodor's Forums

A great resource if you want more than the normal travel-guide tips. Here you can ask all sort of questions of people who have travelled or live in the particular country of interest. Find out the best places to eat, for example, or where you should do your shopping. You can also read people's travel reports or submit your own if you have information that will be of use.

http://www.fodors.com/forums/

Fodor's Travel Online

This incredibly large travel resource from the established guide book company includes comprehensive, customised hotel and restaurant searches, online phrase books, a guide to sports and adventure holidays, as well as region-specific notice boards. However, the highlight of this site is the customised mini-guide facility where you specify your holiday preferences, and it creates an appropriate guide.

http://www.fodors.com/

Foreign Language for Travellers

This very useful site enables you to read and listen to handy phrases in over 70 different languages. It also translates between any two languages and not just English. For convenience, the languages have been alphabetically organised. Simply select the language you speak and then select the language you want to learn.

http://www.travlang.com/languages/

Great Outdoor Recreation Pages

The writers of GORP have used their own experiences to create a web site that 'offers the freshest and most unique travel destinations and inspires viewer participation in everything from an afternoon hike to a week-long biking adventure. GORP visitors recount their own experiences and share information through a sophisticated menu of online forums, contests, discussions and cross-marketing initiatives'. There certainly is a lot of useful information here, although much of it is primarily aimed at US travellers.

http://www.gorp.com/

The Guide
This site is an online guide to a few of the major cities in England and Wales. It is very easy to use and contains good graphics. Most importantly, though, the guide is updated reguarly with the latest information. Currently the cities covered are Bath, Bournemouth, Brighton, Bristol, Cambridge, Canterbury, Cardiff, Carlisle, Chester, Edingbrugh, Harrogate, Kendal, London, Newcastle, Nottingham, Oxford, Plymouth, Stratford, Windsor and York. The guide points out all the places to eat, sleep, shop and visit. Worthwhile if you are planing a holiday or even a day trip to any of these places.

http://www.demon.co.uk/GRA/eat@j/index.html

Holiday Deals
Exactly that! Bargain holidays and cheap flights, especially for last-minute holidays.

http://www.holidaydeal.co.uk

Holiday Rentals
This online brochure is UK-based but has over 1,500 private homes to rent in over 42 countries around the world. You can browse the site by country, for listings with colour photos and prices. There are also special sections for ski chalets and golf properties. You can check availability online, but reservations must currently be made directly with the owners.

http://www.holiday-rentals.co.uk/

Holiday Tales
This travel library collates individual stories of people's trips. If you do not want to rely solely on the guide books and brochures, get a more personal description of a trip here and relive the experiences of others. The trips are organised by continent, then by country.

http://www.travel-library.com/

Hostelling International
With 4,500 hostels in more than 60 countries, Hostelling International helps provide cheap, practical accommodation for budget travellers

around the world. Look up the addresses and telephone numbers of hostels here and find out more by clicking through to their individual web sites.

http://www.iyhf.org

Hotel World

The Hotel World guide contains information on nearly 9,000 hotels in 204 countries, all of which can be booked online. Information in the guide ranges from simple to comprehensive and may include a page listing room facilities and rates and often a brochure with pictures. Hotels in the premier collection include a deluxe brochure and the guide also identifies hotels suitable for conferences. Finally, there are details of some of the hotel groups whose hotels are in the guide.

http://www.hotelworld.com/index.html

Irish Tourist Board

The official web site to tell you everything you need to know about a holiday in Ireland, from views to information on how to get there, hotels and an interactive route finder.

http://www.irlenad.travel.ie/home/

Late Deals

This site is run by Thomson and offers a selection of last-minute holiday destinations.

http://www.latedeals.com

Leisurehunt

Leisurehunt is a worldwide accommodation search that lets you select the type of establishment you require. It includes hostels, campsites and B&Bs as well as hotels, and you can select your preferred price range and facilities. Once you have found a place to stay you can make your reservation online.

http://www.leisurehunt.com/

Leisureplanet

One of the best travel resources on the web, this site contains an incredible amount of holiday information, together with very good pictures and excellent colour maps. You can take a slide tour of any country you want and view the hotels and facilities in most cases. There is also an endless amount of other 'things to see and do' here.

http://www.leisureplanet.com/

London Town

The official web site for London, this offers you maps, lists of events, a directory of places to go, and information on pubs, restaurants and accommodation. Request an Essential London e-mail guide and find out all the latest to maximise your visit.

http://www.londontown.com/

London Tourist Information

A page devoted to finding your way around London and seeing the best of Britain's capital city.

http://www.london-pages.demon.nl/

Lonely Planet

Lonely Planet publishes some of the world's best guide books for independent travellers. Their books are known worldwide for reliable, insightful travel information, maps, photos and background historical and cultural information. On their site they have every continent covered with an ever-increasing list of travel guides, atlases, phrase books and travel literature. Everything that is listed in their guidebooks is here for you to view on the web site. There are even hints and tips from other travellers.

http://www.lonelyplanet.com/

Lonely Planet Health Guide

This site contains important information on 'pills, ills and bellyaches'. It states, 'successful travelling is healthy travelling. All it takes is a bit of planning, eating carefully while you're away, and recognising the early warning signs of possible health-care disasters.' Find out more about what you need to know here. This is a site well worth checking out before you start trekking out!

http://www.lonelyplanet.com/health/health.htm

Maiden Voyages

More than ever, intrepid women travellers are circling the globe and this site has been written by women travellers to give practical advice and stories of interest to fellow women travellers. If you do not want to go it alone and you need a partner to share expenses and help you enjoy the view, you can post your request here too.

http://www.maiden-voyages.com/

Middletons Caravanning and Camping Guide

This claims to be the most comprehensive camping and caravanning site in the UK. It includes a directory of UK caravan sites, caravan, camping and motor homes for sale, caravan repairs, servicing and insurance, plus help and advice for caravan owners.

http://www.pair.com/caravan/

National Caravan Council

The NCC is the representative trade association for the UK caravan and park home industries and this site is essentially a directory. Here you can easily find park-home estates, caravan sites, manufacturers of caravans, caravan dealers, resorts and much more. It is sorted by name or by county and covers the whole of Britain.

http://www.martex.co.uk/ncc/index.htm

Paris

This site is 'a collection of everything regarding the City of Light'. Go on a virtual tour of Paris and see the sights.

http://www.paris.org

Paris Anglophone

Parisians have long endured a reputation for being rude and unwelcoming to English speakers. As a method of rectification, the Paris Anglophone has been set up to enable you to plan all that you need to do before you leave for the city. It is an all-in-English guide that covers everything from what to do on a weekend break to renting an apartment on a short-term lease, to relocation. The site also lists thousands of English-friendly businesses.

http://www.paris-anglo.com

Planet Rider

Having read, rated and reviewed thousands of sites, and keeping only most informative and useful ones to create this unique system, Planet Rider allows you to make your travel decisions quickly and effectively. A lot of countries are covered here, so you are bound to find something to suit you. Go on some of the 10-minute vacations, compact tours of the world's most popular destinations which contain lots of relevant links.

http://www.planetrider.com/

Rail Watch

Rail Watch is a non-profit American organisation which is supported by local officials, victims of railroad accidents, other concerned citizens and shippers from around the country. It is dedicated to educating the public about rail safety issues and to holding the nation's railroads accountable for their actions.

http://www.railwatch.org/home.htm

Scotland

A site dedicated to the interests of those in Scotland and providing news, weather, features and information about Scotland – you can even find your own tartan.

http://www.scotland.com

Scottish Tourist Board

The official site of the Scottish Tourist Board, containing all kinds of information related to holidays in Scotland, from accommodation to travel and details of the regions.

http://www.holiday.scotland.net/

Signpost Premier Hotel Guide

Signpost publish an annual directory of premier hotels in the UK, with full information on location, services and quality levels. This is their online service where you can find out about all the very best hotels in the UK, whether for business or pleasure.

http://www.signpost.co.uk

Small Luxury Hotels of the World

This site is aimed at millionaires who can afford to pay hotel bills that resemble an average monthly mortgage repayment! If you want to see how the other half lives, search through the top-class luxury hotels on offer here, either by exotic location or by holiday theme. For dreamers and lottery winners.

http://www.slh.com/slh/

The Subway Page

At this site you can download maps of the subway systems in use in many major cities in the world. The site also contains links to many subway information sites around the world. A particularly useful part of the site is the city and area transit guides.

http://www.reed.edu/~reyn/transport.html

Theme Parks

These sites have information on theme parks and thrill rides throughout the world.

http://www.thrillride.com

http://www.screamscape.com

This is Britain

This is a mine of information on what is going on, from regional news to international sporting events.

http://www.thisisbritain.co.uk/

This is London

Created by the London *Evening Standard*, this is a great site for keeping up to date on what is happening in Britain's capital city.

http://www.thisislondon.com/

Timeshares – a TUG between the Pros and Cons

Timeshare properties can either be a good investment or a risky one. The Timeshare Users Group (TUG) provides some advice to prospective buyers and current owners. The site rates timeshares, runs a chat room and provides a forum to buy and sell timeshare accommodation.

http://www.tug2.net/

The Trainline

The Trainline web site provides impartial information on train times and tickets on mainland UK routes. It is as accurate and up-to-date as possible, and the site uses current timetable and fares information. Also available is the chance to buy your tickets online with their secure online booking form. Once they are purchased, the tickets will be sent to you free of charge at home or work anywhere in the UK.

http://www.thetrainline.co.uk/trainline.html

Travel

Last-minute and other holiday deals are to be found by accessing the search facilities on this site.

http://www.trrravel.com

Travel Companies and Agents

There are many different travel companies offering a vast array of holidays. Like the companies themselves, the respective web sites seem to offer a huge range of facilities. Some only offer holiday details or information and do not have online booking facilities, while other sites offer a complete service that enables you to spot bargains and snap them up. Here is a list of some of the reputable travel companies that you can find on the net.

Club Med: http://www.clubmed.com/

Flightline: http://www.flightline.co.uk/

Kuoni: http://www.kuoni.co.uk/

Lunn Poly http://www.lunn-poly.com/

Sunsail: http://www.sunsail.com/

Thomas Cook: http://www.thomascook.co.uk/

Thomson Holidays: http://www.thomson-holidays.com/

Trailfinders: http://www.trailfinders.co.uk/

Travel Select

From this site, you can book airline flights, car-hire, Eurostar and hotels with a bonded travel agent. Easy to use.

http://www.travelselect.com

The Trip

This excellent business travel site provides information about flights, hotels and cabs at the click of a button. It is useful for both the small-business owner and the executive of a large corporation. Whether you travel on business on the odd occasion or you are schedule-weary because you travel all too often, you will find this is an effective and convenient tool that makes any travel experience more manageable and enjoyable.

http://www.theTrip.com/

UCL Hospital for Tropical Diseases

For information on the in-patient and out-patient services are offered by the tropical diseases specialists at UCL, look up this site. You will also find that the consultants offer both pre- and post-travel advice.

http://www.uclh.org/medical/tropical/services.htm

US Travel Warnings

Travel warnings are issued when the State Department decides, based on all relevant information, to recommend that Americans avoid travel to a certain country. It is essential that you check out a potential hot-spot before you visit it and this is one of the best places to carry out your research. However, it is still advisable then to seek a second opinion (from the British Foreign Office Travel Advice site, for example, see page 376) before you decide whether or not to go on your travels.

http://travel.state.gov/travel_warnings.html

Virtual Tour of Jerusalem

Tour through the old city of Jerusalem and see the holy sites, visit the gates and take a look at the Chagall windows.

http://www.md.huji.ac.il/vjt/

The Virtual Tourist

This site contains thousands of links grouped together by geography and category and quality rated by tourists. One of the biggest travel-related directories in the web, you find services such as online booking of flights/hotels/cars, currency converters and time zones, driving directions service, dictionaries/languages, weather data and more.

http://www.vtourist.com/

Walt Disney World

For anything to do with Walt Disney World in Florida, visit these sites.

http://www.wdwinfo.com

http://www.wdwinfo.co.uk

Welsh Tourist Board

The official site of the Welsh Tourist Board providing information on Wales with scenic tours and all kinds of holidays and tours.

http://www.tourism.wales.gov.uk

World of Holidays

With its own search facilities, this is a good place to find last-minute and other holiday deals.

http://www.worldof.net/holidays

World Executive Hotel Directory

Aimed at the business traveller, this site provides a guide to luxury hotels around the world together with news of available discounts. In addition, it includes information on tipping and dress codes, as well as invaluable guides to getting from the airport to the centre of town.

http://www.worldexecutive.com/index.html

WEATHER

BBC Weather Service

The BBC web site is huge and contains a lot of information, much more than material just related to their own TV programmes. The weather page includes both a UK and world weather forecast, as well as shipping forcasts and pollen forecasts.

http://www.bbc.co.uk/weather/

Dan's Wild Weather

An interactive site for children, where they can learn all about all kinds of weather conditions. Created in the US, it does have an American bias but is interesting and educational nonetheless.

http://www.whnt19.com/kidwx

Impact Weather Services

A British site which aims to provide local weather forecasts, the twice-daily updates mean that you can rely on the information, although it is presented in a rather basic format.

http://www.impactweather.co.uk

El Niño Theme Page

El Niño means 'the little one' in Spanish and is a disruption of the ocean-atmosphere system in the tropical Pacific. It affects the weather all around the world, causing a marked increase in rainfall in the US and devastating bush fires in Australia. For an in-depth understanding of this phenomenon, look up this site.

http://www.pmel.noaa.gov/toga-tao/el-nino/

The Met Office

This site predictably covers every aspect of meteorolgy for those looking for information and forecasts.

http://www.meto.govt.uk

World Climate

This site has been designed for anyone interested in the general historical weather patterns around the world. You will find a range of climate data in an easy-to-use form, with links to other similar sites. The site does not contain weather forecasts or reports. The data is also not suitable for professional or research use.

http://www.worldclimate.com

World Meteorological Organisation

This is the official site of the WMO, the United Nation's specialist agency on weather, water, climate and atmosphere. The site includes everything from weather prediction to air pollution research, climate change activities, ozone layer depletion studies and tropical storm forecasting. The site also catalogues all WMO publications and has links to other UN organisations.

http://www.wmo.ch

Yahooligans Weather

A great site for school projects or for anyone who wants to understand weather conditions but can't get to grips with the meterologists' jargon. Here it is all explained simply and clearly.

http://www.yahooligans.com

WINE

See also Beer, Drink

Australian Wines of Distinction

This site is an excellent resource of information to do with the major wine producers of Australia. The makers listed here are Penfolds, Lindemans, Winns, Seppelt, Seaview, Devil's Lair, and Coldstream Hills. All the wines produced by these makers are listed with good descriptions of the wines and the estates.

http://www.australianwines.co.uk/

Berry Bros. and Rudd

Berry Bros. & Rudd offer exceptional wines, hand picked to reflect both the quality and individuality of regions such as Bordeaux, Burgundy and Champagne, as well as North America, Argentina, Australia, New Zealand, and others. You can order from their selection of fine wines over the internet at the BBR Internet Wine Shop, bringing 300 years of personal service, expertise and an unbeatable range of wines online.

http://www.bbr.co.uk/

German Wine Page

Full of information and opinions on German wine, this site offers help in making selections and buying German wine, including information about vintages and producers, as well as lots lots more. It also contains good links to other German pages, some wine-related and some in English.

http://www.winepage.de/

The Wine Anorak

Jamie Goode, also known as the Wine Anorak, has assembled a selection of features, links and reviews here. Jamie also talks about his own travels to various wine-growing regions and you can see his personal notes on the wines he has recently tasted.

http://www.wineanorak.com

Wine Lovers' Page

This site has everything from basic guides on getting started, to organising your cellar with a sophisticated selection of wines. You will find articles on books about wine, discussions on wine, food and wine, wine on the internet, wine pronunciation, wine and its vintage and, of course, on the enjoyment of wine itself. There is also a huge wine grape glossary to help you find the wine that is to your taste. This site is useful for both the amateur and the connoisseur alike.

http://www.wine-lovers-page.com

Wine Pages

The Wine Pages is one of the world's most popular online wine resources. An independent site, it is updated daily with features, tasting notes and wine news. The site is run by wine tutor Tom Cannavan, who has compiled a handy and instructional wine drinker's guide. He even offers an online course in wine, as well as well-written notes on popular wine regions.

http://www.wine-pages.com/

Wine Place

This site provides a good introduction to the world of wines for the beginner. It has well-written, easy-to-swallow guides to the tasting, storing and drinking of all types of wine. There are also handy hints on the correct pronunciation of wines, how to hold a wine party, as well as lots of other regular features and links to more sites.

http://www.wineplace.nu/

Wine Spectator

This claims to be 'the most comprehensive wine web site in the world' and it certainly packs in the facts about its subject. You will find daily wine news, weekly features, a vast searchable database of wines, tips on choosing the right wine for the right meal, an archive of articles from past issues of the magazine as well as information on wineries and wine auctions. Make sure you know what you are looking for when you visit this huge site, although it is fairly easy to navigate, despite its size.

http://www.winespectator.com/

The World Wine Web

This site is a great resource of wine information for everybody interested in wines around the world. It uses three themes: World, Wine and Web. The main feature of the World theme is the world wine encyclopedia, where you will find information on wine-producing countries, wine-growing regions and wine producers of the world. The Wine section allows them to share their wine recommendations selected from a list of recently tasted wines. To learn more about wine, you should also visit the wine taster's tools and the wine knowledge sections. The Web section links you to other excellent wine sites, to some web sites dedicated to fine cuisine, and to other wine lovers. The site is available in either English or French.

http://www.winevin.com/default.htm

WEDDINGS

Confetti.co.uk

This internet service has been designed to make your wedding experience enjoyable and stress free by giving you all the information and advice you want, when you want it. It aims to meet the needs of everyone involved in the wedding and not just the bride and groom.

http://www.confetti.co.uk/

Web Wedding

If you want ideas for your wedding, this is the place to come and browse. It has an impressive database of over 10,000 wedding suppliers – for everything from the dress to the honeymoon – with some special offers and competitions as well. There are also links to online wedding stores.

http://www.webwedding.co.uk

Wedding Bells

This is the web site of the American magazine with the same name. It is published twice a year, with many of the articles being free for you to browse on the web site. Here you can find out information for the best man, parents of the bride and groom, guidance on stag and hen parties and lots more. Also available are lots of different speeches and information about the wedding ceremony.

http://www.weddingbells.com

Weddings and Brides

Weddings and Brides UK have pulled together all essential wedding information and put it into one place. You will even find out what the potential pitfalls are at this site. For example, is your wedding car reliable and is there a back-up available if your car breaks down? It also has details of products and services for weddings and honeymoons. This site is a must for anyone planning a wedding.

http://www.weddings-and-brides.co.uk/

Wedding Channel

Weddings are often one of the most stressful, complex and expensive endeavours people undertake. Wedding Channel is aimed at helping both men and women through process of planning a wedding and starting a new home. This is a comprehensive and useful wedding-related site.

http://www.weddingchannel.com/

Wedding Guide UK

This site offers information and advice to anyone planning a wedding. It has a comprehensive product and service section, giving details of hen and stag activities, marquee hire and wedding insurance – right through to where you can buy all your bridal wear.

http://www.weddingguide.co.uk/

WOMEN'S INTERESTS

See also Business, Children, Employment, Parenting

Advancing Women

More of a 'webazine' for women filled with articles on the workplace, international women, personal finances and current affairs.

http://www.advancingwomen.com/

Centre for Reproductive Law and Policy

The CRLP is a 'non-profit legal and policy advocacy organisation dedicated to promoting women's reproductive rights'. The site, a review of these rights for women all around the world, is presented as a series of to-the-point statistics. It provides a valuable information resource on the status of women across the globe.

http://www.crlp.org

Every Woman

There are a number of sections in this site, including health, cooking, gardening, travel, finance and law, all designed to cater for the interests of women in the UK.

http://www.everywoman.co.uk

The Feminist Majority

This massive resource is not militant. It avoids stridency and instead provides daily news, articles on women in sports and in the arts, information on breast cancer and violence against women. It contains links to a variety of feminist journals and an online feminist store.

Included is information on a number of ongoing campaigns to end injustice to women around the world.

`http://www.feminist.org/`

Handbag

This site is trying to offer the most useful place on the internet for British women. Handbag includes expert features, advice, questions and answers, combined with a multitude of online services edited and customised for women in the UK, as well as free web access, e-mail, news, information, interactivity and online shopping. Handbag has its own editors and a range of expert writers covering topics from arts and education to relationships and travel. Visitors can have their questions answered and take part in online discussions.

`http://www.handbag.com/`

National Federation of Women's Institutes

The Women's Institute (WI), reaching further into urban areas from its traditional rural roots, claims to be an organisation that is changing. Educational and physical-activity courses are now offered, and the WI campaigns on a number of national and international issues. However, you will still find plenty of references to home economics and crafts!

`http://www.nfwi.org.uk/`

New Woman

This fun-filled and informative magazine site for women is one of the best on the web. There are fashion pages that tell you about the latest bargains and give lots of practical tips, and pages on all aspects of beauty care, including a virtual beautician who can help you improve on the looks nature gave you!

`http://www.newwomanonline.co.uk/`

Women Networking

This site is from a professional internet company and it is a great resource for the everyday busy working women. Here they try to help women sort out all the useless sites and replace them with sites that they need. The site is dedicated to helping busy working women get ahead and through the day in a practical way. Includes money and job advice, menus and shopping.

http://www.women-networking.com/

Women's Wire

Whatever you want to do, you can probably do it here. Whether it is checking on your stocks and shares, decorating your home, looking for a job or starting a business, this American-based site can provide light-hearted articles and quizzes to help you. There are also resident experts ready and waiting to consult you about any aspect of your life.

http://www.womenswire.com/

Index

Note: Web site addresses in this index are given without the http://www. prefix. A few addresses have different prefixes – these are shown in full in the index and filed under the first letter after http:// so, for example, http://barnesandnoble.com is filed under 'b'.

08004homes.com 318
2busystitching.com/ 276
4thenet.co.uk 279
24hourmuseum.org.uk 298
101cd.com 304
1001-villa-holidaylets.com/ 374
AA (Automobile Association) 290
a2bairports.com/ 375
a2btravel.com 374
a-uk.co.uk/ 301
abacuses 322
abebooks.com/ 157
about.com 343
about.com/travel 374
aboutdesign.co.uk 140
abtanet.com/ 376
Academy Awards 218
ACAS 283
acas.org.uk 283
accessgenealogy.com/ 249
accessibility options 73
accessnewage.com 308
accountants 220
ace.org.uk/ 312
achievement.org/galleryachieve.html 271
achievers 271, 330
    women 270
achuka.co.uk/ 157
acmenet.net/~dna 298, 342
acmepet.petsmart.com 133
activemind.com/ 322
activemostwanted.com 283
actwin.com/fish/index.cgi 135
addict.com 300
addictive behaviours 262
address toolbar 65
adobe.com 176
adoption.com 313
adultcheck.com/ 281
adultpass.com/ 281
advancingwomen.com/ 396
adventure sports 360
adventuresurf.com/ 371
advertising
    junk email (spam) 123, 177
    law 284
advertisinglaw.com/home.html 284
Aesop's Fables 157
afl.com.au 361
Age Concern 312
AIDS patchwork quilt 140
aifs.org/ 198
aim-irl.com/greenguide/ 211
aint-it-cool-news.com/ 215
air tickets 375, 378
air travel 374, 375, 378, 379, 381, 388, 389
    safety 376
airports 375
airtickets.co.uk 375
ajb.dni.us 206
Alcott, Louisa M. 162
alcottweb.com 162
Alexander technique 307
Alice in Wonderland 162

all-hotels.com/ 375
allexperts.com/default.asp 176
allgame.com/ 241
allmovie.com 216
allmusic.com 300
allpets.com 134
alltheweb.com 343
aloud.com 207
alphabetstreet.com 164
altavista.com/ 343
alternative therapies 262, 268
alternatives.com/crime/ 286
altmed.net/ 264
http://alt.venus.co.uk/vpub/welcome.htm 155
ama-assn.org/special/migraine/ 263
amazon.com/ 157
amazon.co.uk/ 157
American football 360
American Institute for Foreign Study 197–198
americanmall.co.uk/ 212
Amnesty International 254
amnesty.org 254
anagramgenius.com/ 233
anagrams 233
anatomy 265, 339, 340
anbg.gov.au 305
ancestors.co.uk 249
angels 335
angling 361
animals 133–138, 306
animation 80, 234, 260
annefrank.nl/ 269
annoyances.org/ 188
anti-virus software 13–16
antiques 139, 142, 196
anxiety disorders 260–261, 262, 268
http://anywho/aboutus.html 345
AOL (America on Line) 45, 46
apple.com/quicktime/ 176
aprilia.com/ 286
aquatic animals 134–135, 137
Arab world 376
arabia.bigfoot.com 177
arab.net 376
architecture 142
argos.co.uk 349
arsenal.co.uk 363
art 140–142, 177, 376
    by teenagers 172
art-connection.com 140
archive.com/ 140
artguide.org 141
artlex.com/ 141
artsusa.org/clearinghouse/ 141
artswire.org/Artswire/www/dance/dance.html 192
asap.unimelb.edu.au/hstm/hstm_bio.htm 342
Asia, and business 165, 168
asiannet.com/ 165
askjeeves.com/ 343
assertahome.com 319
Association of British Travel Agents (ABTA) 376
astrology 142–143
astrologycom.com/ 143
astronet.com/ 143

1000 Really useful web sites

astronomy 144–147, 174
astrostar.com 233
astro.wisc.edu/~dolan/constellations/ 144
astr.ua.edu/4000ws/4000WS.html 338
athletics 361
atlases 252
atmpage.com 342
atpour.com/frameset.asp 371
auctions 148–149, 278, 319, 349
audi.com 291
audioreview.com 300
audiostreet.co.uk 300
Austen, Jane 162
Australian Botanical Gardens 305
Australian Rules football 361
australianwines.co.uk/ 392
authors 158, 159, 162–163
autism 261
autism.org 261
autobytel.com/ 291
autosport.com 367
autotrader.co.uk 291
aviation safety 376
avon.com 349
axl.com 241

B&Q 194
http://babelfish.altavista.digital.com 322
babies 313–314, 317–318
    see also children; parenting; pregnancy
Baby Bio 244–245
baby names 313
babynames.com/ 313
babyonline.com/ 317
babyworld.co.uk/ 314
back buttons
    Internet Explorer 65
    Netscape Navigator 86–87
ballet 190–191
ballet.co.uk 191
ballroom dancing 191
bank holidays 332
banking 150–151
    see also finance
barbecuen.com/ 189
barbecues 188–189
barclaycard.co.uk 150
Barclays Bank 150
barclays.com 150
http://barnsandnoble.com 158
bartleby.com/qq/ 323
baseball 362
basketball 362
bbc.co.uk 216
bbc.co.uk/education/schools 198
bbc.co.uk/news 308
bbc.co.uk/weather/ 390
http://bbc.co.uk/webguide 177
bbr.co.uk/ 392
beakman.com 176
beauty 151–154, 215, 397
http://beautylink.com/ 152
beautysoul.com/ 152
beautytech.com/nailtech/ 154
because-we-can.com/ebayla/index.htm 148
bed and breakfast 382
    see also holidays; hotels; travel
beer 154–156
beerinfo.com 154
beerstalker.co.uk/ 155
bennetts.co.uk 292
Berry Bros & Rudd 392
bet.co.uk 240
bgs.org.uk/ 261, 347
bham.wednet.edu/explore.htm 271
bhglive.com/homeimp/ 195

Bible 334
    see also religion
http://bible.gospelcom.net 334
biblemagazine.com/ 334
bibliofind, com 158
bibliomania.com/ 159
bibliomania.com//Reference/PhraseAndFable/index.html 323
bigbluedog.com 202
bigfoot.com/ 177
bigfoot.de/ 177
bigrom.co.uk 177
bigsave.com 350
bigyellow.com/ 165
bikenet.com/ 286
biofeedback 267
biographies 269–270, 271, 323, 341, 342
biography.com/ 270
biology 265, 338, 339–340
biorhythms 261
bio.uk.co 245
bird boxes 134
birds 137
birminghamzoo.com/ao/ 134
bizproweb.com/index.html 166
bizproweb.com/pages/features/home_office.html 167
blackstar.co.uk/ 216
blind sports 365
blocking software 17–18, 81–84
    see also children, site access; internet protection
bloomberg.co.uk 220
bluemountain.com/ 169
bluesqu.com 239
blvd.org/ 376
bmf.co.uk/ 287
bmw.com 292
bnm.com 375
boarding schools 199
boardingschools@hobsons.com 199
Bond, James 217
bonus.com 171
bookpages.com 164
books 156–165
    children 156–157, 159, 160–161, 162–164, 171
    out-of-print 157, 158
bookshop.co.uk 164
booksunlimited.co.uk 159
boots.co.uk 350
borders.com 160
boxing 362
boxing.com 362
Bradford Robotic Telescope Observatory 144
brainstorm.co.uk/utils/std-codes.html 330
breadrecipe.com/ 227
breakupgirl.com/ 171
breworld.com/ 155
bristolstreet.co.uk/ 350
Britain 387
British Geriatrics Society 261, 347
British Humanist Association 334–335
British Motorcyclists' Federation 287
British Telecom 348
britishliterature.com/ 160
britishmagazines.co.uk 160
britishmuseum.co.uk 298
broadcast.com 321
broadcast./ 207
broadcasting 320–322
brochurebank.com/ 377
Brontë family 160
browsers 54–58, 176, 178, 183–184
browserwatch.com 178
browsing 96–103
http://bt.com 348
buddhanet.net/ 335
Buddhism 335, 337
bullnet.co.uk/auctions/ 148

bus timetables 374
business 165–169, 177, 252, 376
    companies 220–221
butlers 203
butlersguild.com/ 203
buy-to-let.com 319
buy.co.uk 348
buyinguide.com/ 178

cabaret 373
calculator.com 323
calculators 323
camcentral.com/ 253
Camelot Project 160
camping 382, 384
capital-gardens.co.uk 245
caravans 296–297, 382, 384
cardcentral.net/ 170
cards 169–170
    animated 170, 171
care2.com/ 170
careers 171, 199, 202–206, 263
    see also employment
careersolutions.co.uk/ 202
carehomes.co.uk/index.htm 261
carltonplc.co.uk 220
carnoisseur.com 292
carphonewarehouse.com 350
Car.Quote.co.uk 355
Carroll, Lewis 162
cars 290–297
    buying 291, 292, 295, 350
    classic 293–294
    hiring 374, 375, 389
carsdiy.co.uk/ 293
carsource.co.uk 292
http://cartalk.cars.com/ 292
casino-network.com 239
casinococo.com 239
casinos 239, 240
caso.com/ 199
cassandraeason.co.uk 307
castles/fortifications 274
castletown.com/brendan.htm 270
http://catalog.com/vivian 327
http://catalog.savvy.com 351
Catholicism 335, 336
http://catless.ncl.ac.uk/vmg/ 138
cats 135, 136
cddirect.co.uk 351
cdnow.com 301
CDs 160, 300, 303, 304, 351, 354
    buying guide 301
    see also music
ceco.co.uk/ 261
cellsalive.com 338
cemeteries
    pets 138
    Tomb Town 219
    war graves 270
    see also death
Center for Mars Exploration 144
centraal.com 346
Central Intelligence Agency (CIA) 255, 298, 342
cfkc.demon.co.uk 135
changeslives.com/ 152
channels button 66, 68
charcolonline.co.uk 220
charities 135, 312
chat rooms 9, 17
checkaprice.com 351
chelseaclocks.co.uk 139
chem4kids.com/ 338
chemicalelements.com 341
chemistry 338, 341
chess 277

chevrolet.com 293
chicagohs.org/fire/ 271
chickclick.com/ 171
chicojr.chico.k12.ca.us/staff/gray/animals.html 134
childbirth 314, 317–318
childcare-info.co.uk/ 314
childnet-int.org/ 314
children 170–176, 231
    astronomy 174
    books 156–157, 159, 160–161, 162–164, 171
    charities 312, 314
    and chemistry 338
    childcare 314
    with disabilities 193
    and divorce 332
    educational toys 352
    entertainment 315
    events for 207
    exploitation 316
    and films 207, 218
    and global issues 172
    health 315, 316
    and law 285
    missing 316
    music 172, 174, 175
    myths 207
    and parenting 313–317
    science 174, 176
    search engine for 175
    site access 11, 16–18, 81–84, 281–283
    stories by 172, 173, 174
    United Nations site 259
    and weather 390, 392
    see also teenagers; young people
childrensbookshop.com 161
chinalanguage.com/CCDICT/index.html 250
chinalanguage.com/cgi-bin/name.pl 250
chocolate 227, 231, 253
Church of England 335
cinema 207, 215–219
cinema see films
cis.ohio-state.edu/hypertext/faq/usenet/travel/air/hand-
    book/top.html 375
cities 381, 383, 384–385, 387, 389
city2000.com/entertainer/directory/index.html 155
cizone.com/ 179
clarity.net/~adam/buying-bike.html 290
classic-car-directory.com/ 293
classical.net/ 301
classiccarsworld.co.uk/ 293
classicmotor.co.uk/ 294
classics 158–159
classicscience.co.uk/ 338
clearspring.co.uk/ 227
clicked.com/babytime/ 314
climate
    change 211
    world 391
clinique.com 152
clipart.com 260
clipartconnection.com 260
clocks 139
clothes 352, 353
    see also fashion
clubmed.com/ 388
clubs.psu.edu/aegsa/rome/romec.html 273
http://cmex-www.arc.nasa.gov/ 144
cmhc.com/ 267
cnbc.com 221
CNN 254, 309, 311, 377
cnn.com/ 309
http://cnn.com/ALLPOLITCS/ 254
http://cnnfn.com/ 222
cnnsi.com/ 311
http://coa.acnatsci.org/conchnet 339
cocktails 196–197

http://cocktails.miningco.com/ 196
cofe.anglican.org/ 335
coin-universe.com/index.html/ 277
coins 276–277
colleges 198, 201
colour options 72
comedy 234, 237, 277
comet.co.uk 351
comics-page.com 277
Commonwealth 255
Commonwealth War Graves Commission 270
companiesonline.com 166
companysleuth.com/ 221
compaq.com 179
composer options 94–95
CompuServe 44
computer viruses 11, 12–16
computercpa.com/ 220
computers 19–21, 176–188
    after-sales service 21
    help 176, 178–179, 181, 182, 184, 186
    manufacturers 179
    modems 23, 25–38, 49–53
    personnel recruitment 205
    protocols 48
    software 176, 178, 179, 180–187
    supplies 176–177
    technology 184–185, 186
concert tickets 208, 355, 357
conchology 339
condom.com 351
confectionary 231, 253
confetti.co.uk/ 394
connectingstudents.com 198
connectingstudents.com/lessonplans/potter/index.htm 161
connection icon 88
connection options 76–78
consciousnet.com 307
conspiracy theories 255
conspire.com/ 255
constellations 144
consumer law 284
http://consumer.findlaw.com/congen/index.html 284
Consumers' Association 312
contacts-direct.co.uk 352
Content Advisor 81–84
cooking 188–190, 196
    see also food; recipes
coolbase.com/peepingtom/ 236
cosmetic surgery 153
cosmeticconnection.com 153
cosmetics 151–153, 212, 349–350
cosmetics.com/ 151
cosmomag.com/ 212
Cosmopolitan 212
counselling 333
countrywalks.org.uk/ 277
cowboy.net/native/ 273
crayon.net/ 309
CreditCard.Quote.co.uk 355
cricket 362–363
cricketline.com 363
cricket.org/ 362
crimescene.com/ 241
crlp.org 396
crotchet.co.uk/ 301
cruise industry 203
cruiseservices.co.uk/content.html 203
crystalinks.com 307
culinary.com/index.shtml 189
Culpeper 262
culpeper.co.uk 262
Cult Information Centre 335
cultural exchange programmes 197–198
cultural heritage 271
cultural information 252

currency converters 389
currents.net/resources/dict/dictionary.html 186
cusd.claremont.edu/~tkroll/EastEur/index.html 323
http://customnews.cnn.com/cnews/pna_auth.welcome 309
CVs 202, 204
cvsearch.net/ 202
cwgc.org 270
cyberantiquemall.com/ 139
cybercafés 344
cybercaptive.com 344
cyberdiet.com/ 262
cybereditions.com/aldaily/ 158
cyberpatrol.com/ 281
cyberpsych/main.html 262
cyberteens.com/ctmain.html 172
cycling 363

dailywav.com 302
dalton.org/ms/alice/ 162
daltons.co.uk 352
dance 142, 190–192
dancescape.com/ 191
danceservice.co.uk/ 191
datalake.com/datalake/homepage.htm 198
davecentral.com 179
dbm.com/jobguide/ 205
dcs.hull.ac.uk/public/genealogy/ 329
http://dww.deafworldweb.org/asl/ 329
death
    famous people 324
    natural 267
    see also cemeteries
dejanews.com 180, 344
deliveries 192
dell.com 179
demon.co.uk/GRA/eat@j/index.html 381
Department of Trade and Industry 324
depression 262
deserts 339
desertusa.com/life.html 339
design 140
Design Council 141
design-council.org.uk/ 141
designer clothes 213–215
designeroutlet.com/ 213
designersdirect.com 213
dhl.com 192
Dial-up Networking software 48–53
dialling codes
    international 326
    UK 330
diamondcutters.com/ 277
diamonds 277
dictionaries 324, 327, 328, 330, 332
    of art 141, 142
    foreign languages 326
    medical 266
    see also encyclopedias
dictionary.com 324
dictionary.com/others/ 326
digital-women.com/ 166
digitalcentury.com/encyclo/update/comp_hd.html 178
dine-online.co.uk/welcome.html 228
directories 345–346
disability 193–194, 365
disabilitynet.co.uk/ 193
discussion groups 180
Disney World 172, 389
disney.com 172
disney.co.uk 233
distinguishedwomen.com 270
divorce 332
divorcecentral.com 332
DIY 194–196
diy.com 194
diyfixit.co.uk 194

do it yourself 194–196
do-it-yourself.com 195
dogs 136
doityourself.com/ 194
dorcino.com/dorcino2/ 239
dotmusic.com/ 302
http://dowjones.com 221
download.com 180
http://dpsinfo.com/ 324
draconian.com 233
dragons 233
dream interpretation 234
dreamemporium.com/ 234
dreamlife.com 317
drink 196–197, 253
    beer 154–156
    wine 229, 230, 392–394
drinks-direct.co.uk 253
driving
    in Europe 378
    see also motoring
drudgereport.com 309
drugs, recreational 265
dti.gov.uk 324
ducati.com/ 287
dudley-gateway.co.uk/cz/czindex.htm 332
dumblaws.com/ 284
http://dustygroove.com 302
DVDs 216, 300, 354

e-commend.co.uk 195
e-commerce 166–167, 168, 220
e-garden.co.uk 245
e-mail 9, 42, 104
    filtering 108–112
    junk 123, 177
    Netscape Messenger 112–116
    Outlook Express 104–112
    receiving 121–122
    sending 117–120
    working offline 105
e-mum/com/ 202
e-postcards 142
eaglestardirect.co.uk 221
earlylearningcentre.co.uk 352
earth 306
earthquakes 306
Easter Eggs 180
easyjet.com 378
easynews.com 279
easyshop.co.uk 352
http://eawc.evansville.edu/ 271
ebay.co.uk 148
eb.com 325
ebid.co.uk/ 149
ebookers.com/ 378
http://ecommerce.about.com/ 167
edcampbell.com 308
edirectory.com 346
edit menu 62
education 171–176, 197–201
    see also children
edunet.com/ 198
eeggs.com/ 180
ee.ryerson.ca/~elf/abacus 322
efn.org/~djz/birth/birthindex.html 318
egg.com 222
egreetings.com 170
Egyptology 272, 274
eia.brad.ac.uk/btl/ 144
ekran.no/html/revenge/ 233
El Niño 391
electrical goods 352
Elle 213
elle.com 213
elore.com/elore.htm 271

emailtax.co.uk/ 221
embassysnooker.com/ 370
empireonline.co.uk 217
employment 198, 202–206
    assessment tests 205
    in computer industry 205
    and disability 193
    graduates 204, 206
    overseas 197, 204
    see also careers
http://encyclopedia.com/ 324
encyclopedias 324–325,
    of computer technology 183, 185, 186
    gardening 246
    of home improvement 195
    see also dictionaries
English Tourist Board 378
enn.com/ 209
entertainment 186, 207–208
    broadcasting 320–322
    concert tickets 208, 355, 357
    dance 190–192
    films 207, 215–219
    music 157, 186, 191, 300–305
    television 177, 216
    theatre 142, 207, 373–374
ent.iastate.edu/Misc/InsectsAsFood.html 236
http://envirolink.org 210
environment 209–212
    climate 211, 391
    rain forests 306
epic.org/reports/surfer-beware.html 283
erols.com/amato1/AC/ 184
http://erowid.org/Physcoactives/Physcoactives.shtml 265
http://eserver.org/gender/ 248
eskimo.com/~tiktok/index.html 165
espionage see spies/spying
essay-writing 325
http://etext.virginia.edu/railton/ 163
eto.org.uk/ 256
eu.levi.com/index.html 214
eurekalert.org 339
Euro 255–256
http://europa.eu.int/euro/html/entry.html 256
europages.com/home-en.htmlges 167
europarl.eu.int 256
Europe 256, 377, 378, 379
    driving in 378
    security 258
European companies 167
European Parliament 256
europeantour.com 367
http://europe.cnn.com/TRAVEL/ 377
eurostar.com/ 379
eurotrip.com/ 379
eurunion.org/ 377
events, entertainment 207, 208, 376
eventselector.co.uk 207
eventsworldwide.com/I-codes.htm 326
everton.com/ 249
everywoman.co.uk 396
ex.ac.uk/bugclub/ 171
exams 200
    revision courses 201
exchange programmes 197–198
exchangeandmart.co.uk 353
excite.com 344
exhibitions 357, 376
explore.com 360
explorers 271
extraterrestrial intelligence 147
http://eyewitness.dk.com/ 325

faa.gov/asafety.htm 376
facade.com/attraction/biorhythm/ 261
family trees 249–250

http://familyinternet.about.com/ 282
fantasyanime.com 234
fantasystockmarket.com/ 222
faqs.org/ 181
fashion 212–215, 350, 358, 397
fashion.net 213
fatface.co.uk 353
fathers 313, 316
    see also parenting
fathers.com/ 316
favorites 63, 66, 68
FBI 256, 283
fco.gov.uk 377
fedex.com 192
fedworld.gov 256
feelit.se/siteo 274
fellowshipofisis.com 308
feminism 396–397
    see also women
feminist.org/ 397
fengshuisociety.org.uk/ 307
ferry timetables 374
fi.edu/biosci/heart.html 340
http://fieldingtravel.com/df/index.htm 378
file menu 62
File Transfer Protocol (FTP) 56
films 142, 207, 215–219
filmsite.org/ 217
filtering software 17–18, 81–84
finance 177, 220–226
    calculators 323
    see also banking; insurance
Financial Times 223
find.co.uk 223
findlaw.com 285
first-e.com 150
firstview.com/ 213
fish 134–135, 137
fitness 261, 263, 267
flags 250
flatoday.com/space/ 359
flightline.co.uk/ 388
flowers 226–227
flowersdirectuk.co.uk/ 226
flyer.co.uk 379
flying 376, 378, 379
fodors.com/ 380
fodors.com/forums/ 380
foe.co.uk 210
foia.fbi.gov 256
folk dance 191
food 227–232, 253
    hampers 228, 232, 253, 350
    see also cooking; recipes
food postcards 229
http://food.epicurious.com/ 228
foodlines.com/ 228
foodwine.com/ 229
fool.com 223
football365.co.uk/ 363
football 363–364
    American 360
    Australian Rules 361
football.nationwide.co.uk 363
footballnews.co.uk 364
for-him.com/THEPATH/howlove.htm 265
ford.com 294
Foreign Office Travel Advice 376–377
forteantimes.com 234
forward buttons
    Internet Explorer 65
    Netscape Navigator 87
fourmilab.ch/earthview/vplanet.html 145
fractals 172
fragrancenet.com 353

Frank, Anne 269
fray.com/ 141
fr.bigfoot.com 177
freebase.com/ 302
Freedom of Information Act 257
freegames2000.com/ 241
freeserve.net 181
freeshop.com 353
http://freeweb.pdq.net/headstrong/ 174
freewebspace.net/ 181
frenchhampers.com/ 228
Friends of the Earth 210
fruit 229
fsz.bme.hu/opera/main.html 304
ft.com 223
ftech.co.uk/~webfeet/ 191
FTP transfer 56
FTSE International 223
ftse.com/ 223
full screen button 67
fun 233–238
funny.co.uk/ 234
funschool.com 172
http://futfan.com 161
futuregamer.com/ 241
fylde.demon.co.uk/welcome.htm 272

Gallup Organisation 257
gallup.com 257
gambling 239–240
    National Lottery 237
game-online.com/ 242
gamefaqa.com/ 242
games 172, 238, 239–240, 241–244, 300, 354
    buying 165, 303, 351
games-net.co.uk 242
gamesdomain.co.uk/ 242
gamespot.com/ 243
gamsdirect.co.uk 242
gardenguides.com/ 245
gardening 244–247, 305
    wildlife gardens 212
gardening-uk.com 246
gardening.com 246
gardenweb.com 245–246
gay and lesbian sites 248–249
geishalounge.com 239
genealogy 249–250, 329
genealogy.com 249
genetic modification 210
    see also organic foods
geocities.com/FashionAvenue/1495/ 214
geocities.com/Hollywood/5727/mi6_headquarters.html 217
geocities.com/RainForest/4645/index.html 212
geocities.com/RainForest/Vines/1009/ 306
geocities.com/RainForest/Vines/4030/ 211
geocities.com/RodeoDrive/1415/indexd.html 336
geography 250–253
gerbils 133
gerbils.org.uk/index.html 133
ghost.ltd.uk 214
http://gifs.net/files/ 260
gifts 229, 232, 253–254, 354
giftstore.co.uk 253
gingerbread.org.uk/ 315
girls, and technology 171
girltech.com 171
global warming 211
globalgang.org.uk 172
globalink.com 322
globes 251
go menu 62
goan.com/surflink.html 371
goddesses 308
godiva.com 227
golf 365–367

golfagent.com 365
golfeurope.com/ 366
golftoday.co.uk 366
golfweb.com/ 366
goodasnew.com 295
goodguides.co.uk 155
goodhealthdirectory.com 262
goodvibes.com/ 332–333
gorp.com/ 380
gorp.com/gorp/activity/skiing.htm 369
goto.com 344
government 254, 255–260
    see also USA government
graduates, employment 204, 206
grammar 329
graphics 260
    plug-ins 80
Great Chicago Fire 271
greatestplaces.org 173
greengrocer.com.au 229
Greenpeace International 211
greenpeace.org 211
groveart.com 142
grum.clara.net 156
gsrg.nmh.ac.uk// 306
guardian.co.uk 309
http://guardians.net/egypt/ 272
gw2k.com 179
gwu.edu/~nsarchive/nsa/foia_how_use.html 257

hair 151, 154
hamleys.com 353
Hammicks 159
hampers 228, 232, 253, 350
hamsterdance.com 235
hamsters.co.uk 135
handbag.com/ 397
http://happypuppy.com/ 243
Harley Davidson 287
harmony-central.com 302
harrods.co.uk 354
Harry Potter 161
http://harrypotter.okukbooks.com 161
hawastsoc.org/solar/homepage.htm 147
hd-stamford.com/ 287
headaches 263
health 260–269
    alternative therapies 262, 268
    children 315, 316
    diet 190, 228, 269
    natural products 268–269
    and travel 383–384
health-library.com/ 266
healthfitnessnetwork.com 263
healthgate.com 263
healthlinksusa.com/ 264
healthnbeauty.com/looks.htm 153
heart 339
help menu 63
http://help-site.com/ 181
herbs 262
herbs and spices 190, 230–231, 246
Hergé 162
http://hermes.astro.washington.edu/scied/physics/physbio.ht
    ml 341
hi-techsports.com/ 354
hieroglyphics 276
highland-dress.co.uk 356
Hinduism 336
hinduismtoday.kauai.hi.us/ashram/ 336
history 173, 269–276, 376
history button 66
History Channel 272
history options
    Internet Explorer 72
    Netscape Navigator 92

History Today 272
historychannel.com 272
historytoday.com 272
hmv.co.uk 303
hobbies 276–279
hobsons.co.uk/ 199
holiday rentals 374, 381
holiday-rentals.co.uk/ 381
holidaydeal.co.uk 381
holidays 347, 355, 374–390
    see also travel
holiday.scotland.net/ 386
hollywoodreporter.com 217
home button
    Internet Explorer 66
    Netscape Navigator 87
home improvements 194–196
home pages
    Internet Explorer 69
    Netscape Navigator 92
home workers 166, 167, 315
http://homearts.com/helpers/homecare/00homcc1.htm 195
homeopath.co.uk 264
homeopathy 264
homeopathyhome.com/ 264
homepageeircom.net/~alexandertechnique 307
Home.Quote.co.uk 355
homework 199
homeworkelephant.free-online.co.uk/ 199
Honda 287, 294
honda.com 294
hondamotorcycle.com/index.html 287
horoscopes 142–143
horses 136
hostels 381–382
hotbot.com 344
hotbox.co.uk 253
hotels 374, 375, 382, 386, 390
hotelworld.com/index.html 382
hotgames.com/ 243
hotjobs.com/ 202
Hotmail support 105
house-buying 318–319
houseweb.co.uk 319
how2hq.com 326
howstuffworks.com 340
http://hp.com 179
Hubble Space Telescope 145
humanism.org.uk/ 335
humordatabase.com/ 235
humorscope.com/ 235
humour 235, 236, 238
humournet.com/ 235
hyperlinks 98–99
hypernix.com 181
hyperreal.org/drugs/ 265

iaaf.org/ 361
ibguide.com/ibg.htm 167
ibsa.es 365
ice hockey 367
Iceland (food retailer) 229
iceland.co.uk 229
ichef.com 189
icollector.com 149
icom.org/vlmp/world.html 299
icra.org 283
idrink.com/ 197
idrink.com/home.htm 197
igarden.co.uk 245
iii.co.uk/ 224
illumin.co.uk/artaids/ 140
illustrators 158, 162
imagineradio.com 321
imdb.com 217
impactweather.co.uk 391

indicator bar 63
indo.com/distance/ 250
http://indy4.fdl.cc.mn.us/Eisk/stars/starmenu.html 144
infoseek.com 344
infowar.com 257
Inland Revenue 223
inlandrevenue.gov.uk/home.htm 223
InnerBody.com 265
innovations.co.uk 354
insects
    as pets 171
    recipes 236
Institute of Logistics and Transport 168
insults 170
insurance 221, 223, 225
insure.com/ 223
intelihealth.com 265
intelligence sources 255, 256, 257
intelligence-net.com/asp/index.asp 257
http://intelweb.janes.com 258
interflora.com 226
interior design 195–196
internet 8–10
    advertising blacklist 177
    browsers 54–58, 176, 178, 183–184
    browsing 98–103
    dialling up 48–53
    guides 177, 279–281
    modem connection 25–38, 49–53
    protection 11, 16–18, 81–84, 281–283
Internet Explorer 54–55, 56–57, 59–68
    accessibility option 73
    address toolbar 65
    advanced options 79
    back button 65
    browsing 98–103
    changing options 69–80
    channels button 66, 68
    color options 72
    connection options 76–78
    Content Advisor 81–84
    content options 74–76
    customising toolbars 67–68
    e-mail 104–112, 117–122
    edit menu 62
    favorites 63
    favorites button 66, 68
    file menu 62
    font options 72
    forward button 65
    full screen button 67
    go menu 62
    help menu 63
    history button 66
    history options 72
    home button 66
    home page 69
    indicator bar 63
    language options 72–73
    links button 64
    mail button 67
    menu bar 61–62
    newsgroups 123, 124–127, 131
    Outlook Express 104–112, 117–122, 123, 124–127, 131
    passwords 81–82
    plug-ins 79–80, 98–103
    print button 67
    programs buttons 78–79
    refresh button 66
    scroll bars 63
    search button 67
    security options 73–74
    standard button toolbar 65
    status bar 63–64
    stop button 65

temporary internet files 70–71
    title bar 61
    title bar buttons 63
    toolbars 65
    view menu 62
internet service providers (ISPs) 21, 39–43, 46–47, 124, 181–182
Internet universities 199
internetgarden.co.uk 246
internethoroscopes.com/ 143
inventions 339, 341
investments 222–223, 224–226
investorweb.com/Begin.asp 224
io.com/~hbp/folkdance/fd.html 191
iol.ie/~discover/europe.htm 379
iolt.org.uk 168
iomtt.com/ 288
iorganic.com 230
Ireland, and disabled people 193
http://ireland.iol.ie/infograf/dtour/ 193
irfb.com 368
Irish Tourist Board 382
irlenad.travel.ie/home/ 382
isdesignet.com/ 196
ISDN lines 24
Islam 334, 337
islam.org.au/ 337
Isle of Man TT 287–288
ISPs (internet service providers) 21, 39–43, 46–47, 124
itftennis.com/ 372
iwf.org.uk/ 282
http://ixquick.com 345
iyhf.org 382

jamba.co.uk 243
Jane's 258
jargon 184, 280–281
Jason Project 145
jason.org 145
Jerusalem 389
Jewish religion 336–337
jewishmag.co.il/ 337
jobsearch.co.uk 206
jobserve.com/ 203
jobsite.co.uk/ 204
jokes 235, 236
jokewallpaper.com 236
jpl.nasa.gov/cassini/ 147
juggling 278
june29.com/HLP/ 326
jungle.com 354
junk e-mail 123, 177

kabalarians.com/gkh/your.htm 331
kasparovchess.com/ 277
kawasaki.com/ 288
kaysnet.com 354
kcl.ac.uk/kis/college/careers/links/links.htm 206
kemc.edu/n.html 266
kidpub.org/kidpub/ 173
kids-space.org/ 174
http://kidshealth.org/index2.html 315
kidsworld.com/ 173
kissogram.com.au 236
kitbag.co.uk 354
knowhere.co.uk 326
kodak.com/us/en/nav/takingpics.shtml 278
koi carp 137
koicarp.demon.co.uk/ 137
kuoni.co.uk/ 388
kv5.com/intro.html 274

Landsend (leisurewear) 214
landsend.com 214
http://lang.nagoya-u.ac.jp/~matsuoka/Bronte.html 160
language options 72–73

languages
  central and Eastern European 323
  Chinese 250
  dictionaries 326
  translation 322, 326
  for travellers 380
lastminute.com/ 355
latedeals.com 382
law 283–286
  and internet 10
  legal resources 330–331
  strange laws 236–237
  stupid laws 284
  UK legislation 331
law.net 285
http://learn2.com 173
learn2.com 199
learningstore.co.uk 199
learnthenet.com/english/index.html 280
lectlaw.com/ 285
Leeds Castle 273
leeds-castle.co.uk 273
legalpadjr.com/ 285
Legoland 207
legoland.co.uk 207
leisurehunt.com/ 382
leisureplanet.com/ 383
leonardsloan.com/about/y2k/ 178
letour.com 363
Levi's 214
library.byu.edu/~rdh/wwi/ 276
lib.kth.se/~lg/envsite.htm 210
http://library.advanced.org//11163/gather/cgi-bin/wookie.cgi/
  269
http://library.advanced.org//12740/msie/ 172
http://links2go.com/topic/War 274
links 98–99
links button 64
Linux PCs 179, 180
http://listen.at/RadioNow 322
liszt.com/ 327
literature 142, 159, 160
liveconcerts.com/ 303
location toolbar 89, 92
London 208, 383, 387
  theatre 373
london-pages.demon.nl/ 383
londonstockex.co.uk/ 224
londontown.com/ 383
lonelyplanet.com/ 383
lonelyplanet.com/health/health.htm 384
looksmart.com 345
loot.com 319, 355
http://lottery.merseyworld.com 237
Louvre 298
lunn-poly.com/ 388
lycos.com 345
lycos.co.uk/webguides 251

m-w.com/ 327
Mac computers 19, 181–182
  dialling 48
  internet service provider 181–182
  modem connection 33–38
macconnect.com/ 182
macfixit.com/ 182
macorchard.com 182
macworld.zdnet.com/ 182
http://madsci.org/~lynn/VH/ 339
magazines, British 160
magickeys.com/books/ 161
maiden-voyages.com/ 384
mail button 67
mailameal.com/ 229
mailing lists 183, 327
  special interest groups 327

mailstartplus.com/ 183
majorleaguebaseball.com/ 362
makeupdiva.com/index.html 153
Manchester United 364
manutd.com 364
mapquest.com 251
maps 165, 251, 252
mapworld.com 251
Mars 144
martex.co.uk/ncc/index.htm 384
mastercard.com 150
match-making 333–334
match.com/ 333
matchmaker.com 333
http://math-www.uni-paderborn.de/~axel/BL/ 177
mathematics 173
  abacuses 322
  fractals 172
maven.co.il/ 337
mcnews.com/mcn.htm 288
McGraw-Hill 199–200
md.huji.ac.il/vjt/ 389
mdle.com/ClassicFilms/ 219
medical students 265
medicines 267
med.nyu.edu/Psych/screens/depres.html 262
megaconverter.com 327
megalithic sites 274
megastar.co.uk 310
http://members.aol.com/JuliannaA/scary.html 237
http://members.home.net/daveandlois/ 291
http://members.tripod.com/~lklivingston/essay/ 325
mental health 266–267
mentalhealth.com/ 266
menu bar
  Internet Explorer 61–62
  Netscape Navigator 88
menumaster.co.uk 230
Mercedes-Benz.com 294
http://mercurio.iet.unipi.it/home.html 379
http://messages.yahoo.com/yahoo/business_and_finance/sto
  cks/index.html 222
Messier Catalogue 146
meto.govt.uk 391
mgcars.org.uk/ 295
mhonlinelearning.com/ 200
microscopes 145, 338
Microsoft products 183
  Dial-up Networking 48–53
  see also Internet Explorer; Windows
microsoft.com 183
microsoft.com/insider/internet/default.htm 280
microwarehouse.co.uk 183
military history 257, 274–275
milkround.com 204
mindspring.com/~zoonet/gallery.html 138
http://mineral.galleries.com/default.htm 306
minerals 306
mirror.co.uk 310
missile bases 209
missingkids.org 316
http://mistral.culture.fr/louvre/louvrea.htm 298
mobile phones 348, 350
modem, support 183
modemhelp.com/ 183
modems 21–23, 25–38, 47, 49–53
momsnetwork.com/ 315
mondus.com/index.htm 168
moneyextra.co.uk 225
moneygator.com 224
monster.com/ 204
monster.co.uk 204
morebusiness.com 166
mortgages 220, 320
mothers 202, 313, 315
  see also parenting

motor homes 296–297
motorcycles 286–290
motorcycleworld.co.uk/ 289
motoring 290–297
    see also cars
motorsport.com/ 367
motorsports 367–368
movingmusic.co.uk/ 303
mp3.com 303
mrshowbiz.com/ 218
msf-usa.org/ 288
MSN (Microsoft Network) 45
msnbc.com/ 310
mt.net/~watcher/ 255
mtv.com/ 303
http://multimap.com 251
museums 298–299
music 157, 186, 191, 300–305
    children 172, 174, 175
    classical 301
    opera 136, 304–305
    see also CDs
musical instruments 301
musicals 373
musicnewswire.com 304
muslims 334
my-meals.com 230
mycemetary.com/my/pet_menu.html 138
mythology 325

nail care 153–154
names 331
    babies 313
nara.gov/ 259
NASA 359
nasa.gov 359
National Grid for Learning 200
National Lottery 237
National Science Foundation 340–341
National Security Agency, US 258
national-holidays.com/ 331–332
nationalgeographic.com 251
nationalsavings.co.uk 225
Native American
    astronomy 144
    history 273
NATO 258
nato.int/ 258
natural history, books 163
Natural History Museum 299
nature 177, 305–306
Natwest Bank 150
natwest.com 150
navigation toolbar 86
nba.com 362
NCH Action for children 312
nchafc.org.uk 312
ndirect.co.uk/~law/bentham.htm 284
needlework 276
Neighbourhood Watch 313
neoworx.com/ 187
netbanker.com 151
netgrocer.com 229
netlingo.com/ 280
netnanny.com/ 282
netradio.net 321
Netscape Collabra 123, 127–131, 132
Netscape Communicator 85
    e-mail 112–116
    newsgroups 123, 127–131, 132
Netscape Messenger 112–116
Netscape Navigator
    applications option 92
    back button 86–87
    browsing 98–103
    changing options 90–97

closing toolbars 89
composer options 94–95
connection icon 88
forward button 87
history options 92
home button 87
home page options 92
location bar history 92
location toolbar 89
menu bar 88
navigation toolbar 86
offline options 95–97
personal toolbar 88–89
plug-ins 79–80, 98–103
print button 87
reload button 87
roaming access 93–94
search button 87
security button 87
server icon 88
smart browsing 92
startup page options 92
status bar 88
stop button 87
title bar 86
title bar buttons 86
toolbar options 91
viewing window 88
netscape.com 184
netsource-asia.com/info/resource.htm 168
http://netvet.wustl.edu/e-zoo.htm 306
http://netvet.wustl.edu/vet.htm 136
new age 307–308
    see also astrology
New Musical Express 304
news 252, 308–312
    environmental 209, 211
    exclusive 309, 311
    finance 222–223
    political 254
newsgroups 9, 42, 123–124, 180, 279, 344
    Frequently Asked Questions (FAQs) 180–181
    Netscape Collabra 123, 127–131, 132
    Outlook Express 123, 124–127, 131
    sending messages 131–132
newstrawler.com/nt/nt_home.html 310
newwomanonline.co.uk/ 397
nfl.com/ 360
nfwi.org.uk/ 397
ngfl.gov.uk/ngfl/ 200
nhbs.co.uk 163
nhl.com 367
nhm.ac.uk// 299
http://nichcy.org/ 193
nimh.nih.gov/anxiety/ 260
nintendodirect.co.uk 243
nme.com 304
nmsi.ac.uk// 299
http://noahsarktopiary.com 247
Northern Lights 146
northernlight.com 345
Nova Television 341
nsa.gov:8080/ 258
nsf.gov/ 341
nursing homes 261
nuttysites.com 236
nwatch.org.uk/ 313

ob-ultrasound.net 318
Object Linking Embedding (OLE) 55
oceanblue.com/ 371
odci.gov 255
odci.gov/cia/publications/factbook/index.html 253
officer.com 286
officiallondontheatre.co.uk/ 373
offline options 95–97

offline working 68
OLE (Object Linking Embedding) 55
on-broadway.com/ 373
onelook.com/ 327–328
oneworld.net 310
online service providers (OSPs) 44–47
online-commerce.com/ 166
on.the.sauce.dial.pipex.com 156
opel.com/ 295
Open University 200
open.ac.uk/frames.html 200
open.gov.uk 255
open.gov.uk/ukpass/ukpass.htm 331
opera 136, 142, 304–305
Opera (web browser) 57–58
http://operabase.com/ 305
http://oposite.stsci.edu/pubinfo/BestOfHST95.html 145
organic shopping 355
    foods 229, 230, 231, 355
organicsdirect.com 230, 355
organised crime 286
oscar.com 218
Oscars 218
osce.org/ 258
OSPs (online service providers) 44–47
ou.edu/oupd/kidsafe/inet.htm 282
outdoor recreations 380
Outlook Express 104–112, 117–122, 123, 124–127, 131
    customising toolbars 108
    newsgroups 123, 124–127, 131
    receiving e-mail 121–122
    sending e-mail 117–120
OutRage 248
outrage.cygnet.co.uk/ 248
overseasjobs.com/ 204
http://owl.english.purdue.edu/writers/by-topic.html 329
oxalis.co.uk 245
Oz, world of 164, 165
ozemail.com.au/~vital1/free.htm 267
ozone layer 211

pacificnet.net/~johnr/aesop/ 157
packard-bell.com 179
pair.com/caravan/ 384
Palestine 259
palmistry 308
palmistry.com 308
pampers.com/index.html 316
panda 136
pantheon.org/mythica/ 325,
parascope.com/ 360
parenting 313–317
parentsoup.com/ 316
parentsplace.com/ 317
Paris 298, 384–385
paris-anglo.com 385
paris.org 384
passports 331
passwords 81–82
PatelsCornerShop.com/ 337
patent applications 167, 169
patent.gov.uk 169
patents.ibm.com/ 167
pathfinder.com 208
pathfinder.com/time/time100/ 330
paulsmith.co.uk 214
pbs.org/wgbh/nova/ 341
pcgame.com/ 244
pcmech.com/ 184
PCs 19–20
    modem connection 25–32, 49–53
    protocols 48
pcshowandtell.com/ 184
pctechguide.com/ 184
pcwebopedia.com/ 185
peevish.co.uk/slang 324

pemberley.com/janeinfo.html 162
pension schemes 225
peoplebank.com/ 204
perfumes 352, 353
periodic table 341
perp.com/whale/ 235
personal development 267, 317
personal.u-net.com/~thepub/beers.html 156
Peter Rabbit 163
peterrabbit.co.uk/ 163
petoftheday.com/ 136
pets 133–138
    insects 171
pets-pyjamas.co.uk 137
petspark.com/ 137
peugeot.com/ 295
pewclimate.org/ 211
pharmaceutical products 267
pharmacy2u.co.uk 267
phobias 262
photography 278
phrases 323, 332
phys.com 267
piaggio.com 295
pickabook.co.uk 163
PICS (Platform for Internet Content) 84
pinkpassport.com/ 248
http://place.scholastic.com/Goosebumps/index.htm 161
planetark.org/new/worldnews.html 211
planetrider.com/ 385
planetrugby.com 368
plants
    medicinal and poisonous 266
    see also gardening
http://plasma.nationalgeographic.com/mapmachine/ 252
plastic surgery 153
Platform for Internet Content (PICS) 84
play247.com 216
playstationdirect.co.uk 244
http://play.yahoo.com 238
plug-ins 79–80, 99–103, 176, 178
pmel.noaa.gov/toga-tao/el-nino/ 391
pna.net 259
poetry 159
police officers 286
politics 254–260
pollution 210, 211
popcorn.co.uk 218
porsche.com 296
portobelloroad.co.uk/ 139
positive thinking 267
postcodes 328
Potter, Beatrix 163
pregnancy 267, 314, 317–318
pregnancycalendar.com 318
http://presentpicker.com/ppp/ 254
pricejam.com 205
print button
    Internet Explorer 67
    Netscape Navigator 87
printers 355
Print.Quote.co.uk 355
productreviewnet.com/home.html 372
programs options 78–79
property 318–320, 352
    auctions 148, 319
property-sight.co.uk 320
propertybroker.co.uk 320
propertyfind.co.uk 319
protocols 48
prs.net/midi.html 301
psychology 262
pub guides 155–156
Public Record Office 328
http://publicrecord.com 328
punctuation 329

qed-uk.com 352
quackwatch.com/ 268
queendom.com/soc_anx.html 268
QuickTime 80
quinion.demon.co.uk/words/ 332
quotations 164, 323, 328
quotes 355, 357
qvc.com 356
qvc.de/ 356
qvcuk.com 356
qxl.com 149

rabi.phys.virginia.edu/HTW/ 340
racer.com/ 368
radio 177, 320–322
    plug-ins 80
radio-directory.com 321
railwatch.org/home.htm 385
railways 279
    safety 385
    timetables 374, 379, 387
rain forests 306
rainbows 338
RASCi (Recreational Software Advisory Council rating service) 84
rbge.org.uk 247
real ale 155, 156
Real Audio 80
Real Player 80, 185, 186
real-ale-guide.co.uk/ 156
realaudio.com/ 185
real.com 185
realmeat.co.uk 230
realtime.net/anr/vitamins.html 269
recipes 189–190, 227, 229, 230, 232
    cocktails 196–197
    with herbs and spices 231
    insect 236
    special diets 230
recipexchange.com/ 189
recruitment *see* employment
http://reed.com 205
reed.edu/~reyn/transport.html 386
refdesk.com/ 328
reference 322–332
    BBC Webguide 177
    see also dictionaries; encyclopedias
reflexology.org/ 264
refresh button 66
refugees 252
regiments.org/bd/tintin.html 162
related button 68
relate.org.uk 333
relationships 170–171, 262, 332–334
religion 334–337
reload button 87
residential care homes 261
restaurants 230, 231
retail.co.uk 356
review.co.uk/index.htm 205
http://rick.stanford.edu/opera/main.html/ 304
Riley Guide 205
rinkworks.com/bookaminute/ 159
rleague.com 369
roaming access 93–94
Robin Hood Project 163
Roget's Thesaurus 329
rolls-royceandbentley.co.uk/home.html 296
Roman History 273
roses 247
roses.co.uk 247
Royal Botanic Garden Edinburgh 247
royal families 270
Royal Shakespeare Company 373
Royal Society for the Prevention of Cruelty to Animals 137

Royal Society for the Protection of Birds 137
royal.gov.uk/ 270
royalmail.co.uk/athome 278
royalmail.co.uk/paf/ 328
royalmint.com/ 276
rri.org/envatlas/ 209
rsc.org.uk/ 373
rspb.com 137
rspca, org.uk 138
rugby 368–369
rugbyclub.co.uk 368
rugbymail.co.uk/ 368
runtrackdir.com/ 361

s9.com/biography 323
safesurf.com/lifegard.htm 282
saga.co.uk/ 347
sailing 369
sailing.org/ 369
Sainsbury's 230
sainsburys.co.uk 230
saints 335
http://saints.catholic.org/index.shtml 335
samlearning.co.uk/ 200
sancho.com/poker 240
sandiegozoo.org/special/pandacam/index 136
Saturn 146–147
scambusters.org/ 185
schools, on internet 188
schoolzone.co.uk/ 200
schwartz.co.uk 231
science 338–342
    for children 174, 176
    museums 299
Science Museum 299
scientific instruments 338
scils.rutgers.edu/special/kay/author.html 162
scils.rutgers.edu/special/kay/snowwhite.html 164
scoot.co.uk 329
Scotch Corner 356
scotch-corner.co.uk 254
Scotland 385–386
http://scotland.com 385
screamscape.com 234, 386
screenit.com/search_movies.html 218
http://screentrade.co.uk 225
screentrade.co.uk/ 358
scri.fsu.edu/~dennisl/CMS/activity/math_magic.html 173
script-o-rama.com/ 216
scroll bars 63
scrum.com 369
http://seamonkey.ed.asu.edu/oz/ 164
search button
    Internet Explorer 66
    Netscape Navigator 87
search engines 342–347
    for children 175
searchenginewatch.com 346
seasoned.com/ 190
seasports 370–371
seaworld.org 134
secondsounds.com 305
secret services 259
secretadmirer.com/ 334
security, international 258
security button 87
security options 73–74
http://seds.lpl.arizona.edu/nineplanets/ 146
seds.org/messier/ 146
self-employment 166
http://sellitontheweb.com/ 168
senior citizens 261, 347–348
    Age Concern 312
seniorssearch.com/ 348
sentex.net/~mmcadams/spelling.html 330
sepnet.com/cycle/index.htm 289

services 348
seti-inst.edu/ 147
sex 333
sex aids 351
sexuality 248
Shakespeare, William 164
shambhalasun.com/ 337
Shareware 185
shareware.com 185
shells 339
shlgroup.com/ 205
Shockwave 80, 98–102
shoes 214, 354
shopping 349–358
  antiques 139
  art works 140, 141
  beauty products 151, 154, 212
  books 157, 158, 159–161, 163, 164–165
  CDs 160, 300, 303, 304, 351, 354
  clothes 212–214, 352, 353
  computers 179
  e-commerce 166–167, 168, 220
  food 189, 228, 229, 230, 231, 232
  games 165, 303, 351
  gifts 229, 232, 253–254, 354
  product reviews 372
  software 176, 178, 179
  see also auctions
shopsmart.com 357
shopsonthenet.com/ 356
showbizwire.com 219
shrubs 247
shrubsdirect.com 247
sign language 330
signpost.co.uk 386
simonsays.com/kids/mtb/index.cfm 158
simplerpensions.org.uk/ 225
simplyfood.co.uk 231
single parents 315
sipu.com/sa/index.html 249
size button 68
skicentral.com 370
skiing 369–370
skin care 151–153
Sky Broadcasting Corporation 219
sky.co.uk/ 219
skynews.co.uk/ 310
skysports.co.uk 365
skyview.gsfc.nasa.gov/skybview.html 147
slang 327
slashdot.org/ 186
sleep 234
slh.com/slh/ 386
small businesses 166, 168
smart browsing 92
smarterwork.com 168
snooker 370
Snow White 164
soccernet.com/index.html 364
software
  buying 176, 178, 179
  Dial-up Networking 48–53
  for disabled people 194
  downloading 180, 187
  filtering 17–18, 81–84, 281–283
  TCP/IP 48, 51
  tracing 187
  viruses 11, 12–16
  for visually impaired 194
softwarefirst.co.uk/ 244
solar system 146, 147
sony.com/ 357
http://soundreach.simplenet.com/psp/ 341
http://southpark.comedycentral.com/southpark/ 237
space 359–360
spam 123

spankmag.com 315
spartacus.schoolnet.co.uk/ 274
speciality-foods.com 231
spectacles and contact lenses 351–352
speechtml.com/ 194
speedtrap.com/ 296
speedtraps 296
spellbound-online.co.uk 308
spelling 330
spiceguide.com 190
spies/spying 259, 298, 342
  see also intelligence sources
spikemagazine.com/ 142
spikesys.com/webville.html 279
sporting-life.com 240
sportingbet.com/ 240
sports 177, 310, 311, 321, 360–372
  footwear 354
  news 310, 311, 321
  tutorials 199
  see also gambling; motorcycles; motorsports
sportsline.com 365
sportslive.net/ 321
sportsweb.com 365
stamp collecting 278
stampworld.com/index.html 278
stanleygibbons.com 278
Star Wars 219, 359
http://starchild.gsfc.nasa.gov/docs/StarChild/StarChild.html 174
starlingtech.com/quotes/ 328
starnames.co.uk/ 254
stars see astrology; astronomy
starwars.com 359
starwarsnet.com/ 219
status bar
  Internet Explorer 63–64
  Netscape Navigator 88
Stevenson, Robert Louis 164
stock markets 222–223, 224
stone age 274
stonepages.com/ 274
Stonewall 248
stonewall.org.uk/ 248
stop button
  Internet Explorer 65
  Netscape Navigator 87
stories 207–208
  by children 172, 173, 174
  fables 157, 323
  urban myths 237
strangemag.com/ 208
stress management 267
  see also books
student-world.co.uk/ 201
studentuk.com 201
stud.ifi.uio.no/~hermunda/Snooker/ 370
subway systems 386
summer jobs, US 197
sunday-times.co.uk 311
sundaymirror.co.uk 310
sunsail.com/ 388
sunsite.unc.edu/herbmed/faqs/herbfaqs.html 246
superstitions 237
surfing 370–371
surgery.com/ 153
surgerydoor.co.uk/ 268
suzuki.com/ 289
suzuki.co.uk/ 289
swiftleisure.co.uk/ 297
symantec.com/ 186

tartans 356
tax, self-assessment 221
TCP/IP software 48, 51
http://teach.virginia.edu/go/frog 340

team.net/sol/solwebs.html 296
teamtalk.com/ 364
-tech.mit.edu/Shakespeare/works.html 164
technology 340, 372
  and careers for girls 171
techstocks.com 225
techweb.com/horoscope/ 143
teenadvice.org/ 174
teenagers 172
  advice line 174
  beauty 152
  see also children; young people
teldir.com/ 330
teleflorist.co.uk 226
telegraph.co.uk 311
telephone directories 330
telescopes 144, 145, 147, 342
television 177, 216
temporary internet files 70–71
tennis 371–372
tennis.com/ 372
Tesco 231
tesco.com 231
tesco.co.uk 229
the-times.co.uk 311
http://theaa.co.uk 290
theatre 142, 207, 373–374
  tickets 208, 355, 357
theauctionchannel.com/ 148
thebestofbritish.com 350
thebirdbox.com 134
thebookplace.com 159
thebookseller.com 159
thecommonwealth.org 255
thehistorychannel.com 273
thehistorynet.com 173
thehorse.com/ 136
thehungersite.com 312
theideabox.com/ 315
theme parks 172, 234, 386
theoldie.co.uk/ 347
therepertoire.com/ 190
thesaurus.com 329
thesaurus.co.uk/ 349
thesite.org.uk 268
thesmokinggun.com/ 311
thetrainline.co.uk/trainline.html 387
theTrip.com/ 388
thevirtualbar.com/ 197
thevirtualmall.co.uk/ 358
theweekly.co.uk/ 238
theyarn.com 165
thinknatural.com/ 269
thirdage.com/ 348
thisisbritain.co.uk/ 387
thisislondon.com/ 387
thomascook.co.uk/ 388
thomasthetankengine.com/ 174
thomson-holidays.com/ 388
thorntons.co.uk 231
thrillride.com 386
tias.com/ 139
ticketmaster.au 208, 357
ticketmaster.com 208, 357
ticketmaster.co.uk/ 208, 357
tickets, booking 207, 208, 357
http://tickets.priceline.com/ 349
Time magazine 208, 254, 330
Time Out 208
time zones 331, 389
timeanddate.com/worldclock/ 331
timecast.com 186
timeout.com 208
The Times 311
timeshare properties 387
TinTin 162

title bar
  Internet Explorer 61, 63
  Netscape Navigator 86
title bar buttons, Netscape Navigator 86
tombtown.com/ 219
toolbars
  customising 67–68
  Internet Explorer 65
  Netscape Navigator 86, 88–89, 91, 92
topiary 247
topjobs.net/ 206
tops.co.uk 357
Topshop 357
toshiba.com 179
totalgames.net/ 244
tourism.wales.gov.uk 390
towns, UK 326
toyota.com 297
toys 353
  collectible 144
  educational 352
traffic reports 374
trailfinders.co.uk/ 388
training resources 169
trainingzone.co.uk 169
trains
  safety 385
  timetables 374, 379, 387
  underground 386
http://translator.go.com/ 326
transport
  for disabled people 193
  and environment 210
  see also cars; motorcycles; railways; trains
travel 177, 355, 374–390
  agents and companies 376, 388
  auctions 149
  cybercafés 344
  and health 383–384, 389
  maps 165, 251, 252
  warnings 377–378, 389
  see also air travel; holidays; motoring; railways
travel-library.com/ 381
travelengland.org.uk/ 378
travelselect.com 388
http://travel.state.gov/travel_warnings.html 389
travlang.com/languages/ 380
travlang.com/signs 378
Treasure Island 164
triumph.co.uk/ 289
tropical diseases 389
trrravel.com 387
tucows.com 187
tudocs.com/ 232
tug2.net/ 387
Twain, Mark 162

ubl.com/ 305
ub.rug.nl/camelot/ 160
ub.rug.nl/camelot/rh/rhhome.htm 163
ucalgary.ca/~dkbrown/ 171
ucas.com 201
uclh.org/medical/tropical/services.htm 389
ucmp.berkeley.edu/diapsids/dinosaur.html 135
uforesources.com/ 187
UFOs 360
uftree.com 250
uit.no/npt/homepage-npt.en.html 146
UK Patent Office 169
uk-invest.com 226
uk.bigfoot.com 177
ukdads.co.uk/ 313
ukexnet.co.uk/hort/index.htm 246
UKkids.co.uk 175
ukmums.co.uk/ 313
ukoln.ac.uk/services/treasure/ 164

ukparents.co.uk 317
ukplus.co.uk 346
ukstate.com 331
umass.edu/aesop/ 157
http://umgweb.com/ 290
unbeatable.co.uk 352
underoneroof.co.uk 320
unhcr.ch/ 252
unidata.ucar.edu/staff/blynds/rnbw.html 338
United Nations 259
        world hunger 312
universities 198, 199, 200, 201
Universities and Colleges Admission Service (UCAS) 201
unn.ac.uk/societies/islamic/ 334
un.org 259
un.org/Pubs/CyberSchoolBus/ 259
upmystreet.com/ 320
ups.com/ 192
urban myths 237
Urbanmyths.com 237
URLs 55, 344, 345
US government documents 256
USA
        car hire 375
        Central Intelligence Agency (CIA) 255, 298, 342
        companies 166
        cultural exchange programmes 197–198
        deserts 339
        discovery of 270
        employment 206
        FBI 256, 283
        government 254, 256–257, 258, 259
        national archives 259
        Native American history 144, 273
        skiing 369–370
        theatre 373
        theme parks 172, 234
        travel warnings 389
        White House 175, 260
usatoday.com 312
uselessknowledge.com/ 238
users.interport.net//~fairrosa/carroll.html 162
users.interport.net//~fairrosa/cl.authors.html 158
http://users.lia.net/dlever/main.asp 305
utmem.edu/personal/thjones/hist/hist_mic.htm 145

value-direct.co.uk 358
vam.ac.uk 299
vatican.va 336
vegan.com/ 190
vegans 190
vegetables 229
http://vegetarian-shoes.co.uk 358
vegetarians
        food 227, 231, 232
        leather 358
veggieheaven.com/ 232
venables.co.uk/legal/ 330
veterinary medicine 136
Victoria and Albert Museum 299
vidalsassoon.com 154
videos 160, 186, 216, 217, 354
        plug-ins 80
view menu 62
viewing window 88
virgin-direct.co.uk 224
virtualflorist.com/ 227
virtualinsults.com/home/ 170
virtualjerusalem.com 336
virtualmakeover.com 154
virtualschool.co.uk 201
virtualstudent.co.uk/ 201
virtualvegas.com 240
viruses 11, 12–16
visa.com 151
visual impairment, blind sports 194, 365

vitamins 269
vivanet.com/~stevemd/juggle1.html 278
vl-theatre.com/ 374
voa.gov 311
vogue.co.uk/ 215
Voice of America 311
volcanoes 252, 306
http://volcano.und.nodak.edu/ 306
Volkswagen 297
volvo.com 297
vtourist.com/ 389
http://vulcan.wr.usgs.gov/Volcanoes/ 252

http://w3.one.net/~alward/ 280
w3.org 187
wackyuses.com 238
Waitrose 232, 358
waitrose.com 232, 358
walking 277
Wall Street Journal 226
Walt Disney company 172, 233
wam.emd.edu/~mct/Plants/index.html 266
war criminals 283
war games 275
war graves 270
warfare 257, 258–259, 274–275
        World War I 272, 275–276
wave.net/upg/immigration/flags.html 250
wcn.co.uk/ 206
wdwinfo.com 389
wdwinfo.co.uk 389
weather 390–392
http://web66.coled.umn.edu/ 188
web browsing *see* browsing
web pages, creating 95
http://webcrawler.com 346
webdirectory.com 209
webofculture.com/ 252
webopedia.com 280
http://webperso.iut.univ-paris8/~rosmord//nomhiero.html
        276
webtender.com/ 197
http://web.ukonline.co.uk/ddlg.uk/ 193
http://web.ukonline.co.uk/fab/ 135
webwedding.co.uk 395
weddingbells.com 395
weddingchannel.com/ 395
weddingguide.co.uk/ 396
weddings 394–396
weddings-and-brides.co.uk/ 395
weight loss 262, 267
Welsh Tourist Board 390
Westminster Abbey 275
westminster-abbey.org 275
whatis.com 281
where-to-fish.com/ 361
which.net/webtrader/wt5.html 312
White House 175, 260
whitehouse.gov 260
whitehouse.gov/WH/kids/html/kidshome.html 175
whnt19.com/kidwx 390
whsmith.co.uk 165
wildlife 170, 212
        urban gardens 212
        see also animals; birds; insects; nature; plants
Windows
        Dial-up Networking 48–53
        flaws 188
        software 179, 180, 187
        see also Internet Explorer
windows.umich.edu/ 147
wine 229, 253, 392–394
        organic 230
wine-lovers-page.com 393
wine-pages.com/ 393
wineanorak.com 393

winepage.de/ 392
wineplace.nu/ 393
winespectator.com/ 394
winevin.com/default.htm 394
winter sports 369–370
wintersports.org/ 370
wired.com 372
Wizard of Oz 164, 165
wj.net/rborek/strange.html 237
wmo.ch 391
womanmotorist.com/ 297
women 396–398
    in business 166
    distinguished 270
    home workers 315
    mothers 202, 313, 315
    motorists 297
    reproductive rights 396
    in science 338
    travellers 384
    see also beauty; fashion
women-networking.com/ 398
Women's Institutes 397
womenswire.com/ 398
womenswire.com/style/ 215
wonka.com/ 175
working mothers 202
World Bank 151
world clock 331
World Meteorological Organisation 391
World War I 272, 275–276
worldbank.org 151
worldclimate.com 391
worldexecutive.com/index.html 390
worldgolf.com/ 366
worldmedia.fr/fashion/catwalk/ 212
worldofinteriors.co.uk/ 196
worldof.net/holidays 390
worldtrans.org/naturaldeath.html 267
worldwar1.com 275
Worldwide Web Consortium 187
worldwide web (www) 9
worldwide-hampers.com/ 232
wowgo.com 238

wrestling 372
wrestling.com 372
wsc.co.uk/wsc/ 364
wsj.com 226
wsu.edu/~dee/WORLD.HTM 275
wtj.com/ 275
wwar.com/ 142
http://www1.playbill.com/playbill/ 373
http://www2.active.ch/~mwuest/s_services/secret_ser-
    vices.htm 259
http://www2.eng.cam.ac.uk/~tpl/env.html 210
http://www2.vw-online.de/international/english/index_2.htm
    297
http://wwwiddv.com/ 195

xenu.net/cic/ 335
xplore.com/xplore500/medium/kids.html 175
xvt.com/users/kevink/silo/ 209

yack.com/ 208
yahoo.com 347
yahooligans.com 175, 392
yama-motor.com 290
yama-motor.co.uk 290
Yellow Pages 329
young people 170–176
    advice for 170–171, 174
    books for 161
    with disabilities 193
    generation gap 314–315
    and girls' careers 171
    see also children; teenagers
yslonline.com/va/index.html 215
yukyuk.com 238
Yves St Laurent 215

zdnet.com 188
zdnet.com/pccomp/besttips/ 279
zdnet.com/yil/selector/getsign.html 143
zoom.com 358
zoos 138